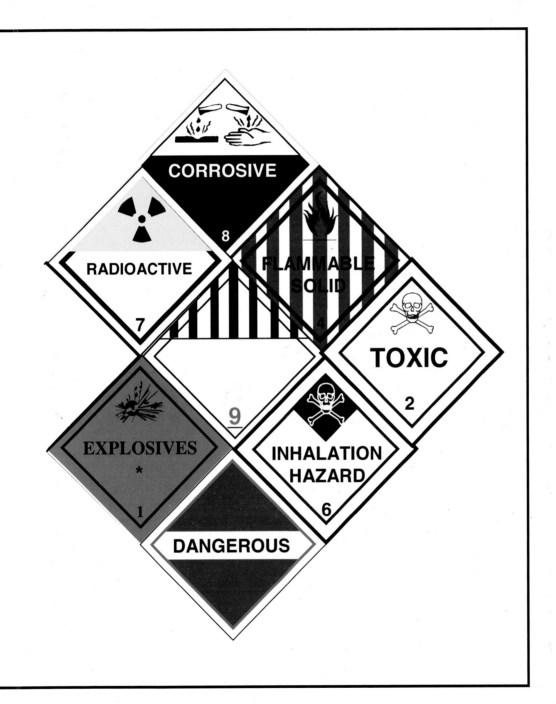

street smart™ chemistry

street smart™ chemistry

EMERGENCY RESPONSE GUIDE
Featuring Weapons of
Mass Destruction

Barry N. Lindley, M.S.
Wayne C. Appleton, Ph.D.

E. I. du Pont de Nemours and Company
Wilmington, DE

Library of Congress Catalogue Number: 2003102021

Freon®, Suva®, Delrin®, and Telfon® are registered trademarks of E. I. du Pont de Nemours and Company.

Halon® is a registered trademark of Allied Corporation.

Plexiglass® is a registered trademark of Rohm & Haas Company.

Lucite® is a registered trademark of Imperial Chemical Industries, Inc.

Miran® is a registered trademark of Thermo Environmental Instruments Inc.

Juicy Fruit® is a registered trademark of W. M. Wrigley Jr. Company.

This book meets the requirements of OSHA 29CFR 1910.120 and NFPA 472.

ISBN 0-9728832-0-7

Printed in the United States of America

About the Authors

Barry Lindley and Wayne Appleton are experts in the field of emergency response. Between them, they have over 32 years of experience and have responded to nearly 650 significant HAZMAT incidents. They consult with DuPont operating facilities, fire departments, and numerous emergency response groups in the area of hazardous chemistry, explosives, environmental monitoring, PPE selection, and hazardous materials handling safety.

Barry has accumulated extensive hazardous materials response experience while serving as a Corporate Integrated Emergency Response and Chemical Incident Response Team leader. He holds a Master of Science in Analytical Chemistry and is an expert on environmental analysis, air dispersal of hazardous materials, and remediation methods. Barry has been a HAZMAT trainer since 1988 and is an instructor at both the West Virginia University Fire School and the Delaware State Fire School.

Wayne holds a doctorate in Physical Organic Chemistry and has experience in process development for organic chemicals, chemical analysis, and environmental chemistry. He is a recognized authority on environmental laws and regulations and is a frequent speaker at environmental conferences and before legislative committees. Wayne is also an educator who teaches chemistry and environmental science at Marshall University, the University of Charleston, and Mountain State University.

Barry and Wayne are also consultants for DuPont Safety Resources' Emergency Response Solutions practice.

DuPont Safety Resources helps companies improve business performance while protecting the lives and livelihoods of employees and contract workers. For over 30 years, more than 500 consultants have been helping hundreds of organizations globally reduce workplace injuries and fatalities. DuPont Safety Resources draws upon the owner-operator experience of DuPont, the company with one of the best industrial safety records in the world and a 200-year heritage of safety as a core business value. DuPont Safety Resources is part of DuPont Safety and Protection, a core DuPont business that provides solutions to protect people, property, and operations. For more information on DuPont Safety Resources, call us at 1-800-532-SAFE or visit our website at www.dupont.com/safety.

Table of Contents

Foreword by Donald W. Walsh, Ph.D., EMT-P   *xiii*
Acknowledgments   *xv*

CHAPTER **1**   **Introduction**   *1*

Definitions   *1*
Units and Measurement   *3*
The Top Twenty Chemicals   *6*

CHAPTER **2**   **Forms and Changes of Matter**   *7*

Recognized Physical Forms   *7*
General Properties of Matter   *8*
    Gases   *8*
    Liquids   *13*
    Solids   *13*
Physical Properties   *14*
Changes of Matter   *15*
Physical Changes   *16*
Chemical Changes   *18*

CHAPTER **3**   **Atoms, Elements, and the Periodic Table**   *21*

Chemistry of the Elements   *24*
    Gases   *24*
    Liquids   *28*
    Solids   *29*

CHAPTER **4**   **Formulas and Bonding of Inorganic Molecules**   *53*

Formulas   *53*
Bonds   *54*

CHAPTER **5**   **Inorganic Chemical Nomenclature**   *55*

   Ionic Compounds   *55*
   Naming Acids   *58*
   Salts   *59*
   Hydrates   *59*

CHAPTER **6**   **Chemical Reactions**   *61*

   Rates of Chemical Reactions   *61*
   Types of Chemical Reactions   *62*

CHAPTER **7**   **Corrosives**   *63*

   Acids and Bases   *63*
   Hazards   *64*
   Concentrated Acids   *64*
   Fuming Acids   *66*
   Strong Bases   *69*
   Weak Bases   *70*
   Cleaning Up Spills of Acids or Bases   *70*

CHAPTER **8**   **Oxidizing Agents**   *71*

   Inorganic Oxidizers   *71*

CHAPTER **9**   **Water- and Air-Reactive Materials**   *73*

   Types of Water- and Air-Reactive Materials   *73*

CHAPTER **10**   **Toxicity**   *75*

   Toxicology   *75*
   Terms   *76*
   Dose   *79*
   Properties of the Individual Chemical   *81*
   Acute Toxicity   *83*
   Chronic Toxicity   *86*
   Individual Susceptibility   *86*

Duration and Frequency of Exposure 87
Route of Exposure 87
Environmental Factors 87
Chemical Combinations 88
Relative Toxicity to Humans and Other Species 89
Environmental Data 89
Environmental Decomposition and Degradation Rates 91
Other Useful Environmental Data 92

CHAPTER **11** **Organic Chemistry** *95*

Alkanes *97*
Alkenes (Olefins) *101*
Alkynes and Dienes *103*
Cyclic Aliphatic Hydrocarbons *104*
Aromatic Hydrocarbons *105*
Halogenated Hydrocarbons *107*
Alcohols *111*
Ethers *113*
Aldehydes and Ketones *114*
Carboxylic Acids *116*
Derivatives of Carboxylic Acids *118*
Organic Sulfur Compounds *122*
Amines *123*
Other Nitrogen-Containing Materials *124*
Phenols *125*
Heterocyclic Compounds *126*
Monomers, Plastics, and Polymers *127*
Organic Peroxides *134*

CHAPTER **12** **Weapons of Mass Destruction** *137*

Biological Hazards *138*
Nuclear Hazards *151*
Incendiary Devices and Reactions *159*
Chemical Hazards *163*
    Choking Agents *168*
    Blood Agents *168*
    Blister Agents *168*
    Nerve Agents *169*
    Crowd-Control Agents *172*

Industrial and Other Chemicals 175
    Psychogenic Materials 175
    Industrial Chemicals 175
The Chemistry of Explosives and Propellants 176
Dissemination Devices 181
Potential Terrorist Targets 182
Responder Actions 183
Choking Agent Chemical Data Sheets 185
Blood Agent Chemical Data Sheets 193
Blistering Agent Chemical Data Sheets 201
Nerve Agent Chemical Data Sheets 221
Crowd-Control Agent Chemical Data Sheets 237

CHAPTER **13** **Environmental Monitoring** 255

Positive Characteristics of Air-Monitoring Instruments 257
Oxygen Indicators 260
Combustible Atmosphere Indicators 262
Colorimetric Indicator Tubes (Detector Tubes) 263
Specific Chemical Monitors 265
Photoionization Detectors (PID) 265
Portable Flame Ionization Detectors (FID) 267
Infrared Spectrophotometer (IR) 268
Aerosol Monitors 268
Accessories/Options 269
Monitoring Pesticides and Highly Toxic Components 269
Methods for Monitoring Weapons of Mass Destruction 274
    Chemical Warfare Agents 274
    Biological Agents 276
    Radiation 277

CHAPTER **14** **Fire** 279

Theories of Fire 279
    The Fire Triangle 279
    The Fire Tetrahedron 282
    The Life Cycle of Fire 283
Theories of Fire Extinguishment 284
Pyrolysis 286

CHAPTER **15** **Pesticides** *289*

Pesticide and Registration *289*
Common Types of Pesticides *290*
Pesticide Toxicity and
    the Corresponding Label Signal Word *292*
Routes of Pesticide Entry into the Human Body *293*
Identify the Signs and Symptoms of Pesticide Poisoning *293*
Identify the Information Found on a Pesticide Label *295*
Formulations Ingredients and the Hazards of
    Inert Pesticide Ingredients *298*
Dangers Involved in Pesticide Fires and Spills *303*
Personal Protective Equipment Requirements
    when Working with Pesticides *304*
Difficulties in Decontamination of Pesticides *305*

CHAPTER **16** **DOT Class Chemistry** *307*

CLASS 1 *307*
CLASS 2 *308*
CLASS 3 *309*
CLASS 4 *309*
CLASS 5 *310*
CLASS 6 *310*
CLASS 7 *311*
CLASS 8 *311*
CLASS 9 *312*

Other Resources *313*

Foreword

My twenty-seven years of experience in Fire Service and Emergency Medical Services operations and management have taught me the importance of being knowledgeable of the effects of chemical, biological, and nuclear hazards. Today, issues such as terrorism, weapons of mass destruction, environmental crimes, and clandestine labs are on virtually everyone's agenda in the Fire Service. These new issues, along with our current responses to hazardous material incidents, just complicate an already complex emergency response system. The rules for First Responders have changed in the United States since September 11, 2001, and we must be ready to respond with the appropriate resources and personnel.

This book has been written for First Responders and chemical management professionals to meet the challenges of today's hazardous material responses. Presented in an easy-to-read format, DuPont's *Street Smart^TM Chemistry* provides new and experienced First Responders with a resource guide that will enable them to upgrade their skills and knowledge of chemistry relative to their profession and public safety.

In providing appropriate mitigation, preparedness, and response to chemical, biological, and nuclear incidents, today's First Responders must be prepared with the tools to manage the hazard, to identify the vulnerability, and for managing risk to minimize losses within the community. This response guide and resource publication can be added to your growing library of references and learning materials and will work as a great review system during your hazardous material training and in-service drills.

In a world concerned with weapons of mass destruction and attacks on our homeland, First Responders have an expanded role within the homeland security community. DuPont's leadership has addressed these priorities by developing this book to prepare the First Responder for the challenges in this new world. DuPont's *Street Smart^TM Chemistry* is like no other emergency response guide.

I hope that you will use this book and add it as part of your personal reference library in your training facilities, offices, fire stations, and rescue trucks. Remember, a knowledgeable First Responder is a safety-first professional. Be safe, and respond appropriately with safety first in mind.

Donald W. Walsh, Ph.D., EMT-P
Assistant Deputy Chief
Chicago, Illinois, USA

Dr. Donald W. Walsh is an Assistant Deputy Chief with the Chicago Fire Department. In addition to his chief officer career with one of the nation's largest fire departments, he is also President and CEO of International Emergency Medicine Disaster Specialist, a disaster management consultant group credited with award-winning disaster planning models used by the international community.

Acknowledgments

We would like to acknowledge the contributions of the DuPont Emergency Response Solutions team located in Belle, West Virginia for their expertise and assistance in the development of this book. They are Charlie Baldwin, Ray Beaudry, Bill Burke, Ron Crede, Tom Keefer, Mike Lacy, Donnie Perry, and Joe Sharp.

We would also like to thank the following people who contributed to the editing and commercialization of the manuscript: Lori Alzamora, Mark Cluff, Bill Collins, Carolyn Luttrell, Chris Sheppard, and Bonnie Swan.

street smart™ chemistry

1

Introduction

Chemistry is the scientific study of the properties, composition, and structure of matter, the changes in structure and composition of matter, and accompanying energy changes.

The purpose of this text is to familiarize emergency response First Responders with chemistry and the terms associated with chemicals. It will not make you a chemist. It will help you recognize when things are starting to go wrong. It should allow you to recognize families of chemicals and make choices on how to monitor for the release of these chemicals into the environment. It will help you to understand the resources available to you and help you to make good decisions based on the information you have.

Definitions

MATTER: Anything that has mass and takes up space. The term matter refers to all the materials, or stuff, making up the universe. Everything you see around you is matter. The paper in front of you, the trees outside your window, the food you ate for lunch, and even you are examples of matter.

ELEMENTS: Substances that cannot be broken down physically or chemically into simpler materials by any non-nuclear reaction. Elements may exist as pure materials, such as pure copper, in mixtures with other elements, like steel, or as part of compounds where the element is chemically bonded with other elements.

ATOMS: The smallest units of an element.

CHEMICAL BONDS: Attractions and interactions between atoms that hold the atoms together in specific patterns and combinations. Think of bonds as glue that holds things together.

MOLECULES: Atoms joined in defined proportions and bonded in specific patterns.

CHEMICAL COMPOUNDS: Substances composed of atoms joined in specific ways by bonds. In contrast to an element, a compound is a pure substance composed of different types of atoms. In other words, compounds are composed of two or more different elements. The different atoms in a compound combine in specific ratios. Atoms from the individual elements will lose their identities when forming compounds. In other words, a compound has properties different from the elements that comprise it. It is possible to take the same atoms and, by changing which atoms are attached or bonded to each other, make many different molecules, each with its own unique physical and chemical properties. As an example, using only carbon and hydrogen, it is possible to make more than 100,000 different molecules with very different properties and hazards. Compounds with the same formula but different structures are called isomers.

MIXTURE: A combination of two or more substances. It is a combination of compounds (molecules) which may have very different chemical and physical properties depending on the amount of each compound in the mixture. Unlike the elements of a compound, the individual components of a mixture retain their identities. A mixture can be described as either homogeneous or heterogeneous.

Homogeneous Mixture

A homogeneous mixture has uniform composition throughout; it is also called a solution. A solution contains a mixture of two or more substances that cannot easily be distinguished from each another. For example, when you create a solution by dissolving sugar in water, distinguishing the sugar molecules from the water molecules is difficult.

Both the air you breathe and the water you drink are good examples of solutions. Air is a mixture of many different gases: about 78 percent nitrogen, 21 percent oxygen and lots of little bits of other gases, like neon and argon. Drinking water is also homogeneous. Water may contain calcium, fluoride, salt, or sugar. The pure substances remain separate, but they mix in with each other to the point at which you cannot see the difference.

Heterogeneous Mixture

A heterogeneous mixture does not have uniform composition throughout. In a heterogeneous mixture, the individual substances can easily be distinguished from one another. Mixtures of sand in water or pebbles in cement are examples of heterogeneous mixtures.

INORGANIC CHEMICALS: Materials that do not contain carbon as their principal element.

ORGANIC CHEMICALS: Materials that do contain carbon as their principal element.

CHEMICAL REACTION: A mixing of some compounds together that may cause them to interact, react, and change composition. This may be accompanied by significant changes in physical properties and significant release of heat.

ENERGY CHANGES: Release or take-up of heat in a reaction or change of physical state. Like matter, energy can be classified in different ways. Two kinds of energy are kinetic and potential.

Kinetic Energy

Kinetic energy is the energy of motion. Gas molecules of a given substance move much more rapidly than do the molecules of that substance in the solid phase. Consequently, gas molecules have more kinetic energy than molecules in the solid phase. For example, water molecules in steam have greater kinetic energy than molecules in liquid water.

Potential Energy

Potential energy is the energy of position, or stored energy. How much potential energy an object possesses depends on its position compared with that of other objects. Therefore, the farther an object is from another object, the more potential energy it has. For example, because individual gas molecules are positioned farther from each other than liquid molecules, the potential energy of a gas is greater than the potential energy of a liquid.

Energy can also be classified based on its source. For example, energy can be electrical, light, mechanical, chemical, or nuclear. Two laws explain the important properties of energy:

Conservation of Energy (also called the First Law of Thermodynamics)
This law states that energy is neither created nor destroyed. Instead, energy is converted from one form to another. Therefore, the total amount of energy in the universe is conserved. For example, during photosynthesis, a plant converts light energy from the sun into chemical energy of the molecules that make up the plant. Next, when animals consume the plant, the chemical energy of the plant's molecules is converted into heat energy. Although the energy has been changed from light energy to chemical energy to heat energy, the total amount of energy involved remains the same.

Increase in Entropy (also called the Second Law of Thermodynamics)
Entropy is a measure of randomness, or disorder. The more disordered a system is, the more entropy it has. As natural processes have a tendency toward maximum disorder, the entropy of the universe is always increasing. For example, when a plant dies, the molecules of the plant break down and become disorganized, and consequently, the entropy of the system increases. You can witness this increase in entropy when you clean your child's room. It immediately starts to become cluttered and messy again.

CONSERVATION OF MASS: The Law of Conservation of Mass states that mass is neither created nor destroyed. Therefore, the total mass of matter before and after a chemical change remains the same. The number of atoms also remains the same. The only thing that changes is the arrangement of the atoms. For example, the sum of the masses of hydrogen and oxygen before they combine to form water is the same as the total mass of the water they form. Furthermore, the sum of the number of atoms of hydrogen and oxygen is the same as the total number of atoms in the water. The only change that occurs in a chemical reaction is in the arrangement of the atoms. Before the reaction, the hydrogen and oxygen atoms are not bonded to one another, and therefore exist separately. However, after the reaction, the hydrogen and oxygen atoms are bonded to one another.

MOLECULAR WEIGHT: For an element, the atomic weight of the weighted average of the atomic masses of the different isotopes of the element; for a molecule or a compound, the sum of the atomic weights of the atoms in the molecule or compound.

Units and Measurement

SI System and Standards
Long ago, people decided that the foot must be standardized. Originally this standard was the King's foot, but that would change with each new ruler. Someone then had the brilliant idea of a standard length for a foot. Then all measurements were made compared to this "standard foot" which was not subject to growth or death. This system of measurement had the drawback of making the math hard–12 inches to a foot, 3 feet to a yard, 5,280 feet in a mile, and so on.

We will be using a newer system of measurement, the System International (SI) system or metric system. We will need to measure three main quantities: length, mass, and time. The SI units for these are meter, kilogram, and second, respectively. Beyond the basic meters, kilograms, and seconds, we define some secondary or derived standards like amperes, moles, and candela. They are defined in terms of meters, kilograms, and seconds.

Units of Measurement
In order for people around the world to agree on quantitative observations, a system of measurement must be defined. Today, scientists worldwide agree on the SI system.

4

The fundamental units of the SI system are listed below:

Physical Quantity	Name of Unit	Abbreviation
Mass	kilogram	kg
Length	meter	m
Time	second	s
Temperature	Kelvin	K
Electric Current	ampere	A
Amount of Substance	mole	mol
Luminous Intensity	candela	cd

Nevertheless, since the fundamental units are not always convenient (e.g., expressing the mass of a sheet of paper in kilograms is ridiculous), prefixes are used to change the size of the unit. For example, 1000 meters can be expressed as 1 km (kilometer). Common prefixes are listed below:

Prefix	Symbol	Factor
exa	E	10^{18}
peta	P	10^{15}
tera	T	10^{12}
giga	G	10^{9}
mega	M	10^{6}
kilo	k	10^{3}
hecto	h	10^{2}
deka	da	10^{1}
—	—	10^{0}
deci	d	10^{-1}
centi	c	10^{-2}
milli	m	10^{-3}
micro	μ	10^{-6}
nano	n	10^{-9}
pico	p	10^{-12}
femto	f	10^{-15}
atto	a	10^{-18}

Besides fundamental units, there are also derived units, which get their units from the fundamental units. An important derived unit in chemistry is the liter (L), which expresses volume. A liter is the volume that a cube with sides of one dm (decimeter) takes up. In other words, $1 \text{ L} = 1 \text{ dm}^3$.

Importance of Keeping Track of Units
Units give numbers a particular meaning. For example, I am 6 feet 2 inches tall. Feet and inches are units. I could have told you that I am six-two. Nevertheless, you would only understand the information if you could figure out that we are talking about my height and that height is usually reported in the archaic English system of feet and inches. Sometimes you can get away without mentioning the units used to measure whatever you are talking about, but chemistry is not one of those times.

Units can be most helpful when you are converting from one system of measurement to another; for example, from English to metric. If you want to convert 300 miles into kilometers, 300 miles x 5,280 feet/mile x 12 inch/feet x 2.54 cm/inch x 1 m/100 cm x 1 km/1000 m = 483 km.

If you look at each multiplier, you will notice that each is the same as an equation, such as 1 mile = 5,280 feet, so each multiplier is the same as multiplying by one. If you go down the equation and cancel units that appear in the numerator (top) and in the denominator (bottom), you start with 300 miles multiplied by one five times, and we finally get to kilometers. To find out how many kilometers there are in 300 miles, you have to do what each multiplier tells you to do. First, multiply 300 by 5,280, then multiply by 12, then multiply by 2.54, then divide by 100, and last divide by 1,000 to get 483 km.

Uncertainty in Measurement

Because people can only measure something to a certain degree of accuracy, realizing that a measurement always has some degree of uncertainty is important. This uncertainty depends on the precision of the measuring device. For example, if you weigh two heads of lettuce on a bathroom scale, the bathroom scale may show that both weigh 1.5 kg. Nevertheless, if you weigh the two on a balance, the balance may show that one weighs 1.488 kg while the other weighs 1.521 kg. So do the two heads have the same mass? Your conclusion depends on the certainty of those measurements. Therefore, showing the uncertainty in any measurement is important. This is done by using significant figures.

Significant Figures

Rules for counting significant figures:

- Nonzero Integers–Nonzero integers always count as significant figures (i.e., three significant figures in the measurement 2.45 g).
- Zeros–Three classes of zeros exist.
  - Leading zeros are zeros that are in front of, to the left of, all nonzero digits. They are never significant (e.g., 0.00057 has only two significant figures).
  - Captive zeros are zeros between nonzero digits. They are always significant (e.g., 90.08 has four significant figures).
  - Trailing zeros are zeros at the right end of the number. They are significant only if the number contains a decimal point, (e.g., 100 has only one significant figure. However, 1.00 x 102 has three significant figures).
- Exact Numbers–Numbers obtained by counting rather than measuring. They are assumed to have infinite significant figures. Numbers that arise from definitions are also exact, e.g., one inch means exactly 2.54 centimeters, so that when 2.54 cm/in is used in a calculation, it will not limit the number of significant figures.

Using Significant Figures in Calculations

- Multiplication and Division–The number of significant figures in the result is the same as the number in the least precise measurement. For example, 4.28 x 8.3 = 35.524 before correction, and after correction of significant figures, the result should be 36, because the limiting term (8.3) has only two significant figures.
- Addition and Subtraction–The result has the same number of decimal places as the least precise measurement used in the calculation. For example, 53.984 + 2.5 = 56.484 before correction, and after correction, the result should be 56.5, because the limiting term has only one decimal place.

6

The Top Twenty Chemicals

The table below lists the top twenty chemicals manufactured in 2001. As we can see, it represents a broad selection of chemicals from corrosives to hydrocarbons to aromatic compounds to heterocyclic compounds. We will talk about many of these individual chemicals in the next chapters.

Top Twenty Manufactured Chemicals in 2001

Rank	Chemical	Rank	Chemical
1	Sulfuric acid	11	Nitric acid
2	Ethylene	12	Ammonium nitrate
3	Lime	13	Urea
4	Phosphoric acid	14	Ethylbenzene
5	Ammonia	15	Styrene
6	Propylene	16	Hydrogen chloride
7	Chlorine	17	Ethylene oxide
8	Sodium hydroxide	18	Cumene
9	Sodium carbonate	19	Ammonium sulfate
10	Ethylene chloride	20	1,3-Butadiene

2

Forms and Changes of Matter

Recognized Physical Forms

SOLID: A material that has distinct shape and form without a container at normal temperatures and pressures.

LIQUID: A fluid that has no distinct shape but will form to the shape of the container at normal temperatures and pressures.

GAS: A formless fluid material that will fill the container at normal temperatures and pressures.

VAPOR: The gaseous phase of a material that is normally a solid or liquid at normal temperatures and pressures.

AEROSOLS: A dispersion of particles of microscopic size in air. These may be solid particles (dust, fume, smoke) or liquid particles (mist, fog).

DUST: Airborne solid particles that range from 0.1 to 50 microns and larger in diameter. Dust particles less than 50 microns cannot be seen without a microscope.

MIST: An aerosol of suspended liquid droplets.

FOG: A visible aerosol of a liquid formed by condensation.

Most materials may exist in any of these physical forms, depending on their temperature. A compound or mixture that is normally a solid may melt to become a liquid as the temperature rises and boil to become a gas or vapor as the temperature increases. Similarly, a liquid at room temperature may freeze as the temperature cools, solidifying and expanding. This may significantly change and increase the hazards to emergency response First Responders. In responding to emergencies involving hazardous materials, considering both chemical and physical changes that take place is important because of changing weather conditions that may make the materials more hazardous.

8

General Properties of Matter

COMPRESSIBILITY: In a liquid or a solid, most of the space is taken up by the molecules, and therefore, compressing them into a smaller volume by applying pressure is very difficult. Gases can be compressed quite easily, because their molecules are further apart.

DIFFUSION: Occurs rapidly in gases, slowly in liquids, and hardly at all in solids. This is because there is less space between molecules in liquids and solids for a substance to diffuse through.

RETENTION OF VOLUME AND SHAPE: Gases can change their volumes and shapes depending on the pressure and the container. Liquids generally do not change their volumes but can change their shape depending on the container. The volumes or shapes of solids are much harder to change.

SURFACE TENSION: A characteristic of liquids. Attractions felt at the liquids' surface and those within are different. Molecules at the surface want to move back into the center. You can see this when you fill a glass with water. Molecules at the surface can make the water look like a skin because you can fill a glass above the rim.

WETTING: The spreading of a liquid across a surface. Because of surface tension, beads of liquid form where it was spread.

EVAPORATION: Liquids and solids have a tendency to evaporate. This involves changing state from liquid to gas or from solid to gas.

Gases

One of the most amazing things about gases is that, despite wide differences in chemical properties, all the gases essentially obey the gas laws. The gas laws deal with how gases behave with respect to pressure, volume, temperature, and amount.

Pressure

Gases are the only state of matter that can be compressed very tightly or expanded to fill a very large space. Pressure is force per unit area, calculated by dividing the force by the area on which the force acts. The earth's gravity acts on air molecules to create a force, which is the air pushing on the earth. This is called atmospheric pressure.

The units of pressure that are used are known as the pascal (Pa), standard atmosphere (atm), and torr. One atm is the average pressure at sea level. It is normally used as a standard unit of pressure. The SI unit though, is the Pa. One atm is equal to 101,325 Pa. The bar is also used. For pressure:

$$1 \text{ atm} = 760 \text{ mm Hg} = 407 \text{ inches } H_2O = 14.7 \text{ psi} = 101 \text{ kPa} = 1 \text{ torr}$$
$$1 \text{ bar} = 14.5 \text{ psi}$$
$$1 \text{ ft } H_2O = 0.43 \text{ psi}$$

For laboratory work though, the atm is very large. A more convenient unit is the torr; 760 torr equals one atm. A torr is the same unit as the mm Hg (millimeter of mercury). It is the pressure needed to raise a tube of mercury one-millimeter.

THE GAS LAWS: Pressure Volume Temperature Relationships

In all these laws we use the SI units, so we need to know temperatures in Kelvin (K), pressure in atmospheres, and volume in liters.

BOYLE'S LAW: The Pressure-Volume Law. Boyle's law, or the pressure-volume law, states that the volume of a given amount of gas held at constant temperature varies inversely with the applied pressure when the temperature and mass are constant. In other words, when pressure goes up, volume goes down. When volume goes up, pressure goes down. The equation for this law is $P_1V_1 = P_2V_2$. A practical application of this law is in scuba diving. Think of a diver: for every 33 feet, pressure increases by 1 atmosphere, and volume is decreased by ½. If you went down 165 feet, the pressure is 5 atmospheres and volume is 1/5 of your lung capacity. If you take a full breath at 165 feet and hold it to come to the surface, your lungs will over-pressurize and explode.

CHARLES' LAW: The Temperature-Volume Law. This law states that the volume of a given amount of gas held at constant pressure is directly proportional to the Kelvin (K) temperature. In other words, as the volume goes up, the temperature also goes up, or as the temperature goes down, the volume goes down. The equation for this law is $T_2V_1 = T_1V_2$. A practical application is a hot air balloon. You heat the air with a propane torch. The hot air expands the balloon sack. As the air inside the balloon gets hotter, it expands the balloon sack and gets bigger and bigger. The displaced air produces a buoyant force and the balloon lifts from the ground and rises.

GAY-LUSSAC'S LAW: The Pressure-Temperature Law. This law states that the pressure of a given amount of gas held at constant volume is directly proportional to the Kelvin (K) temperature. In other words, as the pressure goes up, the temperature also goes up, or as the pressure decreases the temperature decreases. This is responsible for the coolness of a self-contained breathing apparatus (SCBA) when you remove air from it by breathing. The equation for this is $T_2P_1 = T_1P_2$. A very practical application to the responder is, "when will this cylinder over-pressure and explode?" Let's take a gas cylinder of hydrogen. Typical burst pressure of the cylinder will be about 7000 psi. The typical pressure of the gas in the cylinder will be about 2250 psi. We need to know the temperature at which the cylinder will burst during a fire. So, we need to know the following things: temperature in Kelvin (°C + 273); pressure in atm (psi x 0.068); burst pressure 7000 psi or 476 atm; current pressure 2250 psi or 153 atm; current temperature 35°C or 308 K. So we put it in the equation and solve for the unknown:

$$T_2 = (476 \times 308)/153$$
$$T = 958 \text{ K or } 685°C \text{ or } 1265°F$$

So at a temperature of 1265°F the cylinder pressure will exceed the burst pressure of the bottle and an explosion will occur.

THE IDEAL GAS LAW: The previous laws all assume that the gas being measured is an ideal gas, a gas that obeys all the laws exactly. However, over a wide range of temperature, pressure, and volume, real gases deviate slightly from ideal. For the chemistry of HAZMAT and to simplify, we will assume that all gases act like ideal gases.

10

Compressed Gases and Cryogenic Liquids

COMPRESSED GASES: Compounds and mixtures in gaseous form that are shipped at ambient temperatures in pressurized cylinders. Pressures in the cylinders may range from a few pounds to greater than 15,000 psi.

LIQUEFIED GASES: Gases shipped in pressurized containers, typically shipped at temperatures below ambient. Liquefied gases will vaporize rapidly when the pressure is released.

CRYOGENIC LIQUIDS: Liquefied gases at low temperature. A cryogenic liquid means a refrigerated liquefied gas having a boiling point lower than -90°C (-130°F) at 101.3 kPa (14.7 psi) absolute. There are two generally used definitions of cryogenic liquids:

- One standard defines cryogenics as materials which are liquid with boiling points below -150°C.
- A second standard defines cryogenics as liquids that are stored as a liquid at temperatures below -250°C.

A distinction between cryogenic liquids and liquefied gases is that cryogenics, such as liquid nitrogen or liquid oxygen, remain liquid at atmospheric pressure and do not require pressurized containers to remain liquid at these low temperatures.

Cryogenic liquids, liquefied gases, and compressed gases have their own unique hazards in addition to those associated with the chemical reactions the materials might undergo or the toxicity of the materials. These include:

- The displacement of oxygen by the vaporizing liquid or from the gas released from a pressurized cylinder may cause the danger of asphyxiation.
- The extreme cold of cryogenic liquids and liquefied gases may cause severe frostbite in exposed personnel and destruction of exposed tissue.
- The extreme cold of cryogenic liquids may cause the embrittlement of metals leading to failure of the container, supporting structures, or other exposed metal parts.
- Rapid expansion of liquefied gases or cryogenic liquids can lead to the buildup of extremely high pressure and the violent failure of pressurized equipment. This explosive release of gas is similar in effect to a Boiling Liquid Expanding Vapor Explosion (BLEVE).
- Some pressurized gases may generate large static-electric charges when they are released, leading to the potential to ignite flammable atmospheres.
- Some cryogenic liquids and liquefied gases have unique reactive hazards beyond the hazards associated with the same materials at ambient temperatures. For example, liquid oxygen will react with asphalt to form a powerful and sensitive contact explosive which can be detonated by the pressure of a single footstep. Similarly, liquid chlorine reacts violently with almost any organic material, including wood and cloth, leading to extreme fire danger in the vicinity of a spill.

The End Use Defines the Choice of Shipping Form
It is important to note that some materials may be shipped in more than one form. For example:

- Oxygen may be shipped and stored as a compressed gas at ambient temperatures or may shipped as a cryogenic liquid.
- Nitrogen, helium and argon may be shipped as gases or as cryogenic liquids.
- Carbon dioxide may be shipped as a compressed gas, as a solid (dry ice), or as a liquid under pressure.

- Methane, propane, butane, and mixtures of these gases may be transported in pipelines as gases or shipped as Liquefied Natural Gas, Liquefied Petroleum Gas, etc.
- Ammonia and the simple organic amines may be shipped as compressed gases in small quantities or as liquefied gases in large quantity.

What Determines the Form of Shipment and Storage?

Given the option of shipping these materials in several forms, what determines the choice of the customer as to the form ordered? These decisions are largely based on the application and the amount of material required at a given time. For example, oxygen is shipped in small cylinders as a compressed gas for medical use in ambulances, doctor's offices, etc.; in larger cylinders (as a compressed gas) for use in gas chromatography and for laboratory-scale reactions; and as a cryogenic liquid for large uses, such as the oxygen supply for a hospital or as an oxidant for chemical processes. Materials shipped as cryogenic liquids or as liquefied gases may also be used for their cooling capability: Liquid nitrogen, for example, is used as a coolant to preserve biological samples at low temperature, to rapidly freeze foods, and in traps in gas delivery lines to freeze out low-boiling impurities in the gas stream.

Common Compressed Gases, Liquefied Gases, and Cryogenic Liquids Shipped In Quantity

Compound	Use	Shipping Form	Temperature	Special Hazard
Hydrogen	Instrument gas, chemical reactant	Compressed gas	Ambient under high pressure	Heats on expanding, self-ignites, highly flammable
Nitrogen	Inerting gas, fire prevention, coolant	Compressed gas, cryogenic liquid	Boiling point -195.8°C	Asphyxiant, severe cold
Oxygen	Medical gas, oxidizer	Compressed gas, cryogenic liquid	Boiling point -188°C	Powerful oxidizer, spontaneous fires contact explosive formation with oils
Chlorine	Powerful oxidizer, sterilizing water	Compressed gas, liquefied gas under pressure	Ambient, but evaporation of liquid may cause extreme cooling and frost formation	Highly toxic Powerful oxidizer may cause spontaneous fires on contact with organics, including wood
Fluorine	Powerful oxidizer, fluoropolymers, uranium refining	Compressed gas, cryogenic liquid	Boiling point -180.05°C	Powerful oxidizer, highly toxic, severe burns, etches glass
Helium	Instrument gas, coolant for nuclear reactors, inert gas for arc welding, balloons/blimps, Mixed gases for deep-sea diving	Compressed gas, cryogenic liquid	Boiling point -268.9°C	Coldest cryogenic liquid shipped
Ammonia	Refrigerant, chemical reactant	Compressed gas, liquefied gas, solutions	Boiling point -33°C	Toxic, corrosive, Solutions are strong bases
Sulfur Dioxide	Strong oxidizer, chemical reactant, sulfuric acid/oleum, bleaching paper	Compressed gas, liquefied gas	Boiling point -10°C	Forms corrosive solutions, strong oxidizer, highly toxic
Carbon Dioxide	Coolant, fire extinguishers, dry cleaning, decaffeinating coffee	Compressed gas, liquefied gas, solid "dry ice"	Boiling point -79°C	Asphyxiation, freeze burns

Street Smart^{TM} Chemistry

Liquids

The physical properties of the states are controlled by the strengths of intermolecular attractions. There are only weak interactions between gas molecules; stronger interactions occur between molecules in a liquid, and very strong interactions occur in a solid. The main types of intermolecular attractions for liquids are dipole-dipole attractions, hydrogen bonds, and London forces.

Dipole-dipole attractions are the attractions between polar molecules. Opposite poles of different molecules attract each other. They are about one percent as strong as a covalent bond.

Hydrogen bonds are similar to dipole-dipole attractions, but they involve hydrogen because it is very electronegative. F-H, O-H, and N-H bonds are very polar, and molecules that have those bonds generally attract each other strongly. They are about five percent as strong as a covalent bond.

London forces are responsible for attractions in nonpolar molecules. Because electrons are constantly moving, the movement of electrons in one particle will influence the electrons in another particle. Sometimes, the electrons may even move synchronously all to one side, creating a short-lived dipole, or instantaneous dipole.

Solids

Solids are particles packed in an orderly fashion. There are three main types of solids.

	Crystalline	**Amorphous**	**Polymerics**
Example	Diamond	Glass	Polythene
Structure	Crystalline solids are based upon a simple pattern of arrangement of molecules that is repeated many times throughout the molecule. Often there will be boundaries in the material where the pattern cannot be continued. These produce the edges of crystals and a polycrystalline material.	Amorphous solids have no regular arrangement of their molecules and appear like an instantaneous photo of a liquid; some, like glass, flow very slowly.	Polymeric solids are made up of long chain molecules, wrapped around each other. The polymer chains are made up of repeated monomers.

14

Physical Properties

Materials can be characterized by their physical properties: appearance, density, specific gravity, vapor density, viscosity, and odor.

Elements, compounds, and mixtures have a characteristic appearance consistent with their composition. A description of the appearance of a material (physical state, color, etc.) will normally appear on a Material Safety Data Sheet (MSDS). How the material appears is very important. If the material does not look the way it should, DO NOT handle it until you understand why it has changed. A change such as the addition of another substance may have occurred to alter the original substance with a significant effect on physical properties and hazards. (Special note: For many industrial products the color listed on the MSDS may represent an "average," and the product shipped may vary significantly in color and still be the same product. On the other hand, a significant difference in color may also show contamination or high levels of impurities which may have their own hazards. Continue with caution if the material's appearance is significantly different from the MSDS description.)

DENSITY: A measure of how heavy a unit volume of a substance is, or the mass of a known volume. It is often expressed in lbs/gal, g/c^3, lbs/ft^3. The density of a substance changes with temperature. Usually, as things get colder, they get more dense. As things get warmer, they get less dense. The comparison of densities tells you whether an item will sink or float in a liquid. A wax candle will float in water, but sinks in rubbing alcohol. This is because wax is less dense than water but more dense than the rubbing alcohol.

SPECIFIC GRAVITY: The relative density of liquids compared to water. It is the ratio of the weight of a volume of liquid or solid to the weight of an equal volume of water (the specific gravity of water is, therefore, 1.0). A substance with a specific gravity that is greater than 1.0 will sink in water, whereas one with a specific gravity of less than 1.0 will float on water.

VAPOR DENSITY: Measures the weight of a given vapor as compared with an equal volume of air, with air as a value of 1.0. A vapor density that is greater than 1.0 shows that it is heavier than air and therefore will sink, while a value of less than 1.0 shows that it is lighter than air and therefore will rise. The Compressed Gas Association (CGA) uses specific gravity of the gas for vapor density. They are the same numbers so do not be confused. We can estimate the vapor density of a material when we cannot find it listed in the resource material. We only need to know the molecular weight of the material. Divide it by the average molecular weight of air, which is 29, to get the estimated vapor density. For example, let's look at chlorine, which has a molecular weight of 71. Divide 71 by 29, which is 2.45. In the reference material, the vapor density of chlorine is 2.49. This is more than adequate for the street-smart responder.

When we look at vapor density, we also have to look at the temperature of the vapor. Hot vapors will rise, but unless totally dispersed they will sink once they have cooled off. Cold vapors are very dense and will tend to rise when they warm up. Most materials are heavier than air. A list of materials that are known to be lighter than air is presented in the table that follows.

Materials Lighter Than Air

Hydrogen	0.0696
Helium	0.138
Methane	0.554
Illuminating gas	Mixture of natural gases–primarily methane and ethane
Ammonia	0.597
Neon	0.696
Acetylene	0.906
Hydrogen cyanide	0.947
Diborane	0.952
Carbon monoxide	0.967
Nitrogen	0.967
Ethylene	0.978

VISCOSITY: A measure of the thickness or flowability of a liquid at a given temperature. Viscosity will determine the ease of flow. Temperature affects viscosity. Usually the hotter a liquid gets, the thinner it becomes; the cooler it gets, the thicker it becomes. Liquids with high viscosities, such as heavy oils, have to be heated to increase their fluidity.

ODOR: An expression of how chemicals smell. Some chemicals have little or no odor, while others have a strong characteristic odor. Some characteristic odors can help identify a material. An unexpected odor may be a warning that a substance has escaped from its container. The ability to smell or sense an odor is highly individual. Some people can smell a given compound at a much lower level than others can. Other people may not be able to smell a particular compound even at very high concentrations in the air. There are published tables of odor thresholds that list the concentration in air at which the average person can smell a particular compound. Never attempt to use odors to define areas of safety; some compounds which are highly toxic may cause significant damage at a concentration below the odor threshold and may be at toxic levels long before their odor is detected!

ANHYDROUS: Dry, without water. Material contains no water and is usually pure, for example, anhydrous ammonia.

HYDROPHOBIC: Water-hating or repelled by water.

HYDROPHILIC: Water-loving, attracted to water, or wetted by water.

Changes of Matter

Remembering that materials do not always stay the same is important. Understanding the kinds of changes a chemical can undergo will help you to control or prevent unwanted changes from occurring. There are two kinds of predictable changes that matter can undergo: physical and chemical.

Physical Changes

In a physical change, the state of a substance is altered but the substance itself is not. Boiling water to make steam is an example of a physical change.

TEMPERATURE CHANGES
Given the right conditions, matter can change its state from a solid to a liquid, from a liquid to a gas, and back again. Water changes from a solid (ice), to a liquid (water), to a gas (steam). Yet its chemical composition is unchanged. It is still H_2O. Water is water regardless of its state.

MELTING POINT: The temperature at which a solid turns into its liquid phase.

BOILING POINT: The temperature at which the vapor pressure of a liquid is equal to the atmospheric pressure and the liquid boils. More simply put, the boiling point is reached when bubbles of vapor rise to the surface of a liquid and escape. Boiling is simply rapid evaporation.

FREEZING POINT OR CRYSTALLIZATION: When a liquid is cooled to its melting point, we call it the freezing point, the temperature at which it will solidify or crystalize. The freezing point and melting point are usually the same temperature.

CRITICAL TEMPERATURE: The minimum temperature above which a gas cannot be liquefied no matter how much pressure is applied.

CRITICAL PRESSURE: The minimum pressure above which a gas cannot be liquefied no matter what the temperature is.

SUBLIMATION: Occurs when a substance evaporates going directly from the solid state to the vapor state, without passing through the liquid state. Solids such as naphthalene, moth balls, or dry ice are examples of materials that sublime readily.

DEPOSITION: Occurs when a substance deposits out of the vapor state directly to the solid state without passing through the liquid state. Solids such as iodine and high temperature materials that cool rapidly are examples of materials that will undergo deposition.

EVAPORATION RATE: The speed at which some material changes from a liquid to a gas. Temperature will affect evaporation rates. The hotter the temperature, the faster the evaporation rate. The colder the temperature, the slower the rate.

VOLATILITY is another word for an evaporation rate. Some materials change to a gas more easily than others. Those that change more readily to gases are called volatile. Volatility is usually reported as a comparative value versus another compound. For example: volatility = 1.3 (butyl acetate = 1.0). This is not generally useful unless you know the relative rate of the comparison compound. However, the higher the volatility numbers, the more easy a liquid usually converts into gas. The lower the boiling point of a material, the higher the volatility. That is not to say high boiling materials do not have high volatility. We can estimate the volatility of a material:

$$V = (16020 \times MW \times VP)/Kelvin$$

V	= volatility
MW	= Molecular weight
VP	= vapor pressure in mm Hg
Kelvin	= °C + 273

Example of volatility estimation for phosgene:

MW	= 100
VP	= 1173 mm Hg @ 20°C (68°F)
V	= [(16020 x 100 x 1173)/293] = 6,400,000 mg/m^3

Volatility of phosgene from literature is 6,340,000 mg/m^3.

VAPOR EXPANSION: When a material volatilizes or evaporates, the vapors occupy a specific volume. The ratio of how much vapor to the volume of the original liquid or solid is called the vapor expansion ratio. Some compounds that are shipped as liquids under pressure or as cryogenic liquids will expand to many hundred times their original volume on evaporation.

VAPOR PRESSURE: The pressure exerted by the vapor of a substance in a closed container. It is a measure of a substance's tendency to emit or give off vapors. The higher the vapor pressure, the more volatile the substance, thus the more vapor given off. The lower the material's boiling point, the higher the vapor pressure. Vapor pressure increases with temperature. If we can cool off a container we can reduce the boiling. You could cool the container by putting a colder material through the cooling coils if equipped, or possibly spraying water on it. You could also reduce pressure by venting the container and therefore provide cooling. This should only be done in extreme circumstances, as an environmental problem could occur.

CONCENTRATION: When a material dissolves, the result is a mixture. The amount of each component in a mixture can be measured. Measures of how much of each compound is present in the mixture are expressed as concentrations. Concentration is usually expressed in percentages: parts per million (ppm), parts per billion (ppb), or milligrams per cubic meter (mg/m^3). Usually, when dealing with hazardous materials, the concentration of the mixture will have a significant impact on the hazard. Low concentrations will normally be less hazardous than high concentrations. For example, one percent caustic (sodium hydroxide) will be a skin irritant and can cause skin burns over a long time if not washed off; 50 percent caustic will cause serious burns immediately on contact.

DISSOLVING AND SOLUBILITY: When a material dissolves, it is undergoing another type of physical change. Dissolving occurs when one material physically moves inside and disperses into another. Upon dissolving, a compound's chemical composition (e.g., which atoms bond to which other atoms) stays the same. Sugar dissolved in tea is still sugar–it has not changed its composition because it is in solution.

SOLUBILITY: How well a material will dissolve in a liquid is shown by a property called solubility. Tables listing solubility in water and in common organic solvents are available and this data is frequently found on Material Safety Data Sheets. The values listed are normally the maximum amounts of material that will dissolve in the listed solvent at room temperature. Solubility depends on temperature; compounds that dissolve very poorly in cold water may be very soluble in hotter water.

Chemical Changes

Chemical reactions change the structures of the original substances involved and create new materials with unique properties. The physical characteristics of the new compounds may be very different from those of the starting materials, and the hazards associated with the new compounds may also be very different. For example, sodium metal and chlorine gas chemically react to form sodium chloride, or ordinary table salt. The salt has properties different from the individual properties of the sodium and chlorine that chemically combined to form it. During a chemical reaction, chemical bonds are broken and formed.

STABLE substances are ones that do not change composition under ordinary conditions over long periods of time. Unstable substances are more likely to change composition rapidly and/or unexpectedly.

COMPATIBLE: Materials can coexist in a stable and nonreactive manner when they are mixed. Other materials when mixed are incompatible and react with each other and may create hazardous conditions. Incompatible materials should always be separated and segregated.

Knowing which materials are stable, unstable, compatible, and incompatible will permit you to handle them more safely and avoid chemical reactions.

CORROSIVITY AND pH: Corrosion is a process of material degradation. Technically, corrosivity is the ability of a material to attack and destroy metals, flesh, or other materials. A corrosive agent is a reactive compound or element that produces a destructive chemical change in the material upon which it is acting. Common corrosives are halogens (bromine, chlorine, fluorine, iodine), ozone, strong acids, and strong bases.

The most common measure of corrosivity is pH. pH is a scale for measuring how acidic or basic (alkaline) a material is. The scale ranges from 0 to 14. Those materials with a low pH (less than 7) are known as acids. Stomach acid is an example of a substance with a low pH. Vinegar is less acidic. Pure water, with a pH of seven, is neutral. Those with higher pH (greater than 7) are known as bases. Up the scale are weak bases like antacids. Strong basic chemicals such as drain cleaner top the scale. The closer the pH is to 0 or 14 the stronger the acid or base. pH is a "logarithmic" scale meaning that the difference between pH=2 and pH=3 or pH=9 and pH=10 is actually a 10x increase in acid or basic strength or concentration.

COMBUSTIBILITY: The ability of a material to act as a fuel. Materials that can be readily ignited and sustain a fire are considered combustible, while those that do not are called noncombustible.

FLAMMABILITY: The ability of a material to generate a sufficient concentration of combustible vapors under normal conditions to be ignited and produce a flame. Having a proper fuel-to-air ratio expressed as the percentage fuel in air, is necessary to allow combustion. Usually, there is a range of fuel concentrations in air for each material that is optimal for the ignition and sustenance of combustion. This is called the flammable range. A flammable material is considered highly combustible if it can burn at ambient temperature. A combustible material is not necessarily flammable, because it may not be easily ignited or the ignition cannot be maintained.

Lower Flammable Limit (LFL) or Lower Explosibility Level (LEL)
The minimum concentration of vapor to air below which the propagation of a flame will not occur in the presence of an ignition source.

Upper Flammable Limit (UFL) or **Upper Explosibility Limit (UEL)**
The maximum vapor to air concentration above which propagation of a flame will not occur. If a vapor to air mixture is below the LFL, it is described as too lean to burn; if it is above the UFL, it is "too rich" to burn. When the vapor to air ratios are somewhere between the LFL and UFL, fires and explosions can occur. The mixture is said to be in the flammable or explosive range.

FLASH POINT: The lowest temperature at which vapor is given off in sufficient concentration to form an ignitable mixture with air near its surface. Combustion does not continue as a sustained burn at the flash point.

FIRE POINT: The lowest temperature at which a liquid produces sufficient vapor to flash near its surface and continue to burn. The fire point is usually 10 to 30°C higher than the flash point.

AUTO-IGNITION TEMPERATURE: The lowest temperature at which a substance will ignite in air when there is no ignition source.

SADT: Self Accelerating Decomposition Temperature. Temperature above which the decomposition of an unstable substance continues unimpeded, regardless of the ambient or external temperature.

MAXIMUM SAFE STORAGE TEMPERATURE: The maximum safe temperature at which a product can be stored. This temperature is well below the SADT.

GAS OR VAPOR EXPLOSIONS: Very rapid, violent releases of energy. If combustion is extremely rapid, large amounts of energy, heat, and gaseous products are produced and released. The major factor contributing to the explosion is the confinement of a flammable material. When vapors of gases cannot freely dissipate, they enter the combustion reaction more rapidly. Confinement also increases the energy associated with these materials that enhances the explosive process. Poorly ventilated buildings, sewers, drums, and bulk liquid containers are examples of places where potentially explosive atmospheres may exist.

Explosions in liquid containers are usually known as BLEVE (Boiling Liquid Expanding Vapor Explosion). BLEVEs have been known and recorded to hurl pieces of tank cars 4000 to 5000 feet from the initial scene. You do not have to have a fire present to have a BLEVE. A steam-drum explosion is an example of a BLEVE.

While working at a HAZMAT scene where flammable materials are present, the concentration of combustible gas must be monitored and any potential ignition source(s) must be kept out of the area.

Some examples of hazards related to fires and explosions are listed below, but not limited to:
- Physical destruction due to shock waves, heat, and flying objects
- Initiation of secondary fires or creation of flammable conditions
- Release of toxic and corrosive compounds into the surrounding environment

3

Atoms, Elements, and the Periodic Table

Each atom is made up of several different parts. At the center of the atom is a nucleus or core surrounded at a distance by electrons. In the nucleus are protons, which are positively charged, and neutrons that have no charge. Electrons surrounding the nucleus are negatively charged. In an atom of the "pure" element the number of protons and electrons are exactly equal and the atom is electrically neutral.

Elements differ from one another by the number of protons in the nucleus. The fact that hydrogen has one proton in its nucleus is what makes the atom a hydrogen atom. A nucleus that has eight protons in its nucleus is always an oxygen atom. An atom that has 16 protons is always a sulfur, etc. The periodic table is a listing of the elements based on the number of protons in each nucleus. The periodic table also gives the internationally recognized name and symbol for each element. The atomic number is the number of protons; the number of protons always equals the number of electrons in an atom. The atomic mass is the weight of an atom; it is determined by the number of neutrons and protons that are present in the nucleus.

The molecular weight of an element is the sum of all nuclide (isotope) masses multiplied by their natural abundance. This weighted average is the relative mass listed in the periodic table. The molecular weights of molecules and compounds are the sum of their atomic masses.

The periodic table is an efficient and compact arrangement for all the known chemical elements. Once you understand the organization of the periodic table, you can probably use it quickly to obtain a wealth of information about any of the more than 112 elements. Besides obtaining the name, symbol, atomic number, and atomic mass for any element, you can probably use the table to help you predict an element's chemical behavior. However, to realize its full potential as a valuable chemical resource, you must understand its organization. Looking at the periodic table, you can see that the elements are arranged horizontally by order of increasing atomic number. Notice that the table consists of several horizontal rows. These horizontal rows are called periods. The vertical rows found in the periodic table are called groups, or families. Elements within a specific group have similar chemical properties. As we will discuss in the next section, the similar chemical properties of elements within a group occur because these elements have the same number of electrons in their outer shells. These groups can be divided into three categories: metals, nonmetals, and metalloids. Overall, the diagonal line (that resembles a staircase) in the right-hand side of the periodic table separates the metals from the nonmetals. Let us see what specific groups are included among the various categories:

METALS
Elements below and to the left of the diagonal line:
>Alkali Metals (Group IA)
>Alkaline Earth Metals (Group IIA)
>Transition Metals
>Inner Transition Metals

The Heavier Elements in:
>Group III (Al, Ga, In, Tl)
>Group IV (Sn, Pb)
>Group V (Bi)

NONMETALS
Elements above and to the right of the diagonal line

METALLOIDS
Seven of the elements touching the diagonal line that cannot be classified as metals or nonmetals: B, Si, Ge, As, Sb, Te, and Po

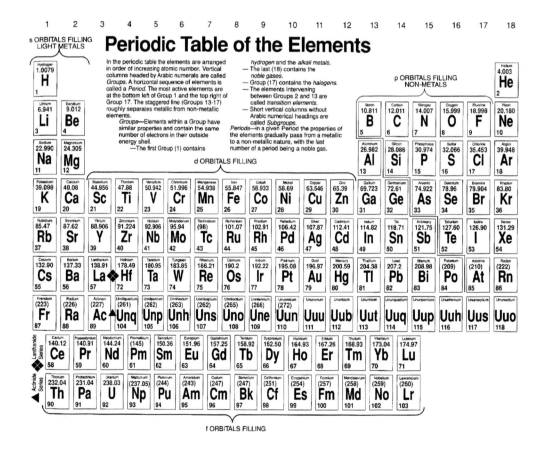

Each element may also have different numbers of electrically neutral neutrons in its nucleus. These different combinations are called isotopes. For example, hydrogen has three isotopes. Each hydrogen nucleus has one proton (this is what makes it hydrogen). The isotope that has no neutrons in its nucleus is traditionally called hydrogen and is the most abundant isotope. Hydrogen (with or without its accompanying electron) is the most abundant element in the universe. There is also an isotope of hydrogen that has one proton and one neutron (called deuterium) and a second isotope that has one proton and two neutrons (called tritium). All three species (hydrogen, deuterium, and tritium) are isotopes of the same element because they all have one proton in their nucleus.

Similarly, carbon has six protons in its nucleus. The most abundant isotope of carbon also has six neutrons in its nucleus, but there are also isotopes with seven neutrons and eight neutrons. These are sometimes designated as C^{12}, C^{13}, and C^{14} to show that they are isotopes but that they have a different number of neutrons in their nucleus.

We normally hear about isotopes only when the topic involves radioactivity. Some elements have radioactive isotopes that decompose to release radiation. However, most elements have isotopes that are stable and are not radioactive, so the term isotope itself does not necessarily imply a radiation hazard.

Each element has a name approved by the International Union of Pure and Applied Chemistry and an intentionally recognized abbreviation or symbol. The symbols often do not resemble the English names for the element. Many symbols were chosen based on the ore the element was first isolated from, the country, the region where the element was found in abundance, or the ancient name for the element. When writing names of elements, a chemist usually uses abbreviations, since they are quicker to write than the names. The abbreviations that we use are called symbols. None of the symbols contains more than two letters; the first one is always capitalized and the second, if any, is always lower case. Of course there are some exceptions, such as Hydrogen (H), Carbon (C), Oxygen (O), etc. Let us look at some examples: W for tungsten, since tungsten was first isolated from the ore called Wolframite; or Cu for copper, from the ancient Latin name for Cyprus (Cuprum) where copper was mined in antiquity; or Pb for lead, from the Latin name Plumbum; or Fe for Ferrum, the ancient Roman name for iron. Do not forget that the second letter of the symbol is never capitalized. If it is, then it represents a molecule; for example, CO represents a molecule of carbon monoxide. The symbols for all known elements are given in the periodic table. The following table shows the symbols for some of the elements found in the periodic table.

Symbols for Elements in the Periodic Table

Element	Symbol	Atomic Weight	Element	Symbol	Atomic Weight
Aluminum	Al	26.98	Magnesium	Mg	24.31
Antimony	Sb	121.75	Manganese	Mn	54.93
Argon	Ar	39.95	Mercury	Hg	200.59
Arsenic	As	74.92	Neon	Ne	20.18
Barium	Ba	137.34	Nickel	Ni	58.71
Bismuth	Bi	208.98	Nitrogen	N	14.01
Boron	B	10.81	Oxygen	O	16.00
Bromine	Br	79.91	Phosphorus	P	30.97
Cadmium	Cd	112.40	Platinum	Pt	195.09
Calcium	Ca	40.08	Potassium	K	39.10
Carbon	C	12.01	Radium	Ra	226
Chlorine	Cl	35.45	Silicon	Si	28.09
Chromium	Cr	52.00	Silver	Ag	107.87
Cobalt	Co	58.93	Sodium	Na	22.99
Copper	Cu	63.54	Strontium	Sr	87.62
Fluorine	F	19.00	Sulfur	S	32.10
Gold	Au	196.97	Tin	Sn	118.69
Helium	He	4.00	Titanium	Ti	47.90
Hydrogen	H	1.01	Tungsten	W	183.85
Iodine	I	126.90	Uranium	U	238.03
Iron	Fe	55.85	Zinc	Zn	65.37
Lead	Pb	207.19	Zirconium	Zr	91.22
Lithium	Li	6.939			

Chemistry of the Elements

Gases

FLUORINE: Fluorine is the most reactive of all elements; no chemical substance is capable of freeing fluorine from any of its compounds. For this reason, fluorine does not occur freely in nature and was extremely difficult for scientists to isolate. The first recorded use of a fluorine compound dates to around 1670, to a set of instructions for etching glass that called for Bohemian emerald (CaF_2). Chemists attempted to identify the material that was capable of etching glass. George Gore was able to produce a small amount of fluorine through an electrolytic process in 1869. Unknown to Gore, fluorine gas explosively combines with hydrogen gas. That is exactly what happened in Gore's experiment when the fluorine gas that formed on one electrode combined with the hydrogen gas that formed on the other electrode.

Ferdinand Frederic Henri Moissan, a French chemist, was the first to successfully isolate fluorine in 1886. He did this through the electrolysis of potassium fluoride (KF) and hydrofluoric acid (HF). He also completely isolated the fluorine gas from the hydrogen gas, and he built his electrolysis device completely from platinum. His work was so impressive that he was awarded the Nobel Prize for chemistry in 1906. Today, fluorine is still produced through the electrolysis of potassium fluoride and hydrofluoric acid as well as through the electrolysis of molten potassium acid fluoride (KHF_2).

Fluorine as fluoride salts are added to city water supplies in the proportion of about one part per million to help prevent tooth decay. Sodium fluoride (NaF), stannous(II) fluoride (SnF_2), and sodium monofluorophosphate (Na_2PO_3F) are all fluorine compounds added to toothpaste, to help prevent tooth decay. Hydrofluoric acid (HF) is used to etch glass, including most of the glass used in light bulbs. Uranium hexafluoride (UF_6) is used to separate isotopes of uranium. Crystals of calcium fluoride (CaF_2), also known as fluorite and fluorspar, are used to make lenses to focus infrared light. Fluorine joins with carbon to form a class of compounds known as fluorocarbons. Some of these compounds, such as dichlorodifluoromethane (CF_2Cl_2), were widely used in air conditioning and refrigeration systems and in aerosol spray cans, but have been phased out due to the damage they were causing to the earth's ozone layer.

Fluorine is a clear to yellow cryogenic liquid (-306°F) or gas. The liquid is denser than water and will sink and boil. The expansion ratio is 980:1. The vapors are visible (pale yellow), very irritating (odor threshold 0.035ppm), and extremely poisonous (TWA 0.1ppm). It is the strongest known oxidizing element and will react with most common materials. When it is wet, it is extremely corrosive. It is one of the few materials that will corrode glass and porcelain. When water is present, it reacts to form hydrogen fluoride, oxygen, and oxygen difluoride gases. It produces toxic gases in fire situations.

CHLORINE: Chlorine is a greenish yellow liquid (-29°F) or gas. The liquid is denser than water and will sink and boil. The expansion ratio is 460:1. The vapors are visible, very irritating (odor threshold 3.5ppm), and extremely poisonous (TWA 0.5 ppm). Concentrations of 1000 parts per million can be fatal after a few deep breaths. When it is wet, it is extremely corrosive. It is a very strong oxidizer and reacts with water to produce hydrogen chloride gas. Chlorine fires produce very toxic gases. Chlorine gas was used as war gas in World War I and caused many casualties.

Since it combines directly with nearly every element, chlorine is never found free in nature. Chlorine was first produced by Carl Wilhelm Scheele, a German chemist, when he combined the mineral pyrolusite (MnO_2) with hydrochloric acid (HCl) in 1774. Although Scheele thought the gas produced in his experiment contained oxygen, Sir Humphry Davy proved in 1810 that it was actually a distinct element. Today, most chlorine is produced through the electrolysis of aqueous sodium chloride (NaCl).

Chlorine is commonly used as an antiseptic and is used to make drinking water safe and treat swimming pools. Large amounts of chlorine are used in many industrial processes, such as in the production of paper products, plastics, dyes, textiles, medicines, antiseptics, insecticides, solvents, and paints.

Two of the most familiar chlorine compounds are sodium chloride (NaCl) and hydrogen chloride (HCl). Sodium chloride, commonly known as table salt, is used to season food and in some industrial processes. Hydrogen chloride, when mixed with water (H_2O), forms hydrochloric acid, a strong and commercially important acid. Other chlorine compounds include: chloroform ($CHCl_3$), carbon tetrachloride (CCl_4), potassium chloride (KCl), lithium chloride (LiCl), magnesium chloride ($MgCl_2$), and chlorine dioxide (ClO_2).

HYDROGEN: Composed of a single proton and a single electron, hydrogen is the simplest and most abundant element in the universe. It is estimated that 90 percent of the visible universe is composed of hydrogen. Hydrogen is an odorless, colorless, and very flammable gas. It burns with an almost invisible flame (3700°F) and will self-ignite when released from a container under pressure. The flammable range is very broad: LEL 4 percent to UEL 75 percent. Hydrogen is different from most gases in that it heats up when released under pressure. This heating will cause ignition of the hydrogen gas. As a liquid it will float and boil rapidly on water. The vapor density is less than air but will displace oxygen. It can be shipped as a cryogenic liquid with a boiling point of -423°F and a vapor expansion of 860:1. Hydrogen is a commercially important element. Large amounts of hydrogen are combined with nitrogen from the air to produce ammonia (NH_3) through a process called the Haber process. Hydrogen is also added to fats and oils, such as peanut oil, through a process called hydrogenation. Liquid hydrogen is used in the study of superconductors and, when combined with liquid oxygen, makes an excellent rocket fuel. Hydrogen has three common isotopes. The simplest isotope, called protium, is just ordinary hydrogen. The second, a stable isotope called deuterium, was discovered in 1932. The third isotope, tritium, was discovered in 1934.

HELIUM, NEON, AND ARGON : These gases are known as the inert or noble gases. They are colorless, odorless, nonreactive, and nonflammable. Helium is less dense than air, but the remaining gases are more dense. They can be shipped as compressed gases or cryogenic liquids. The boiling points are helium at -452°F, neon at -411°F, and argon at -302°F. They are nontoxic, but will displace oxygen from the air. The expansion ratios are helium 700:1, neon 1445:1, and argon 840:1. These gases will not react with any other chemicals under normal conditions. Liquid helium trapped in a closed container can vaporize and generate 15,000 psi of pressure. These gases can create significant asphyxiation hazards by displacing air as they evaporate.

Helium

Helium, the second most abundant element in the universe, was discovered on the sun before it was found on the earth. The hunt to find helium on earth ended in 1895. Sir William Ramsay, a Scottish chemist, conducted an experiment with a mineral containing uranium called clevite. He exposed the clevite to mineral acids and collected the gases that were produced. Helium makes up about 0.0005 percent of the earth's atmosphere. This trace amount of helium is constantly lost to space. The earth's atmospheric helium is replaced by the decay of radioactive elements in the earth's crust. Alpha decay, one type of radioactive decay, produces particles called alpha particles. An alpha particle can become a helium atom once it captures two electrons from its surroundings. This newly formed helium can eventually work its way to the atmosphere through cracks in the crust.

Helium is commercially recovered from natural gas deposits, mostly from Texas, Oklahoma, and Kansas. Helium gas is used to inflate blimps, scientific balloons, and party balloons. It is used as an inert shield for arc welding, to pressurize the fuel tanks of liquid fueled rockets, and in supersonic wind tunnels. Helium is combined with oxygen to create an atmosphere for deep-sea divers that prevents them from contracting the bends. Liquid helium is an important cryogenic material and is used to study superconductivity and to create superconductive magnets. The Department of Energy's Jefferson Lab uses large amounts of liquid helium to operate its superconductive electron accelerator.

Neon

Neon is the fourth most abundant element in the universe, but only 0.0018 percent of the earth's atmosphere is neon.

The largest use for neon gas is in advertising signs. Neon is also used to make high voltage indicators and is combined with helium to make helium-neon lasers. Liquid neon is used as a cryogenic refrigerant. Neon is highly inert and forms no known compounds, although there is some evidence that it could form a compound with fluorine.

Argon
Argon was discovered by Sir William Ramsay and Lord Rayleigh, a British chemist, in 1894. Argon makes up 0.93 percent of the earth's atmosphere, making it the third most abundant gas. Argon is obtained from the air as a by-product of the production of oxygen and nitrogen.

Argon is frequently used when an inert atmosphere is needed. It is used to fill incandescent and fluorescent light bulbs to prevent oxygen from corroding the hot filament. Argon is also used to form inert atmospheres for arc welding, grow semiconductor crystals, and in processes that require shielding from other atmospheric gases.

NITROGEN: Discovered by the Scottish physician Daniel Rutherford in 1772, nitrogen is a colorless and odorless gas that makes up most of the air we breathe. By itself it is nontoxic; but it can displace oxygen, leading to asphyxiation. It is the fifth most abundant element in the universe and makes up about 78 percent of the earth's atmosphere, which contains an estimated 4,000 trillion tons of the gas. Nitrogen is obtained from liquefied air through a process known as fractional distillation.

The largest use of nitrogen is for the production of ammonia (NH_3). Large amounts of nitrogen are combined with hydrogen to produce ammonia. Large amounts of ammonia are then used to create fertilizers, explosives, and nitric acid (HNO_3).

Nitrogen gas is largely inert and is used as a protective shield in the semiconductor industry and during certain types of welding and soldering operations. It is used as an inerting material by itself to prevent the formation of a flammable or explosive atmosphere above a flammable liquid. Oil companies use high-pressure nitrogen to help force crude oil to the surface. Liquid nitrogen is an inexpensive cryogenic liquid used for refrigeration, preservation of biological samples, and low temperature scientific experimentation. It is shipped as a compressed gas and a cryogenic liquid (-320°F) with an expansion ratio is 694:1. In some types of fires nitrogen will be oxidized to the different nitrogen oxides, a group of very toxic gases. The nitrogen derivatives can be burnt in a fire to release not only nitrogen oxides, but cyanides as well.

OXYGEN: Oxygen is a colorless gas with a fresh odor. As a cryogenic liquid (-297°F), it is bluish in color, and its expansion ratio is 857:1. It is a nonflammable material, but a very powerful oxidizer. When liquid oxygen (LOX) comes into contact with asphalt, it forms a contact explosive. Liquid oxygen will cause most organic and several inorganic materials to burst into flames on contact. Oxygen is the third most abundant element in the universe and makes up nearly 21 percent of the earth's atmosphere. Oxygen accounts for nearly half of the mass of the earth's crust, two-thirds of the mass of the human body, and nine-tenths of the mass of water. Large amounts of oxygen can be extracted from liquefied air through a process known as fractional distillation.

Oxygen is a highly reactive element and is capable of combining with most other elements. It is required by most living organisms and for most forms of combustion. Impurities in molten pig iron are burned away with streams of high pressure oxygen to produce steel. Oxygen can also be combined with acetylene (C_2H_2) to produce an extremely hot flame used for welding. Liquid oxygen, when combined with liquid hydrogen, makes an excellent rocket fuel. Ozone (O_3) forms a thin, protective layer around the earth that shields the surface from the sun's ultraviolet radiation. Oxygen is also a component of hundreds of thousands of organic compounds.

28

Liquids

BROMINE: Bromine is a dark, reddish-brown, heavy fuming liquid. The vapors are very dense and are extremely harsh and irritating (odor threshold 3.5 ppm). It is extremely corrosive, poisonous (TWA 0.1 ppm), and is a strong oxidizer. It reacts violently with aluminum. It corrodes or reacts with most metals and plastics. Bromine produces toxic gases in fire situations.

The only nonmetallic element that is a liquid at normal room temperatures, bromine was produced by Carl Löwig, a young chemistry student, the summer before starting his freshman year at Heidelberg. When he showed his professor, Leopold Gmelin, the red, smelly liquid he had produced, Gmelin realized that this was an unknown substance and encouraged Löwig to produce more of it so they could study it in detail. Unfortunately, winter exams and the holidays delayed Löwig's work long enough for another chemist, Antoine-Jérôme Balard, to publish a paper in 1826 describing the new element. Balard was credited with the discovery and named it after the Greek word for stench, bromos. Today, bromine is primarily obtained by treating brines from wells in Michigan and Arkansas with chlorine.

Elemental bromine is a hazardous material. It causes severe burns when it comes in contact with the skin, and its vapor irritates the eyes, nose, and throat. Most of the bromine produced in the United States was used in the manufacture of ethylene dibromide($C_2H_4Br_2$), a chemical added to leaded gasolines that prevented the accumulation of lead compounds within the engine. With the discontinuation of leaded gasolines in favor of unleaded gasolines, the demand for bromine has been greatly reduced. Silver bromide (AgBr), a chemical used in photography, now accounts for the largest use of bromine. Other bromine compounds are used in fumigants, in flameproofing agents, and in some compounds used to purify water. Tyrian purple, an expensive purple dye known to ancient civilizations, was produced from an organic bromine compound secreted from a sea mussel known as the murex.

MERCURY: The only liquid metal at room temperature, mercury is very bright, shiny, and very heavy (113 lb/gal). It has a significant vapor pressure, and the vapors are very hazardous to your health (TWA 0.006 ppm). Mercury was known to the ancient Chinese and Hindus and has been found in 3500-year-old Egyptian tombs. Mercury's chemical symbol (Hg) comes from the Greek word hydrargyrum, which means liquid silver. Mercury is not usually found free in nature and is primarily obtained from the mineral cinnabar (HgS). Spain and Italy produce about half of the world's supply of mercury.

Mercury can be used to make thermometers, barometers, and other scientific instruments. Mercury conducts electricity and is used to make silent, position-dependent switches. Mercury vapor is used in streetlights, fluorescent lamps, and advertising signs.

Mercury easily forms alloys with other metals, such as gold, silver, zinc, and cadmium. These alloys are called amalgams. Amalgams are used to extract gold from its ores, create dental fillings (in the case of silver), and extend the life of dry cell batteries (in the case of zinc and cadmium).

Mercury forms useful compounds with other elements. Mercuric chloride ($HgCl_2$) is a very poisonous salt and was once used to disinfect wounds. Mercurous chloride (Hg_2Cl_2), also called calomel, is an antiseptic used to kill bacteria. Mercuric sulfide (HgS) is used to make a red paint pigment called vermilion. Mercuric oxide (HgO) is used to make mercury batteries.

Mercury is poisonous and can enter the body through the respiratory tract, the digestive tract, or directly through the skin. It accumulates in the body, eventually causing severe illness or death. The derivatives of mercury are used as fungicides and other intermediates. All the derivatives are poisonous. Some organic mercury compounds are among the most toxic materials known.

Solids

ALKALI METALS–LITHIUM(Li), SODIUM(Na), POTASSIUM(K), RUBIDIUM(Rb), AND CESIUM(Cs): Alkali metals react violently with water. This reaction is very exothermic and will cause burning metal to erupt and explode, causing more eruptions and explosions. The relative reactivity of these metals is the following: Li < Na < K < Rb < Cs. The corresponding hydroxides are formed when they react, and the resulting solution is very corrosive. These metals are shipped in vacuum-packed metal cans or in cans with a hydrocarbon base. They are also shipped in tank cars under inert gas. These metals are so reactive that they will start to react in moist air, giving off fumes of the oxides and hydroxides. They will react with just about any molecule that has oxygen in it (like carbon dioxide). However, they will not react with pure, dry oxygen. When these materials are around as powders, you should be aware that reaction rates are explosive! These materials will also react with halogenated hydrocarbons (Halon®), so use a Class D fire extinguisher for fire extinguishment.

Lithium
Many uses have been found for lithium and its compounds. Lithium has the highest specific heat of any solid element and is used in heat transfer applications. It is used to make special glasses and ceramics, including the Mount Palomar telescope's 200-inch mirror. Lithium is the lightest known metal and can be alloyed with aluminium, copper, manganese, and cadmium to make strong, lightweight metals for aircraft. Lithium hydroxide (LiOH) is used to remove carbon dioxide from the atmosphere of spacecraft. Lithium stearate ($LiC_{18}H_{35}O_2$) is used as a general purpose and high temperature lubricant. Lithium carbonate (Li_2CO_3) is used as a drug to treat manic depression disorder. Lithium reacts with water, but not as violently as sodium.

Sodium
Although sodium is the sixth most abundant element on earth and comprises about 2.6 percent of the earth's crust, it is a very reactive element and is never found free in nature. Pure sodium was first isolated by Sir Humphry Davy in 1807 through the electrolysis of caustic soda (NaOH). Since sodium can ignite on contact with water, it must be stored in a moisture-free environment.

Sodium is used in the production of titanium, sodamide, sodium cyanide, sodium peroxide, and sodium hydride. Liquid sodium has been used as a coolant for nuclear reactors. Sodium vapor is used in streetlights and produces a brilliant yellow light.

Sodium also forms many useful compounds. Some of the most common are table salt (NaCl), soda ash (Na_2CO_3), baking soda ($NaHCO_3$), caustic soda (NaOH), Chile saltpeter ($NaNO_3$), and borax ($Na_2B_4O_7 \cdot 10H_2O$).

30

Potassium

Although potassium is the eighth most abundant element on earth and comprises about 2.1 percent of the earth's crust, it is a very reactive element and is never found free in nature. Metallic potassium was first isolated by Sir Humphry Davy in 1807 through the electrolysis of molten caustic potash (KOH). A few months after discovering potassium, Davy used the same method to isolate sodium. Potassium can be obtained from the minerals sylvite (KCl), carnallite ($KCl \cdot MgCl_2 \cdot 6H_2O$), langbeinite ($K_2Mg_2(SO_4)_3$), and polyhalite ($K_2Ca_2Mg(SO_4)_4 \cdot 2H_2O$). These minerals are often found in ancient lake and sea beds. Caustic potash, another important source of potassium, is primarily mined in Germany, New Mexico, California, and Utah.

Pure potassium is a soft, waxy metal that can be easily cut with a knife. It reacts with oxygen to form potassium superoxide (KO_2) and with water to form potassium hydroxide (KOH), hydrogen gas, and heat. During the reaction with water enough heat is produced to ignite the hydrogen gas. To prevent it from reacting with the oxygen and water in the air, samples of metallic potassium are usually stored submerged in mineral oil. Potassium forms an alloy with sodium (NaK) that is used as a heat transfer medium in some types of nuclear reactors.

Potassium forms many important compounds. Potassium chloride (KCl) is the most common potassium compound. It is used in fertilizers, as a salt substitute, and to produce other chemicals. Potassium hydroxide (KOH) is used to make soaps, detergents, and drain cleaners. Potassium carbonate (K_2CO_3), also known as pearl ash, is used to make some types of glass and soaps and is obtained commercially as a by-product of the production of ammonia. Potassium superoxide (KO_2) can create oxygen from water vapor (H_2O) and carbon dioxide (CO_2) through the following reaction: $4KO_2 + 2H_2O + 2CO_2 \rightarrow 2KHCO_3 + 2KOH + 3O_2$. It is used in respiratory equipment and is produced by burning potassium metal in dry air. Potassium nitrate (KNO_3), also known as saltpeter or nitre, is used in fertilizers, matchheads, and pyrotechnics.

Cesium

Cesium was discovered in 1860 by the German chemists Robert Wilhelm Bunsen and Gustav Robert Kirchoff through the spectroscopic analysis of Durkheim mineral water. They named cesium after the blue lines they observed in its spectrum. Today, cesium is primarily obtained from the mineral pollucite ($CsAlSi_2O_6$). Obtaining pure cesium is difficult because cesium ores are frequently contaminated with rubidium, an element that is chemically similar to cesium. To obtain pure cesium, cesium and rubidium ores are crushed and heated with sodium metal to 650°C, forming an alloy that can then be separated by fractional distillation. Metallic cesium is too reactive to easily handle and is usually sold in the form of cesium azide (CsN_3). Cesium is recovered from cesium azide by heating it.

Cesium has the second-lowest melting point of all metallic elements, which limits its uses. Cesium readily combines with oxygen and is used as a getter, a material that combines with and removes trace gases from vacuum tubes. Cesium is also used in atomic clocks, in photoelectric cells, and as a catalyst in the hydrogenation of certain organic compounds. Since it is easily ionized and has a high mass, cesium ions may one day be used as a propellant in ion engines on spacecraft.

Cesium reacts violently with water and ice, forming cesium hydroxide (CsOH). Cesium hydroxide is the strongest base known and will attack glass. Cesium chloride (CsCl) and cesium nitrate ($CsNO_3$) are cesium's most common compounds and are primarily used in the production of other chemicals.

ALUMINUM: Pure aluminum is a bright, shiny metal. It is the most abundant metal on earth. It melts at 1220°F and ignites at about the same temperature. It burns with a brilliant white light. Aluminum dust is a very powerful explosive and is water-reactive to the point of ignition for the entire mass of powder. Aluminum powder makes the very bright, white light and loud explosion in the production of fireworks.

Although aluminum is the most abundant metal in the earth's crust, it is never found free in nature. All of the earth's aluminum has combined with other elements to form compounds. Two of the most common compounds are alum, such as potassium aluminum sulfate ($KAl(SO_4)_2·12H_2O$), and aluminum oxide (Al_2O_3). About 8.2 percent of the earth's crust is composed of aluminum.

Scientists suspected that an unknown metal existed in alum as early as 1787, but they did not have a way to extract it until 1825. Hans Christian Oersted, a Danish chemist, was the first to produce tiny amounts of aluminum. Two years later, Friedrich Wöhler, a German chemist, developed a different way to obtain aluminum. By 1845, he was able to produce samples large enough to determine some of aluminum's basic properties. Wöhler's method was improved in 1854 by Henri Étienne Sainte-Claire Deville, a French chemist. Deville's process allowed for the commercial production of aluminum. As a result, the price of aluminum dropped from around $1200 per kilogram in 1852 to around $40 per kilogram in 1859. Unfortunately, aluminum remained too expensive to be widely used.

Two important developments in the 1880s greatly increased the availability of aluminum. The first was the invention of a new process for obtaining aluminum from aluminum oxide. Charles Martin Hall, an American chemist, and Paul L. T. Héroult, a French chemist, each invented this process independently in 1886. The second was the invention of a new process that could cheaply obtain aluminum oxide from bauxite. Bauxite is an ore that contains a large amount of aluminum hydroxide ($Al_2O_3·3H_2O$), along with other compounds. Karl Joseph Bayer, an Austrian chemist, developed this process in 1888. The Hall-Héroult and Bayer processes are still used today to produce nearly all of the world's aluminum.

With an easy way to extract aluminum from aluminum oxide and an easy way to extract large amounts of aluminum oxide from bauxite, the era of inexpensive aluminum had begun. In 1888, Hall formed the Pittsburgh Reduction Company, which is now known as the Aluminum Company of America, or Alcoa. When it opened, his company could produce about 25 kilograms of aluminum a day. By 1909, his company was producing about 41,000 kilograms of aluminum a day. As a result of this huge increase of supply, the price of aluminum fell rapidly to about $0.60 per kilogram.

Today, aluminum and aluminum alloys are used in a wide variety of products: cans, foils, and kitchen utensils, as well as parts of airplanes, rockets, and other items that require a strong, light material. Although it does not conduct electricity as well as copper, it is used in electrical transmission lines because of its light weight. It can be deposited on the surface of glass to make mirrors, where a thin layer of aluminum oxide quickly forms that acts as a protective coating. Aluminum oxide is also used to make synthetic rubies and sapphires for lasers.

ANTIMONY: Known since ancient times, antimony is sometimes found free in nature, but is usually obtained from the ores stibnite (Sb_2S_3) and valentinite (Sb_2O_3). Nicolas Lémery, a French chemist, was the first person to scientifically study antimony and its compounds. He published his findings in 1707. Antimony makes up about 0.00002 percent of the earth's crust.

32

Antimony is a brittle metal and is a poor conductor of heat and electricity. Very pure antimony is used to make certain types of semiconductor devices, such as diodes and infrared detectors. Antimony is alloyed with lead to increase lead's durability. Antimony alloys are also used in batteries, low friction metals, type metal, and cable sheathing, among other products. Antimony compounds are used to make flame-proofing materials, paints, ceramic enamels, glass, and pottery. The ancient Egyptians used antimony, in the form of stibnite, for black eye make-up.

ARSENIC: Metallic arsenic comes in two basic forms, yellow and grey metallic. It is used in the manufacture of pesticides, pharmaceuticals, wood preservatives, enamels, and glass. It is easily oxidized into arsenic trioxide or arsenous oxide. Although arsenic compounds were mined by the early Chinese, Greek, and Egyptian civilizations, it is believed that arsenic itself was first identified by Albertus Magnus, a German alchemist, in 1250. Arsenic occurs free in nature, but is most often found in the minerals arsenopyrite (FeAsS), realgar (AsS), and orpiment (As_2S_3). Today, most commercial arsenic is obtained by heating arsenopyrite.

Arsenic and its compounds are poisonous. They have been used to make rat poison and some insecticides. Small amounts of arsenic are added to germanium to make transistors. Gallium arsenide (GaAs) can produce laser light directly from electricity. Arsenic was used as one of the first chemical weapons.

At 28 times standard atmospheric pressure, arsenic melts at a temperature of 1090 K. If it were also measured at a pressure of 28 atmospheres, arsenic's boiling point would be higher than its melting point, as you would expect.

BARIUM: First isolated in 1808 by Sir Humphry Davy, a British chemist, through the electrolysis of molten baryta (BaO), Barium is never found free in nature since it reacts with oxygen in the air, forming barium oxide (BaO), and with water, forming barium hydroxide ($Ba(OH)_2$) and hydrogen gas (H_2). Barium is most commonly found as the mineral barite ($BaSO_4$) and witherite ($BaCO_3$). It is primarily produced through the electrolysis of barium chloride ($BaCl_2$).

Barium sulfate ($BaSO_4$), a common barium compound, is used as a filler for rubber, plastics, and resins. It can be combined with zinc oxide (ZnO) to make a white pigment known as lithophone or with sodium sulfate (Na_2SO_4) to make another white pigment known as blanc fixe. Stones made from impure barium sulfate glow when exposed to light and will glow in the dark for up to six years if intensely heated in the presence of charcoal. These stones, known as Bologna stones, were discovered near Bologna, Italy in the early 1500s and were thought to possess magical properties by alchemists. Although all barium compounds are poisonous, barium sulfate can be safely ingested because it does not dissolve in water. It is also a good absorber of X-rays and, when swallowed, can be used to produce X-ray images of the intestinal tract.

Barium carbonate ($BaCO_3$), another common barium compound, is used in the manufacture of ceramics and some types of glass. It is a component in clay slurries used in drilling oil wells. Barium carbonate is used to purify some chemical solutions and is the primary base material for the manufacture of other barium compounds.

Barium forms several other useful compounds. Barium nitrate ($Ba(NO_3)_2$) burns with a bright green color and is used in signal flares and fireworks. Barium chloride (BaCl) is used as a water softener. Barium oxide (BaO) easily absorbs moisture and is used as a desiccant. Barium peroxide (BaO_2) forms hydrogen peroxide (H_2O_2) when it is mixed with water and is used as a bleaching agent that activates when wet. Barium titanate ($BaTiO_3$) is used as a dielectric material in capacitors. Barium ferrite ($BaO·6Fe_2O_3$) is used to make magnets.

33

BISMUTH: Known since ancient times, bismuth was often confused with lead and tin. Bismuth was first shown to be a distinct element in 1753 by Claude Geoffroy the Younger. Bismuth does occur free in nature and in such minerals as bismuthinite (Bi_2S_3) and bismite (Bi_2O_3). The largest deposits of bismuth are found in Bolivia, although bismuth is usually obtained as a by-product of mining and refining lead, copper, tin, silver, and gold.

Pure bismuth is a white, brittle metal with a slight pink color. Bismuth is usually mixed with other metals, such as lead, tin, iron, or cadmium to form low-melting alloys. These alloys are used in such things as automatic fire sprinkler systems, fire detection systems, and electrical fuses.

Bismuth oxide (Bi_2O_3), a bismuth compound, is used as a yellow pigment in paints and cosmetics. Bismuth oxychloride (BiOCl) is used to make a pigment known as bismuth white. Bismuth carbonate ($Bi_2(CO_3)_3$) is used to treat diarrhea and gastric ulcers.

BORON: Used in pyrotechnics and flares to produce a green color, boron has also been used in some rockets as an ignition source. B^{10}, one of the naturally occurring isotopes of boron, is a good absorber of neutrons and is used in the control rods of nuclear reactors as a radiation shield and as a neutron detector. Boron filaments are used in the aerospace industry because of their high strength and light weight.

Boron forms several commercially important compounds. The most important boron compound is sodium borate pentahydrate ($Na_2B_4O_7 \cdot 5H_2O$). Large amounts of this compound are used in the manufacture of fiberglass insulation and sodium perborate bleach. The second most important compound is boric acid (H_3BO_3), which is used to manufacture textile fiberglass and is used in cellulose insulation as a flame retardant. Sodium borate decahydrate ($Na_2B_4O_7 \cdot 10H_2O$), better known as borax, is the third most important boron compound. Borax is used in laundry products and as a mild antiseptic. Other boron compounds are used to make borosilicate glasses, enamels for covering steel, and as a potential medicine for treating arthritis.

CARBON: The sixth most abundant element in the universe, carbon has been known since ancient times. Carbon is most commonly obtained from coal deposits, although it usually must be processed into a form suitable for commercial use. Three naturally occurring allotropes of carbon are known to exist: amorphous, graphite, and diamond.

Amorphous
Amorphous carbon is formed when a material containing carbon is burned without enough oxygen for it to burn completely. This black soot, also known as lampblack, gas black, channel black, or carbon black, is used to make inks, paints, and rubber products. It can also be pressed into shapes and is used to form the cores of most dry cell batteries, among other things.

Graphite
One of the softest materials known is a form of carbon that is primarily used as a lubricant. Although it does occur naturally, most commercial graphite is produced by treating petroleum coke, a black tar residue remaining after the refinement of crude oil, in an oxygen-free oven. Naturally-occurring graphite occurs in two forms, alpha and beta. These two forms have identical physical properties but different crystal structures. All artificially produced graphite is of the alpha type. In addition to its use as a lubricant, graphite, in a form known as coke, is used in large amounts in the production of steel. Coke is made by heating soft coal in an oven without allowing oxygen to mix with it. Although it is commonly called lead, the black material used in pencils is actually graphite.

34

Diamond

The third naturally occurring form of carbon, diamond is one of the hardest substances known. Although naturally occurring diamond is typically used for jewelry, most commercial quality diamonds are artificially produced. These small diamonds are made by squeezing graphite under high temperatures and pressures for several days or weeks and are primarily used to make things like diamond-tipped saw blades. Although they posses very different physical properties, graphite and diamond differ only in their crystal structure.

A fourth allotrope of carbon, known as white carbon, was produced in 1969. It is a transparent material that can split a single beam of light into two beams, a property known as birefringence. Very little is known about this form of carbon.

Large molecules consisting only of carbon, known as buckminsterfullerenes, or buckyballs, have recently been discovered and are currently the subject of much scientific interest. A single buckyball consists of 60 or 70 carbon atoms (C60 or C70) linked together in a structure that looks like a soccer ball. They can trap other atoms within their framework, appear to be capable of withstanding great pressures, and have magnetic and superconductive properties.

C^{14}, a radioactive isotope of carbon with a half-life of 5,730 years, is used to find the age of formerly living things through a process known as radiocarbon dating. The theory behind carbon dating is fairly simple. Scientists know that a small amount of naturally occurring carbon is C^{14}. Although C^{14} decays into N^{14} through beta decay, the amount of C^{14} in the environment remains constant because new C^{14} is always being created in the upper atmosphere by cosmic rays. Living things tend to ingest materials that contain carbon, so the percentage of C^{14} within living things is the same as the percentage of C^{14} in the environment. Once an organism dies, it no longer ingests anything. The C^{14} within that organism is no longer replaced and the percentage of C^{14} begins to decrease as it decays. By measuring the percentage of C^{14} in the remains of an organism, and by assuming that the natural abundance of C^{14} has remained constant over time, scientists can estimate when that organism died. For example, if the concentration of C^{14} in the remains of an organism is half of the natural concentration of C^{14}, a scientist would estimate that the organism died about 5,730 years ago, the half-life of C^{14}.

There are nearly ten million known carbon compounds. An entire branch of chemistry, known as organic chemistry, is devoted to their study. Many carbon compounds are essential for life as we know it. Some of the most common carbon compounds are carbon dioxide (CO_2), carbon monoxide (CO), carbon disulfide (CS_2), chloroform ($CHCl_3$), carbon tetrachloride (CCl_4), methane (CH_4), ethylene (C_2H_4), acetylene (C_2H_2), benzene (C_6H_6), ethyl alcohol (C_2H_5OH), and acetic acid (CH_3COOH).

CALCIUM: Although calcium is the fifth most abundant element in the earth's crust, it is never found free in nature since it easily forms compounds by reacting with oxygen and water. Metallic calcium was first isolated by Sir Humphry Davy in 1808 through the electrolysis of a mixture of lime (CaO) and mercuric oxide (HgO). Today, metallic calcium is obtained by displacing calcium atoms in lime with atoms of aluminum in hot, low-pressure containers. About 4.2 percent of the earth's crust is composed of calcium.

Due to its high reactivity with common materials, there is very little demand for metallic calcium. It is used in some chemical processes to refine thorium, uranium, and zirconium. Calcium is also used to remove oxygen, sulfur, and carbon from certain alloys. Calcium can be alloyed with aluminum, beryllium, copper, lead, and magnesium. Calcium is also used in vacuum tubes as a getter, a material that combines with and removes trace gases from vacuum tubes.

Calcium carbonate ($CaCO_3$) is one of the common compounds of calcium. It is heated to form quicklime (CaO) which is then added to water (H_2O). This forms another material known as slaked lime ($Ca(OH)_2$) which is an inexpensive base material used throughout the chemical industry. Chalk, marble, and limestone are forms of calcium carbonate. Calcium carbonate is used to make white paint, cleaning powder, toothpaste, and stomach antacids, among other things. Other common compounds of calcium include: calcium sulfate ($CaSO_4$), also known as gypsum, which is used to make dry wall and plaster of Paris; calcium nitrate ($Ca(NO_3)_2$), a naturally occurring fertilizer; and calcium phosphate ($Ca_3(PO_4)_2$), the main material found in bones and teeth.

CADMIUM: Friedrich Strohmeyer, a German chemist, discovered cadmium in 1817 while studying samples of calamine ($ZnCO_3$). When heated, Strohmeyer noticed that some samples of calamine glowed with a yellow color while other samples did not. After further examination, he determined that the calamine that changed color when heated contained trace amounts of a new element. There is only one mineral that contains significant amounts of cadmium, greenockite (CdS), but it is not common enough to mine profitably. Fortunately, small amounts of cadmium are found in zinc ores, and most of the cadmium produced today is obtained as a by-product of mining and refining zinc.

Cadmium is a poisonous metal and its use is somewhat limited for this reason. Like zinc, cadmium can be electroplated to other materials to protect them from corrosion. Cadmium easily absorbs neutrons and is used to make control rods for nuclear reactors. Cadmium is also used in rechargeable nickel-cadmium batteries.

Cadmium is alloyed with silver to form solder, a metal with a relatively low melting point used to join electrical components, pipes, and other metallic items. Cadmium-based solders must be handled with care to prevent cadmium poisoning. Cadmium alloys are also used to make low friction bearings that are highly resistant to fatigue.

Hydrated cadmium sulfate ($3CdSO_4 \cdot 5H_2O$), one of cadmium's compounds, is used in a device called a Weston cell, a type of battery that produces a precise voltage used to calibrate medical and laboratory equipment. Cadmium sulfide (CdS), another cadmium compound, is a yellow powder that is used as a pigment. Other cadmium compounds are used in the phosphors of black and white television sets and in the blue and green phosphors in color television sets.

CHROMIUM: Chromium was discovered by Louis-Nicholas Vauquelin, in 1797, while experimenting with a material known as Siberian red lead, also known as the mineral crocoite ($PbCrO_4$). He produced chromium oxide (CrO_3) by mixing crocoite with hydrochloric acid (HCl). Although he believed a method for isolating chromium did not yet exist, Vauquelin was pleasantly surprised in 1798 to discover that he was able to obtain metallic chromium by simply heating chromium oxide in a charcoal oven. Today, chromium is primarily obtained by heating the mineral chromite ($FeCr_2O_4$) in the presence of aluminum or silicon.

Chromium is a blue-white metal that is hard, brittle, and very corrosion-resistant. Chromium can be polished to form a very shiny surface and is often plated to other metals to form a protective and attractive covering. Chromium is added to steel to harden it and to form stainless steel, a steel alloy that contains at least 10 percent chromium. Other chromium-steel alloys are used to make armor plate, safes, ball bearings, and cutting tools.

Chromium forms many colorful compounds that have industrial uses. Lead chromate ($PbCrO_4$), also known as chrome yellow, has been used as a yellow pigment in paints. Chromic oxide (Cr_2O_3), also known as chrome green, is the ninth most abundant compound in the earth's crust and is a widely used green pigment.

36

Rubies and emeralds also owe their colors to chromium compounds. Potassium dichromate ($K_2Cr_2O_7$) is used in the tanning of leather while other chromium compounds are used as mordants, materials that permanently fix dyes to fabrics. Chromium compounds are also used to anodize aluminum, a process that coats aluminum with a thick, protective layer of oxide. Chromite, chromium's primary ore, is used to make molds for the firing of bricks because of its high melting point, moderate thermal expansion, and stable crystal structure. Chromium VI compounds are very toxic.

COBALT: Cobalt was discovered by Georg Brandt, a Swedish chemist, in 1739. Brandt was attempting to prove that the ability of certain minerals to color glass blue was due to an unknown element and not to bismuth, as was commonly believed at the time. Cobalt's primary ores are cobaltite (CoAsS) and erythrite $Co_3(AsO_4)_2 \cdot 8H_2O$. Cobalt is usually recovered as a by-product of mining and refining nickel, silver, lead, copper, and iron.

Although cobalt is used in electroplating to give objects an attractive surface that resists oxidation, it is more widely used to form alloys. Alnico, an alloy consisting of aluminum, nickel and cobalt is used to make powerful permanent magnets. Stellite alloys, which contain cobalt, chromium, and tungsten, are used to make high speed and high temperature cutting tools and dyes. Cobalt is also used to make alloys for jet engines and gas turbines, magnetic steels, and some types of stainless steels.

Co^{60}, a radioactive isotope of cobalt, is an important source of gamma rays and is used to treat some forms of cancer and as a medical tracer. Co^{60} has a half-life of 5.27 years and decays into Ni^{60} through beta decay.

Cobalt compounds have been used for centuries to color porcelain, glass, pottery, tile, and enamel. Some of these compounds are known as cobalt blue, ceruleum, new blue, smalt, cobalt yellow, and cobalt green. In addition to being used as a dye, cobalt is also important to human nutrition, as it is an essential part of Vitamin B_{12}.

COPPER: Archaeological evidence suggests that people have been using copper for at least 11,000 years. Copper is relatively easy to mine and refine; people discovered methods for extracting copper from its ores at least 7,000 years ago. The Roman Empire obtained most of its copper from the island of Cyprus, which is where copper's name originated. Today, copper is primarily obtained from the ores cuprite (Cu_2O), tenorite (CuO), malachite ($CuCO_3 \cdot Cu(OH)_2$), chalcocite (Cu_2S), covellite (CuS), and bornite (Cu_6FeS_4). Large deposits of copper ore are located in the United States, Chile, Zambia, Zaire, Peru, and Canada.

Used in large amounts by the electrical industry in the form of wire, copper is second only to silver in electrical conductance. Since it resists corrosion from the air, moisture, and seawater, copper has been widely used in coins. Although once made nearly entirely from copper, American pennies are now made from zinc that has been coated with copper. Copper is also used to make water pipes and jewelry, as well as other items.

Pure copper is usually too soft for most uses. People first learned about 5,000 years ago that copper can be strengthened if it is mixed with other metals. The two most familiar alloys of copper are bronze and brass. Bronze, the first alloy created by people, is a mix of copper that contains as much as 25 percent tin. Early people used bronze to make tools, weaponry, containers, and ornamental items. Brass, a mix of copper that contains between 5 percent and 45 percent zinc, was first used about 2,500 years ago. The Romans were the first to make extensive use of brass, using it to make such things as coins, kettles, and ornamental objects. Today, brass is also used in some musical instruments, screws, and other hardware that must resist corrosion.

Hydrated copper sulfate ($CuSO_4 \cdot 5H_2O$), also known as blue vitrol, is the best known copper compound. It is used as an agricultural poison, as an algicide in water purification, and as a blue pigment for inks. Cupric chloride ($CuCl_2$), another copper compound, is used to fix dyes to fabrics. Cuprous chloride ($CuCl$) is a poisonous white powder that is chiefly used to absorb carbon dioxide (CO_2). Copper cyanide ($CuCN$) is commonly used in electroplating.

GALLIUM: First proposed to exist by Dmitri Mendeleyev in 1871 based on gaps in his newly created Periodic Table of Elements, gallium was discovered spectroscopically by the French chemist Paul-Émile Lecoq de Boisbaudran in 1875. Later that same year, Lecoq was able to obtain pure gallium through the electrolysis of a solution of gallium hydroxide ($Ga(OH)_3$) in potassium hydroxide (KOH). Trace amounts of gallium are found in diaspore, sphalerite, germanite, and bauxite, as well as in the by-products of burning coal.

Gallium melts near room temperature and has one of the largest liquid ranges of any metal, so it has found use in high temperature thermometers. Gallium easily forms alloys with most metals and has been used to create low melting alloys. Gallium is used as a doping material for semiconductors and has been used to produce solid-state items like transistors and light-emitting diodes. Gallium arsenide ($GaAs$) can produce laser light directly from electricity. Large amounts of gallium trichloride ($GaCl_3$) have been gathered to build the Gallium Neutrino Observatory, an observatory located in Italy. The observatory was built to study particles called neutrinos which are produced inside the sun during the process of nuclear fusion.

GOLD: An attractive and highly valued metal, gold has been known for at least 5,500 years. Gold is sometimes found free in nature, but it is usually found in conjunction with silver, quartz (SiO_2), calcite ($CaCO_3$), lead, tellurium, zinc, or copper. There is roughly 1 milligram of gold dissolved in every ton of seawater, although extracting it currently costs more than the gold is worth. It has been estimated that all the gold that has currently been refined could be placed in a cube measuring 20 meters on a side.

Gold is the most malleable and ductile of all known metals. A single ounce of gold can be beaten into a sheet measuring roughly 5 meters on a side. Thin sheets of gold, known as gold leaf, are primarily used in arts and crafts for gilding. One sheet of gold leaf can be as thin as 0.000127 millimeters, or about 400 times thinner than a human hair.

Pure gold is soft and is usually alloyed with other metals such as silver, copper, platinum, or palladium to increase its strength. Gold alloys are used to make jewelry, decorative items, dental fillings, and coins. The amount of gold in an alloy is measured with a unit called a carat. One carat is equal to one part in twenty-four, so an 18-carat gold ring contains 18 parts pure gold and 6 parts alloy material.

Gold is a good conductor of heat and electricity and does not tarnish when it is exposed to the air, so it can be used to make electrical connectors and printed circuit boards. Gold is also a good reflector of infrared radiation and can be used to help shield spacecraft and skyscrapers from the sun's heat. Gold-coated mirrors can be used to make telescopes that are sensitive to infrared light.

A radioactive isotope of gold, Au^{198}, is used for treating cancer. Gold sodium thiosulfate ($AuNa_3O_6S_4$) is used as a treatment for arthritis. Chlorauric acid ($HAuCl_4$) is used to preserve photographs by replacing the silver atoms present in an image.

IODINE: Iodine was discovered by the French chemist Barnard Courtois in 1811. Courtois was extracting sodium and potassium compounds from seaweed ash. Once these compounds were removed, he added sulfuric acid (H_2SO_4) to further process the ash. He accidentally added too much acid and a violet colored cloud erupted from the mass. The gas condensed on metal objects in the room, creating solid iodine. Today, iodine is chiefly obtained from deposits of sodium iodate ($NaIO_3$) and sodium periodate ($NaIO_4$) in Chile and Bolivia.

Trace amounts of iodine are required by the human body. Iodine is part of thyroxin, a hormone produced by the thyroid gland that controls the body's rate of physical and mental development. A lack of iodine can also cause a goiter, a swelling of the thyroid gland. Iodine is added to salt (iodized salt) to prevent these diseases. Large amounts of iodine are toxic.

Iodine is used as a test for starch which turns a deep blue when it comes in contact with starch. Potassium iodide (KI) is used to make photographic film and, when mixed with iodine in alcohol, as an antiseptic for external wounds. A radioactive isotope of iodine, I^{131}, is used to treat some diseases of the thyroid gland.

Care should be taken in handling and using iodine. It can burn the skin and damage the eyes and mucous membranes. Pure iodine is poisonous if ingested. Iodine will sublime at room temperature to give a purple gas and iodine deposits. It can also be found in meth labs.

IRIDIUM: Iridium was discovered at the same time as osmium by the British chemist Smithson Tennant in 1803. Iridium and osmium were identified in the black residue remaining after dissolving platinum ore with aqua regia, a mixture of 25 percent nitric acid (HNO_3) and 75 percent hydrochloric acid (HCl). Today, iridium is still obtained from platinum ores and as a by-product of mining nickel.

Pure iridium is very brittle and is nearly impossible to machine. It is primarily used as a hardening agent for platinum. Platinum-iridium alloys are used to make crucibles and other high temperature equipment. Iridium is also alloyed with osmium to make the tips of fountain pens and compass bearings.

Iridium is the most corrosive-resistant metal known. For this reason, the standard meter bar was created from an alloy of 90 percent platinum and 10 percent iridium. This bar was replaced as the definition of the meter in 1960 when the meter was redefined in terms of the orange-red spectral line of Kr^{86}.

A thin, worldwide layer of iridium exists in a layer of sediment that was put down at the end of the Cretaceous period. Since meteors and asteroids contain a higher percentage of iridium than the earth's crust, this iridium-enriched layer is seen as evidence that the earth was struck by a large meteor or asteroid at that time. Dust from the impact would have spread around the globe, depositing the iridium. The dust also would have blocked the sun for a time, resulting in the extinction of many plant and animal species, including the dinosaurs.

IRON: Archaeological evidence suggests that people have been using iron for at least 5,000 years. Iron is the cheapest and one of the most abundant of all metals, comprising nearly 5.6 percent of the earth's crust and nearly all the earth's core. Iron is primarily obtained from the minerals hematite (Fe_2O_3) and magnetite (Fe_3O_4). The minerals taconite, limonite ($FeO(OH)\cdot nH_2O$), and siderite ($FeCO_3$) are other important sources.

Huge amounts of iron are used to make steel, an alloy of iron and carbon. Steel typically contains between 0.3 percent and 1.5 percent carbon, depending on the desired characteristics. The addition of other elements can give steel other useful properties. Small amounts of chromium improves durability and prevents rust (stainless steel); nickel increases durability and resistance to heat and acids; manganese increases strength and resistance to wear; molybdenum increases strength and resistance to heat; tungsten retains hardness at high temperatures; and vanadium increases strength and springiness. Steel is used to make paper clips, skyscrapers, and everything in between.

In addition to helping build the world around us, iron helps keep plants and animals alive. Iron plays a role in the creation of chlorophyll in plants and is an essential part of hemoglobin, the substance that carries oxygen within red blood cells. Iron sulfate ($FeSO_4$) is used to treat the blood disease anemia.

Iron pentacarbonyl ($Fe(CO)_5$) is a heavy, toxic liquid that can burst into flame on contact with air.

LEAD: Known since ancient times, lead is sometimes found free in nature, but it is usually obtained from the ores galena (PbS), anglesite ($PbSO_4$), cerussite ($PbCO_3$), and minium (Pb_3O_4). Although lead makes up only about 0.0013 percent of the earth's crust, it is not considered to be a rare element since it is easily mined and refined. Most lead is obtained by roasting galena in hot air, although nearly one-third of the lead used in the United States is obtained through recycling efforts.

Lead is a soft, malleable, and corrosion-resistant material. The ancient Romans used lead to make water pipes, some of which are still in use today. Unfortunately for the ancient Romans, lead is a cumulative poison and the decline of the Roman empire has been blamed, in part, on lead in the water supply. Lead is used to line tanks that store corrosive liquids, such as sulfuric acid (H_2SO_4). Lead's high density makes it useful as a shield against X-ray and gamma-ray radiation, and it is used in X-ray machines and nuclear reactors. Lead is also used as a covering on some wires and cables to protect them from corrosion, as a material to absorb vibrations and sounds, and in the manufacture of ammunition. Today, most lead is used in the production of lead-acid storage batteries, such as the batteries found in automobiles.

Several lead alloys are widely used. Solder, an alloy that is nearly half lead and half tin, is a material with a relatively low melting point that is used to join electrical components, pipes, and other metallic items. Type metal, an alloy of lead, tin, and antimony, is a material used to make the type used in printing presses and plates. Babbit metal, another lead alloy, is used to reduce friction in bearings.

Lead forms many useful compounds. Lead monoxide (PbO), also known as litharge, is a yellow solid that is used to make some types of glass such as lead crystal and flint glass, in the vulcanizing of rubber, and as a paint pigment. Lead dioxide (PbO_2) is a brown material that is used in lead-acid storage batteries. Trilead tetraoxide (Pb_3O_4), also known as red lead, is used to make a reddish-brown paint that prevents rust on outdoor steel structures. Lead arsenate ($Pb_3(AsO_4)_2$) has been used as an insecticide although other, less harmful, substances have now largely replaced it. Lead carbonate ($PbCO_3$), also known as cerussite, is a white, poisonous substance that was once widely used as a pigment for white paint. Lead carbonate in paints has largely been replaced by titanium dioxide (TiO_2). Lead sulfate ($PbSO_4$), also known as anglesite, is used in a paint pigment known as sublimed white lead. Lead chromate ($PbCrO_4$), also known as crocoite, is used to produce chrome yellow paint. Lead nitrate ($Pb(NO_3)_2$) is used to make fireworks and other pyrotechnics. Lead silicate ($PbSiO_3$) is used to make some types of glass and in the production of rubber and paints.

MAGNESIUM: Pure magnesium is a bright, shiny metal. It ignites at about 1200°F and burns with an intense white flame. Its demand for oxygen is so great that it will burn under water and in pure carbon dioxide. Powdered magnesium is even more dangerous than powdered aluminum. Damp materials have been known to detonate when shocked.

Although it is the eighth most abundant element in the universe and the seventh most abundant element in the earth's crust, magnesium is never found free in nature. Magnesium was first isolated by Sir Humphry

Davy, a British chemist, through the electrolysis of a mixture of magnesium oxide (MgO) and mercuric oxide (HgO) in 1808. Today, magnesium can be extracted from the minerals dolomite ($CaCO_3 \cdot MgCO_3$) and carnallite ($KCl \cdot MgCl_2 \cdot 6H_2O$), but it is most often obtained from seawater. Every cubic kilometer of seawater contains about 1.3 billion kilograms of magnesium (12 billion pounds per cubic mile). Magnesium burns with a brilliant white light and is used in pyrotechnics, flares, and photographic flashbulbs. Magnesium is the lightest metal that can be used to build things, although its use as a structural material is limited since it burns at relatively low temperatures. Magnesium is frequently alloyed with aluminum, which makes aluminum easier to roll, extrude, and weld. Magnesium-aluminum alloys are used where strong, lightweight materials are required, such as in airplanes, missiles, and rockets. Cameras, horseshoes, baseball catchers' masks, and snowshoes are other items that are made from magnesium alloys.

Magnesium oxide (MgO), also known as magnesia, is the second-most-abundant compound in the earth's crust. Magnesium oxide is used in some antacids, in making crucibles and insulating materials, in refining some metals from their ores, and in some types of cements. When combined with water (H_2O), magnesia forms magnesium hydroxide ($Mg(OH)_2$), better known as milk of magnesia, which is commonly used as an antacid and as a laxative.

Hydrated magnesium sulphate ($MgSO_4 \cdot 7H_2O$), better known as Epsom salt, was discovered in 1618 by a farmer in Epsom, England, when his cows refused to drink the water from a certain mineral well. He tasted the water and found that it tasted very bitter. He also noticed that it helped heal scratches and rashes on his skin. Epsom salt is still used today to treat minor skin abrasions.

Other magnesium compounds include magnesium carbonate ($MgCO_3$) and magnesium fluoride (MgF_2). Magnesium carbonate is used to make some types of paints and inks and is added to table salt to prevent caking. A thin film of magnesium fluoride is applied to optical lenses to help reduce glare and reflections.

MANGANESE: Proposed to be an element by Carl Wilhelm Scheele in 1774, manganese was discovered later that year by Johan Gottlieb Gahn, a Swedish chemist, by heating the mineral pyrolusite (MnO_2) in the presence of charcoal. Today, most manganese is still obtained from pyrolusite, although it is usually burned in a furnace with powdered aluminum or is treated with sulfuric acid (H_2SO_4) to form manganese sulfate ($MnSO_4$), which is then electrolyzed.

Nearly 90 percent of all of the manganese produced each year is used in the production of steel. Manganese is added to molten steel to remove oxygen and sulfur; it is alloyed with steel to make it easier to form and work with and to increase steel's strength and resistance to impact. Railroad tracks, for example, are made with steel that contains as much as 1.2 percent manganese. Manganese is also used to give glass an amethyst color and is responsible for the color of amethyst gemstones.

Manganese dioxide (MnO_2), the most common compound of manganese, makes up about 0.14 percent of the Earth's crust. It is used in dry-cell batteries to prevent the formation of hydrogen, to remove the green color in glass that is caused by the presence of iron contaminants, and as a drying agent in black paints.

MOLYBDENUM: Carl Welhelm Scheele, a Swedish chemist, discovered molybdenum in 1778 in a mineral known as molybdenite (MoS_2) which had been confused as a lead compound. Molybdenum was isolated by Peter Jacob Hjelm in 1781. Today, most molybdenum is obtained from molybdenite, wulfenite ($PbMoO_4$), and powellite ($CaMoO_4$). These ores typically occur in conjunction with ores of tin and tungsten. Molybdenum is also obtained as a by-product of mining and processing tungsten and copper.

Molybdenum has a high melting point and is used to make the electrodes of electrically heated glass furnaces. Some electrical filaments are also made from molybdenum. The metal is used to make some missile and aircraft parts and is used in the nuclear power industry. Molybdenum is also used as a catalyst in the refining of petroleum.

Molybdenum is primarily used as an alloying agent in steel. When added to steel in concentrations between 0.25 percent and 8 percent, molybdenum forms ultra-high-strength steels that can withstand pressures up to 300,000 pounds per square inch. Molybdenum also improves the strength of steel at high temperatures. When alloyed with nickel, molybdenum forms heat and corrosion-resistant materials used in the chemical industry. Molybdenum disulphide (MoS_2), one of molybdenum's compounds, is used as a high temperature lubricant. Molybdenum trioxide (MoO_3), another molybdenum compound, is used to adhere enamels to metals. Other molybdenum compounds include molybdic acid (H_2MoO_4), molybdenum hexafluoride (MoF_6), and molybdenum phosphide (MoP).

NICKEL: Discovered by the Swedish chemist Axel Fredrik Cronstedt in the mineral niccolite (NiAs) in 1751, today most nickel is obtained from the mineral pentlandite ($NiS \cdot 2FeS$). Most of the world's supply of nickel is mined in the Sudbury region of Ontario, Canada. It is believed that this large deposit of nickel ore is a result of an ancient meteor impact.

Nickel is a hard, corrosion-resistant metal. It can be electroplated onto other metals to form a protective coating. Finely divided nickel is used as a catalyst for the hydrogenation of vegetable oils. Adding nickel to glass gives it a green color. A single kilogram of nickel can be drawn into 300 kilometers of wire. Nickel is also used to manufacture some types of coins and batteries.

Nickel is alloyed with other metals to improve their strength and resistance to corrosion. Nickel is alloyed with steel to make armor plate, vaults, and machine parts. It is alloyed with copper to make pipes that are used in desalination plants. Very powerful permanent magnets, known as Alnico magnets, can be made from an alloy of aluminum, nickel, cobalt, and iron. Nickel alloys with materials to form one of the stainless steel families. Materials like 316 and 304 stainless steel have nickel as a major component.

Nickel carbonyl ($Ni(CO)_4$) is a pyrophoric liquid that is extremely toxic, decomposes violently just slightly above its boiling point, and is a human carcinogen.

OSMIUM: This metal is lustrous, bluish white, extremely hard, and brittle even at high temperatures. It has the highest melting point and the lowest vapor pressure of the platinum group. The metal is very difficult to fabricate, but the powdered or spongy metal slowly gives off osmium tetroxide, which is a powerful oxidizing agent and has a strong smell. The tetroxide (OsO_4) is highly toxic, although it is a solid at room temperature (melting point of 40°C); it sublimes and distills well below its boiling point (130°C) where as little as 10^{-4} mg/m^3 causes damage to the eyes and lungs. Osmium tetroxide is also used around electron microscopes for staining tissues and to make fountain pen tips, instrument pivots, phonograph needles, and electrical contacts.

PALLADIUM: Discovered by William Hyde Wollaston, a British chemist, in 1803, while analyzing samples of platinum ore that were obtained from South America. Although it is a rare element, palladium tends to occur along with deposits of platinum, nickel, copper, silver, and gold and is recovered as a by-product of mining these other metals.

Palladium is used to make springs for watches, surgical instruments, electrical contacts, and dental fillings and crowns. Finely divided palladium acts as a catalyst and is used in hydrogenation and dehydrogenation processes. Palladium at room temperature can absorb up to 900 times its own volume of hydrogen. Hydrogen will easily pass through heated palladium, a property that allows for the easy purification of hydrogen. Palladium alloys are used to make jewelry and, when alloyed with gold, forms a material known as white gold.

Palladium dichloride ($PdCl_2$), a palladium compound, can absorb large amounts of carbon monoxide (CO) gas and is used in carbon monoxide detectors.

PHOSPHORUS: This element can be many colors due to different crystal structures. Phosphorus has three main allotropes: white, red, and black. White phosphorus is poisonous and can spontaneously ignite when it comes in contact with air. For this reason, white phosphorus must be stored under water, and it is not usually used to produce phosphorus compounds. Red phosphorus is formed by heating white phosphorus to 250°C (482°F) or by exposing white phosphorus to sunlight. Red phosphorus is not poisonous and is not as dangerous as white phosphorus, although frictional heating is enough to change it back to white phosphorus. Red phosphorus is used in safety matches, fireworks, smoke bombs, and pesticides. Red phosphorus is used in meth labs as one of the key ingredients in the illegal manufacture of methamphetamine. Black phosphorus is also formed by heating white phosphorus, but a mercury catalyst and a seed crystal of black phosphorus are required. Black phosphorus is the least reactive form of phosphorus and has no significant commercial uses. All burn with extremely hot fires which produce phosphorus pentoxide. Phosphorus pentoxide is very water-reactive and highly corrosive. Its derivatives are used to make weapons, pesticides, fertilizers, and other useful materials.

In what is perhaps the most unpleasant method of discovering an element, phosphorus was first isolated in 1669 by Hennig Brandt, a German physician and alchemist, by boiling, filtering, and otherwise processing as many as 60 buckets of urine. Thankfully, phosphorus is now primarily obtained from phosphate rock ($Ca_3(PO_4)_2$).

Phosphoric acid (H_3PO_4) is used in soft drinks and to create many phosphate compounds, such as triple super-phosphate fertilizer ($Ca(H_2PO_4)_2 \cdot H_2O$). Trisodium phosphate (Na_3PO_4) is used as a cleaning agent and as a water softener. Calcium phosphate ($Ca_3(PO_4)_2$) is used to make china and in the production of baking powder. Some phosphorus compounds glow in the dark or emit light in response to absorbing radiation and are used in fluorescent light bulbs and television sets.

PLATINUM: Used by the pre-Columbian Indians of South America, platinum was not noticed by western scientists until 1735. Platinum can occur free in nature and is sometimes found in deposits of gold-bearing sands, primarily those found in the Ural mountains, Columbia, and the western United States. Platinum, in the form of the mineral sperrylite ($PtAs_2$), is also obtained as a by-product of the nickel mining operation in the Sudbury region of Ontario, Canada. Credit for the modern rediscovery of platinum is usually given to Antonio de Ulloa.

Platinum is a soft, dense, ductile metal that is very resistant to corrosion. It is used to make jewelry, wire, electrical contacts, and laboratory vessels. Platinum expands at nearly the same rate as soda-lime-silica glass, so it is used to make sealed electrodes in glass systems. Platinum is used to coat missile nose cones, jet engine fuel nozzles, and other devices that must operate reliably for long periods of time at high temperatures. Platinum resistance wires are used in high temperature electric furnaces. Platinum anodes are used in cathodic protection systems to prevent ships, pipelines, and steel piers from corroding in salt water.

Platinum is widely used as a catalyst. It will convert methyl alcohol vapors (CH_3OH) into formaldehyde (H_2CO) on contact, glowing red-hot in the process. This effect is used to make small hand warmers. Platinum is also used in a device called a catalytic converter, a device found in the exhaust systems of most cars. Catalytic converters combine carbon monoxide (CO) and unburned fuel from a car's exhaust with oxygen from the air, forming carbon dioxide (CO_2) and water vapor (H_2O). Platinum is also used as a catalyst in the production of sulfuric acid (H_2SO_4) and in the cracking of petroleum products. Fuel cells, devices that combine hydrogen and oxygen to produce electricity and water, also use platinum as a catalyst.

PLUTONIUM: Plutonium was first produced by Glenn T. Seaborg, Joseph W. Kennedy, Edward M. McMillan, and Arthur C. Wohl by bombarding an isotope of uranium, U^{238}, with deuterons that had been accelerated in a device called a cyclotron. This created Np^{238} and two free neutrons. Np^{238} has a half-life of 2.1 days and decays into Pu^{238} through beta decay. Although they conducted their work at the University of California in 1941, their discovery was not revealed to the rest of the scientific community until 1946 because of wartime security concerns.

Plutonium's most stable isotope, Pu^{244}, has a half-life of about 82,000,000 years. It decays into U^{240} through alpha decay. Pu^{244} will also decay through spontaneous fission.

Only two of plutonium's isotopes, Pu^{238} and Pu^{239}, have found uses outside of basic research. Pu^{238} is used in radioisotope thermoelectric generators to provide electricity for space probes that venture too far from the sun to use solar power, such as the Cassini and Galileo probes. Pu^{239} will undergo a fission chain reaction if enough of it is concentrated in one place, so it is used at the heart of modern day nuclear weapons and in some nuclear reactors.

RADIUM: Discovered by Marie Sklodowska Curie, a Polish chemist, and Pierre Curie, a French chemist, in 1898. Marie Curie obtained radium from pitchblende, a material that contains uranium, after noticing that unrefined pitchblende was more radioactive than the uranium that was separated from it. She reasoned that pitchblende must contain at least one other radioactive element. Curie needed to refine several tons of pitchblende in order to obtain tiny amounts of radium and polonium, another radioactive element discovered by Curie. One ton of uranium ore contains only about 0.14 grams of radium. Today, radium can be obtained as a by-product of refining uranium and is usually sold as radium chloride ($RaCl_2$) or radium bromide ($RaBr_2$), and not as a pure material.

Radium's most stable isotope, Ra^{226}, has a half-life of about 1,600 years. It decays into Rn^{222} through alpha decay or into Pb^{212} by ejecting a C^{14} nucleus.

The Curie, a unit used to describe the activity of a radioactive substance, is based on Ra^{226}. It is equal to the number of atoms in a one gram sample of Ra^{226} that will decay in one second, or 37,000,000,000 decays per second.

Radium had been used to make self-luminous paints for watches, aircraft instrument dials, and other instrumentation, but has largely been replaced by Co^{60}, a less dangerous radioactive source. A mixture of radium and beryllium will emit neutrons and is used as a neutron source. Radium is used to produce radon, a radioactive gas used to treat some types of cancer. A single gram of Ra^{226} will produce 0.0001 milliliters of radon a day.

Radium is about one million times more active than uranium. The lab notebooks used by the Curies are too highly contaminated to be safely handled today.

SELENIUM: Discovered by Jöns Jacob Berzelius, a Swedish chemist, in 1817, after analyzing an impurity that was contaminating the sulfuric acid (H_2SO_4) being produced at a particular factory in Sweden. Originally believing the material was tellurium, Berzelius eventually realized that it was actually a previously unknown element. Selenium occurs in minerals such as eucairite (CuAgSe), crookesite ($Cu_7Tl_{0.75}Ag_{0.25}Se_4$), and clausthalite (PbSe), but these minerals are too rare to use as a major source of selenium. Today, most selenium is obtained as a by-product of refining copper.

Selenium's resistance to the flow of electricity is greatly affected by the amount of light shining on it. The brighter the light, the better selenium conducts electricity. This property has made selenium useful in devices that respond to the intensity of light, such as electric eyes, photo cells, light meters for cameras, and copiers. Selenium can also produce electricity directly from sunlight and is used in solar cells. Selenium is also a semiconductor and is used in some types of solid-state electronics as well as in rectifiers, devices that convert alternating current electricity into direct current electricity. In addition to its use in electrical devices, selenium is also used to make a ruby-red color in glasses and enamels, as a photographic toner, and as an additive to stainless steel.

Selenium forms few inorganic compounds, none of which are commercially important. They include selenious acid (H_2SeO_3), selenium dichloride ($SeCl_2$), and selenium oxychloride ($SeOCl_2$). One of the compounds, selenium hydride (H_2Se), is intolerable at 1.5 ppm and most of the other compounds are very toxic. Selenium is what makes Locoweed toxic.

SILICON: Jöns Jacob Berzelius, a Swedish chemist, discovered silicon in 1824 by heating chips of potassium in a silica container and then carefully washing away the residual by-products. Silicon is the seventh most abundant element in the universe and the second most abundant element in the earth's crust. Today, silicon is produced by heating sand (SiO_2) with carbon to temperatures approaching 2200°C.

Two allotropes of silicon exist at room temperature: amorphous and crystalline. Amorphous appears as a brown powder, while crystalline silicon has a metallic luster and a grayish color. Single crystals of crystalline silicon can be grown with a process known as the Czochralski process. These crystals, when doped with elements such as boron, gallium, germanium, phosphorus, or arsenic, are used in the manufacture of solid-state electronic devices, such as transistors, solar cells, rectifiers, and microchips.

Silicon dioxide (SiO_2), silicon's most common compound, is the most abundant compound in the earth's crust. It commonly takes the form of ordinary sand, but also exists as quartz, rock crystal, amethyst, agate, flint, jasper, and opal. Silicon dioxide is extensively used in the manufacture of glass and bricks. Silica gel, a colloidal form of silicon dioxide, easily absorbs moisture and is used as a desiccant.

Silicon forms other useful compounds. Silicon carbide (SiC) is nearly as hard as diamond and is used as an abrasive. Sodium silicate (Na_2SiO_3), also known as water glass, is used in the production of soaps, adhesives, and as an egg preservative. Silicon tetrachloride ($SiCl_4$) is used to create smoke screens. Silicon is an important ingredient in silicone, a class of material that is used for lubricants, polishing agents, electrical insulators, and medical implants.

SILVER: Archaeological evidence suggests that people have been using silver for at least 5,000 years. Silver can be obtained from pure deposits, from silver ores such as argentite (Ag_2S) and horn silver (AgCl), and in conjunction with deposits of ores containing lead, gold, or copper.

Silver and silver compounds have many uses. Pure silver is the best conductor of heat and electricity of all known metals, so it is sometimes used in making solder, electrical contacts, and printed circuit boards.

Silver is also the best known reflector of visible light, but silver mirrors must be given a protective coating to prevent them from tarnishing. Silver has also been used to create coins, although today other metals are typically used in its place. Sterling silver, an alloy containing 92.5 percent silver, is used to make silverware, jewelry, and other decorative items. High capacity batteries can be made with silver and zinc and silver and cadmium. Sliver nitrate ($AgNO_3$) is light-sensitive and is used to make photographic films and papers. Silver iodide (AgI) is used to seed clouds to produce rain.

SULFUR: Usually a yellow solid, sulfur may be orange, tan, brown, or gray. It is odorless and quite brittle. It displays three allotropic forms: orthorhombic, monoclinic and amorphous. The orthorhombic form is the most stable form of sulfur. Monoclinic sulfur exists between the temperatures of 96°C and 119°C and reverts back to the orthorhombic form when cooled. Amorphous sulfur is formed when molten sulfur is quickly cooled. Amorphous sulfur is soft and elastic and eventually reverts back to the orthorhombic form. It may have a faint rotten egg odor from small amounts of hydrogen sulfide. By itself it is nontoxic, but when it burns it liberates large quantities of sulfur dioxide. Sulfur dioxide is a choking toxic gas. Sulfur can be shipped as a dry powder or as a molten solid, which is very flammable. As a molten liquid, the temperature can be as high as 270°F (melting point is 239°F). It has an autoignition temperature of 450°F. The molten liquid has both extreme thermal hazards as well as flammable hazards for the responder. It is highly friction-sensitive in a liquid state and may ignite easily. It is used to manufacture sulfuric acid and many organic derivatives. The organic derivatives have names like sulfide, disulfide, and mercaptan. These materials are very foul-smelling, usually toxic, and burn to liberate sulfur dioxide.

Sulfur, the tenth most abundant element in the universe, has been known since ancient times. Sometime around 1777, Antoine Lavoisier convinced the rest of the scientific community that sulfur was an element. Sulfur is a component of many common minerals, such as galena (PbS), gypsum ($CaSO_4 \cdot 2(H_2O)$), pyrite (FeS_2), sphalerite (ZnS or FeS), cinnabar (HgS), stibnite (Sb_2S_3), epsomite ($MgSO_4 \cdot 7(H_2O)$)), celestite ($SrSO_4$), and barite ($BaSO_4$). Nearly 25 percent of the sulfur produced today is recovered from petroleum refining operations and as a by-product of extracting other materials from sulfur containing ores. The majority of the sulfur produced today is obtained from underground deposits, usually found in conjunction with salt deposits.

Most of the sulfur that is produced is used in the manufacture of sulfuric acid (H_2SO_4). Large amounts of sulfuric acid, nearly 40 million tons, are used each year to make fertilizers, lead-acid batteries, and in many industrial processes. Smaller amounts of sulfur are used to vulcanize natural rubbers, as an insecticide (the Greek poet Homer mentioned pest-averting sulphur nearly 2,800 years ago), in the manufacture of gunpowder, and as a dying agent.

In addition to sulfuric acid, sulfur forms other interesting compounds. Hydrogen sulfide (H_2S) is a gas that smells like rotten eggs. Sulfur dioxide (SO_2), formed by burning sulfur in air, is used as a bleaching agent, solvent, disinfectant, and as a refrigerant. When combined with water (H_2O), sulfur dioxide forms sulfurous acid (H_2SO_3), a weak acid that is a major component of acid rain.

TANTALUM: Anders Gustaf Ekenberg, a Swedish chemist discovered tantalum in 1802 in minerals obtained from Ytterby, Sweden. Many scientists believed that he had only discovered an allotrope of niobium, an element that is chemically similar to tantalum. The issue was finally settled in 1866 when Jean Charles Galissard de Marignac, a Swiss chemist, proved that tantalum and niobium were two distinct elements. The first relatively pure samples of tantalum were first produced in 1907. Today, tantalum is primarily obtained from the minerals columbite ((Fe, Mn, Mg)(Nb, Ta)$_2O_6$), tantalite ((Fe, Mn)(Ta, Nb)$_2O_6$), and euxenite ((Y, Ca, Er, La, Ce, U, Th)(Nb, Ta, Ti)$_2O_6$).

46

Tantalum is a strong, ductile metal that is nearly immune to chemical attack at room temperatures. It can be drawn into a fine wire that is used to evaporate metals, such as aluminum. It has a high melting point and is frequently used as a substitute for platinum, which is more expensive. Tantalum is used to make components for chemical plants, nuclear power plants, airplanes, and missiles. Tantalum does not react with bodily fluids and is used to make surgical equipment. Tantalum also does not irritate the body and is used to make surgical sutures as well as implants, such as artificial joints and cranial plates. Tantalum is alloyed with steel to increase steel's ductility, strength, and melting point. Tantalum pentoxide (Ta_2O_5), one of tantalum's compounds, is a dielectric material and is used to make capacitors. It is also used to make a glass with a high index of refraction that is used in camera lenses. A composite consisting of tantalum carbide (TaC) and graphite is one of the hardest materials known and is used on the cutting edges of high-speed machine tools.

TELLURIUM: Tellurium was discovered by Franz Joseph Müller von Reichenstein, a Romanian mining official, in 1782. Reichenstein was the chief inspector of all mines, smelters, and saltworks in Transylvania. He also had an interest in chemistry and extracted a new metal from an ore of gold, known as aurum album, which he believed was antimony. He shortly realized that the metal he had produced was not antimony at all, but a previously unknown element. Reichenstein's work was forgotten until 1798 when Martin Heinrich Klaproth, a German chemist, mentioned the substance in a paper. Klaproth named the new element tellurium but gave full credit for its discovery to Reichenstein.

Tellurium is found free in nature, but is most often found in the ores sylvanite ($AgAuTe_4$), calaverite ($AuTe_2$), and krennerite ($AuTe_2$). Today, most tellurium is obtained as a by-product of mining and refining copper.

Tellurium is a semiconductor and is frequently doped with copper, tin, gold, or silver. Tellurium is also used to color glass and ceramics and is one of the primary ingredients in blasting caps.

Tellurium is primarily used as an alloying agent. Small amounts of tellurium are added to copper and stainless steel to make them easier to machine and mill. Tellurium is also added to lead to increase its strength and resistance to sulfuric acid (H_2SO_4).

Tellurium forms many compounds, but none that are commercially important. They include: tellourous acid (H_2TeO_3), tellurium tetrachloride ($TeCl_4$), tellurium dichloride ($TeCl_2$), tellurium trioxide (TeO_3), tellurium monoxide (TeO), and sodium telluride (Na_2Te).

THALLIUM: Thallium was discovered spectroscopically by Sir William Crookes, a British chemist, in 1861. Crookes had obtained the sludge left over from the production of sulfuric acid (H_2SO_4) from a friend. After removing all the selenium from the sludge, he inspected it with a device known as a spectroscope to look for signs of tellurium. Rather than seeing the yellow spectral lines produced by tellurium, he observed a bright green line that no one had ever seen before. He named the new element that was producing the green line thallium, after the Greek word for "green twig", thallos. He isolated samples of thallium the next year. Thallium is found in the minerals crookesite ($Cu_7Tl_{0.75}Ag_{0.25}Se_4$), lorandite ($TlAsS_2$), and hutchinsonite ($(Pb, Tl)_2 As_5S_9$), but it is usually obtained as a by-product of the production of sulfuric acid or as a by-product of refining zinc or lead.

There are no uses for metallic thallium since pure thallium quickly combines with oxygen and water vapor from the atmosphere, forming a black, powdery substance. Thallium, used in conjunction with sulfur or selenium and arsenic, forms low melting glass. Thallium sulfate (Tl_2SO_4), an odorless, tasteless thallium compound, was once used as a rat and ant poison, although it has been banned from household use in the

United States since 1974. Thallium sulfide (Tl_2S), thallium iodide (TlI), and thallium bromide (TlBr) are all compounds used in devices to detect infrared radiation.

TIN: Archaeological evidence suggests that people have been using tin for at least 5,500 years. Tin is primarily obtained from the mineral cassiterite (SnO_2) and is extracted by roasting cassiterite in a furnace with carbon. Tin makes up only about 0.001 percent of the earth's crust and is chiefly mined in Malaysia. Two allotropes of tin occur near room temperature. The first form of tin is called gray tin and is stable at temperatures below 13.2°C (55.76°F). There are few, if any, uses for gray tin. At temperatures above 13.2°C, gray tin slowly turns into tin's second form, white tin. White tin is the normal form of the metal and has many uses. Unfortunately, white tin will turn into gray tin if its temperature falls below 13.2°C. This change can be prevented if small amounts of antimony or bismuth are added to white tin.

Tin resists corrosion and is used as a protective coating on other metals. Tin cans are probably the most familiar example of this application. A tin can is actually made from steel. A thin layer of tin is applied to the inside and outside of the can to keep the steel from rusting. Once widely used, tin cans have largely been replaced with plastic and aluminum containers.

Tin is used in the Pilkington process to produce window glass. In the Pilkington process, molten glass is poured onto a pool of molten tin. The glass floats on the surface of the tin and cools, forming solid glass with flat, parallel surfaces. Most of the window glass produced today is made this way.

Tin is used to form many useful alloys. Bronze is an alloy of tin and copper. Tin and lead are alloyed to make pewter and solder. An alloy of tin and niobium is used to make superconductive wire. Type metal, fusible metal, bell metal, and Babbitt metal are other examples of tin alloys.

Tin salts can be sprayed onto glass to make electrically conductive coatings. These can then be used to make panel lighting and frost-free windshields. Stannous fluoride (SnF_2) is used in some types of toothpaste.

TITANIUM: Discovered in 1791 by the Reverend William Gregor, a British pastor, pure titanium was first produced by Matthew A. Hunter, an American metallurgist, in 1910. Titanium is the ninth most abundant element in the earth's crust and is primarily found in the minerals rutile (TiO_2), ilmenite ($FeTiO_3$), and sphene ($CaTiSiO_5$). Titanium makes up about 0.57 percent of the earth's crust.

Titanium is a strong, light metal. It is as strong as steel and twice as strong as aluminum, but is 45 percent lighter than steel and only 60 percent heavier than aluminum. Titanium is not easily corroded by sea water and is used in propeller shafts, rigging, and other parts of boats that are exposed to sea water. Titanium and titanium alloys are used in airplanes, missiles, and rockets where strength, low weight and resistance to high temperatures are important. Since titanium does not react within the human body, it is used to create artificial hips, pins for setting bones, and for other biological implants. Unfortunately, the high cost of titanium has limited its widespread use.

Titanium dioxide (TiO_2) is used as a pigment to create white paint and accounts for the largest use of the element. Pure titanium dioxide is relatively clear and is used to create titania, an artificial gemstone. Titanium tetrachloride ($TiCl_4$), another titanium compound, has been used to make smoke screens.

A final bit of titanium trivia–titanium is the only element that will burn in an atmosphere of pure nitrogen.

TUNGSTEN: Tungsten was discovered by Juan José and Fausto Elhuyar, Spanish chemists and brothers, in 1783 in samples of the mineral wolframite ($(Fe, Mn)WO_4$). Today, tungsten is primarily obtained from wolframite and scheelite ($CaWO_4$) using the same basic method developed by José and Elhuyar. Tungsten ores are crushed, cleaned, and treated with alkalis to form tungsten trioxide (WO_3). Tungsten trioxide is then heated with carbon or hydrogen gas (H_2), forming tungsten metal and carbon dioxide (CO_2) or tungsten metal and water vapor (H_2O).

Pure tungsten is a light gray or whitish metal that is soft enough to be cut with a hacksaw and ductile enough to be drawn into wire or extruded into various shapes. If contaminated with other materials, tungsten becomes brittle and difficult to work with. Tungsten has the highest melting point of all metallic elements and is used to make filaments for incandescent light bulbs, fluorescent light bulbs, and television tubes. Tungsten expands at nearly the same rate as borosilicate glass and is used to make metal to glass seals. Tungsten is also used as a target for X-ray production, as heating elements in electric furnaces, and for parts of spacecraft and missiles that must withstand high temperatures.

Tungsten is alloyed with steel to form tough metals that are stable at high temperatures. Tungsten-steel alloys are used to make such things as high speed cutting tools and rocket engine nozzles.

Tungsten carbide (WC) is an extremely hard tungsten compound. It is used in the tips of drill bits, high speed cutting tools, and in mining machinery. Tungsten disulfide (WS_2) is a dry lubricant that can be used in temperatures as high as 500°C. Tungsten forms compounds with calcium and magnesium that have phosphorescent properties and are used in fluorescent light bulbs.

URANIUM: Uranium was discovered by Martin Heinrich Klaproth, a German chemist, in the mineral pitchblende (primarily a mix of uranium oxides) in 1789. Although Klaproth, as well as the rest of the scientific community, believed that the substance he extracted from pitchblende was pure uranium, it was actually uranium dioxide (UO_2). After noticing that "pure" uranium reacted oddly with uranium tetrachloride (UCl_4), Eugène-Melchoir Péligot, a French chemist, isolated pure uranium by heating uranium dioxide with potassium in a platinum crucible. Radioactivity was first discovered in 1896 when Antoine Henri Becquerel, a French physicist, detected it from a sample of uranium. Today, uranium is obtained from uranium ores such as pitchblende, uraninite (UO_2), carnotite [$K_2(UO_2)_2(VO_4)_2 \cdot 3H_2O$], and autunite ($Ca(UO_2)_2(PO_4)_2 \cdot 10H_2O$), as well as from phosphate rock ($Ca_3(PO_4)_2$), lignite (brown coal), and monazite sand (($Ce, La, Th, Nd, Y)PO_4$). Since there is little demand for uranium metal, uranium is usually sold in the form of sodium diuranate ($Na_2U_2O_7 \cdot 6H_2O$), also known as yellow cake, or triuranium octaoxide (U_3O_8).

Because it is naturally radioactive, uranium, usually in the form of uranium dioxide (UO_2), is most commonly used in the nuclear power industry to generate electricity. Naturally occurring uranium consists of three isotopes: U^{234}, U^{235}, and U^{238}. Although all three isotopes are radioactive, only U^{235} is a fissionable material that can be used for nuclear power.

When a fissionable material is struck by a neutron, its nucleus can release energy by splitting into smaller fragments. If some of the fragments are other neutrons, they can strike other atoms and cause them to split as well. A fissionable material, such as U^{235}, is a material capable of producing enough free neutrons to sustain a nuclear chain reaction.

Only 0.7204 percent of naturally occurring uranium is U^{235}. This is too low a concentration to sustain a nuclear chain reaction without the help of a material known as a moderator. A moderator is a material that can slow down a neutron without absorbing it. Slow neutrons are more likely to react with U^{235} and reactors using natural uranium can be made using graphite or heavy water as a moderator. Methods also exist for concentrating U^{235}. Once the levels of U^{235} have been increased to about 3 percent, normal water can be used as a moderator.

U^{238}, uranium's most common isotope, can be converted into Pu^{239}, a fissionable material that can also be used as a fuel in nuclear reactors. To produce Pu^{239}, atoms of U^{238} are exposed to neutrons. U^{239} forms when U^{238} absorbs a neutron. U^{239} has a half-life of about 23 minutes and decays into Np^{239} through beta decay. Np^{239} has a half-life of about 2.4 days and decays into Pu^{239}, also through beta decay.

Although it does not occur naturally, U^{233} is also a fissionable material that can be used as a fuel in nuclear reactors. To produce U^{233}, atoms of Th^{232} are exposed to neutrons. Th^{233} forms when Th^{232} absorbs a neutron. Th^{233} has a half-life of about 22 minutes and decays into Pa^{233} through beta decay. Pa^{233} has a half-life of about 27 days and decays into U^{233}, also through beta decay. If completely fissioned, one pound (0.45 kilograms) of U^{233} will provide the same amount of energy as burning 1,500 tons (1,350,000 kilograms) of coal.

Uranium is a dense metal that has uses outside of the nuclear power industry. It is used as a target for X-ray production, as ammunition for some types of military weaponry, as a shield against radiation, as a counterweight for aircraft control surfaces, and in the gyroscopes of inertial guidance systems.

Uranium compounds have been used for centuries to color glass. A 2,000-year-old sample of yellow glass found near Naples, Italy, contains uranium oxide. Uranium trioxide (UO_3) is an orange powder and has been used in the manufacture of Fiestaware dishes. Other uranium compounds have also been used to make vaseline glass and glazes. The uranium within these items is radioactive and should be treated with care.

Uranium's most stable isotope, U^{238}, has a half-life of about 4,468,000,000 years. It decays into Th^{234} through alpha decay or decays through spontaneous fission.

VANADIUM: Vanadium was discovered by Andrés Manuel del Rio, a Mexican chemist, in 1801. Rio sent samples of vanadium ore with a letter describing his methods to the Institute de France in Paris, France, for analysis and confirmation. Unfortunately for Rio, his letter was lost in a shipwreck and the Institute only received his samples, which contained a brief note describing how much this new element, which Rio had named erythronium, resembled chromium. Rio withdrew his claim when he received a letter from Paris disputing his discovery. Vanadium was rediscovered by Nils Gabriel Sefstrôm, a Swedish chemist, in 1830, while analyzing samples of iron from a mine in Sweden. Vanadium was isolated by Sir Henry Enfield Roscoe, a British chemist, in 1867, by combining vanadium trichloride (VCl_3) with hydrogen gas (H_2). Today, vanadium is primarily obtained from the minerals vanadinite [$Pb_5(VO_4)_3Cl$] and carnotite ($K_2(UO_2)_2(VO_4)_2 \cdot 3H_2O$) by heating crushed ore in the presence of carbon and chlorine to produce vanadium trichloride. The vanadium trichloride is then heated with magnesium in an argon atmosphere.

Vanadium is corrosion-resistant and is sometimes used to make special tubes and pipes for the chemical industry. Vanadium also does not easily absorb neutrons and has some applications in the nuclear power industry. A thin layer of vanadium is used to bond titanium to steel.

Nearly 80 percent of the vanadium produced is used to make ferrovanadium or as an additive to steel. Ferrovanadium is a strong, shock resistant and corrosion resistant alloy of iron containing between 1 percent and 6 percent vanadium. Ferrovanadium and vanadium-steel alloys are used to make such things as axles, crankshafts and gears for cars, parts of jet engines, springs, and cutting tools.

50

Vanadium pentoxide (V_2O_5) is perhaps vanadium's most useful compound. It is used as a mordant, a material which permanently fixes dyes to fabrics.

Vanadium pentoxide is also used as a catalyst in certain chemical reactions and in the manufacture of ceramics. Vanadium pentoxide can be mixed with gallium to form superconductive magnets. Vanadium compounds tend to be toxic. One of the symptoms of vanadium poisoning that is sometimes exhibited is a "green" tongue.

XENON: Sir William Ramsay, a Scottish chemist, and Morris M. Travers, a British chemist, discovered xenon on July 12, 1898, shortly after their discovery of the elements krypton and neon. Like krypton and neon, xenon was discovered through the study of liquefied air. The earth's atmosphere is about 0.0000087 percent xenon. Xenon produces a brilliant white flash of light when it is excited electrically and is widely used in strobe lights. The light emitted from xenon lamps is also used to kill bacteria and to power ruby lasers. Due to its high atomic weight, xenon ions were used as a fuel in an experimental ion engine aboard the space probe Deep Space 1. Once thought to be completely inert, xenon will form compounds, usually with fluorine, oxygen, and platinum. $XePtF_6$, XeF_2, XeF_4, XeF_6, and XeO_4 are some of the xenon compounds that have been formed.

ZINC: Although zinc compounds have been used for at least 2,500 years in the production of brass, zinc was not recognized as a distinct element until much later. Metallic zinc was first produced in India sometime in the 1400s by heating the mineral calamine ($ZnCO_3$) with wool. Zinc was rediscovered by Andreas Sigismund Marggraf in 1746 by heating calamine with charcoal. Today, most zinc is produced through the electrolysis of aqueous zinc sulfate ($ZnSO_4$).

Roughly one third of all metallic zinc produced today is used in a process known as galvanization. During galvanization, an object that is subject to corrosion, such as an iron nail, is given a protective coating of zinc. The zinc can be applied to an object by dipping it in a pool of molten zinc; but it is most often applied through an electroplating process. Sacrificial zinc anodes are used in cathodic protection systems to protect exposed iron from corrosion. Metallic zinc is also used to make dry cell batteries, roof cladding, and die castings.

Zinc is used to make many useful alloys. Brass, an alloy of zinc that contains between 55 percent and 95 percent copper, is probably the best known zinc alloy. Brass was first used about 2,500 years ago and was widely enforced by the ancient Romans to make such things as coins, kettles, and decorative items. Brass is still used today, particularly in musical instruments, screws, and other hardware that must resist corrosion. Zinc is alloyed with lead and tin to make solder, a metal with a relatively low melting point that is used to join electrical components, pipes, and other metallic items. Prestal, an alloy containing 78 percent zinc and 22 percent aluminum, is a strange material that is nearly as strong as steel but is molded as easily as plastic. Nickel silver, typewriter metal, spring brass, and German silver are other common zinc alloys.

Zinc oxide (ZnO), a common zinc compound, forms when metallic zinc is exposed to the air and forms a protective coating that protects the rest of the metal. Zinc oxide is used in paints, some rubber products, cosmetics, pharmaceuticals, plastics, printing inks, soap, and batteries, among other things. Zinc sulfide (ZnS), another zinc compound, glows when it is exposed to ultraviolet light, X-rays, or electrons and is used to make luminous watch dials, television screens, and fluorescent light bulbs. Zinc chloride ($ZnCl_2$) is another zinc compound that is used to protect wood from decay and insects.

ZIRCONIUM: Martin Heinrich Klaproth, a German chemist, discovered zirconium while analyzing the composition of the mineral jargoon ($ZrSiO_4$) in 1789. Zirconium was isolated by Jöns Jacob Berzelius, a Swedish chemist, in 1824 and finally prepared in a pure form in 1914. Obtaining pure zirconium is very difficult because it is chemically similar to hafnium, an element which is always found mixed with deposits of zirconium. Today, most zirconium is obtained from the minerals zircon ($ZrSiO_4$) and baddeleyite (ZrO_2) through a process known as the Kroll Process.

Zirconium is a corrosion-resistant metal that is used in high performance pumps and valves. Since it also does not easily absorb neutrons, zirconium is widely used in nuclear reactors. The nuclear power industry uses nearly 90 percent of the zirconium produced each year, which must be nearly free of hafnium. Zirconium is also used as an alloying agent in steel, to make some types of surgical equipment, and as a getter, a material that combines with and removes trace gases from vacuum tubes.

Zircon ($ZrSiO_4$) is a zirconium compound that can take many different forms, the most popular of which is a clear, transparent gemstone that can be cut to look like diamond and is frequently used in jewelry. Zirconium dioxide (ZrO_2) can withstand very high temperatures and is used to make crucibles and line the walls of high temperature furnaces. Zirconium carbonate ($2ZrO_2 \cdot CO_2 \cdot H_2O$) is used in lotions to treat poison ivy.

4

Formulas and Bonding of Inorganic Molecules

Formulas

A formula is a single symbol or a group of symbols that represents a substance. The symbols in a formula identify the elements present in the substance. Therefore, NaCl is the formula for sodium chloride (common table salt) and so identifies the elements sodium and chlorine as the constituents of salt.

Subscripts are used in formulas to show the relative numbers of atoms of each type in the compound, but only if more than one atom of a given element is there. The formula for water–H_2O–tells us that each molecule contains two atoms of hydrogen and one atom of oxygen. In other words there are two atoms of hydrogen per one atom of oxygen (2 atoms H/1 atom O).

The formula of sodium chloride, NaCl, shows the presence of equal numbers of atoms of the elements, sodium and chlorine (1 atom Na/1 atom Cl). Note that in the formulas for water and sodium chloride the subscript 1 is omitted, which is the usual practice. The formula for aluminum sulfate, $Al_2(SO_4)_3$, specifies two atoms of aluminum (Al), along with three sulfate-SO_4-groups. Each sulfate group contains one atom of sulfur and four atoms of oxygen. Therefore, the formula shows a total of two atoms of aluminum, three atoms of sulfur, and twelve atoms of oxygen.

The molecular formula of the most common form of sulfur is S_8, showing that each molecule of this element consists of eight atoms. The molecular formulas for elemental hydrogen and oxygen are H_2 and O_2, while the molecular formula for neon is Ne. Note that H_2 and 2H do not mean the same thing. H_2 represents a molecule of hydrogen consisting of two atoms of the element, chemically combined. The expression 2H, on the other hand, states that the two hydrogen atoms are not in combination as a unit, but are completely separate particles.

Bonds

Chemical bonds are the interactions or glue that bonds atoms together. Each element in its electrically neutral state has a number of electrons equal to the number of protons in the nucleus. Electrons are the glue which binds together atoms into molecules. Chemical bonds occur either with the transfer of electrons between atoms or by having two or more atoms share electrons.

IONIC BONDS: Occur when electrons are transferred from one atom to another, giving one atom more electrons than protons and leaving the other atom with fewer electrons than protons. The net result is that one atom is positively charged and the other has a negative charge. The interaction between positive and negatively charged species is called an electrostatic attraction and the resulting bond is very strong.

IONS: Positive and negative charged species resulting from the transfer of electrons between atoms. Ions may exist as single charged atoms (like Na^+ or Cl^-) or may be more complex combinations of atoms like CO_3^{-2} or PO_4^{-3}.

CATIONS: Positively charged ions.

ANIONS: Negatively charged ions.

COVALENT BONDS: Occur when two or more atoms share electrons between themselves, with the electrons spending some time around each atom. This type of bonding is found in complex ions and in all organic compounds.

5

Inorganic Chemical Nomenclature

Ionic Compounds

Many compounds do not contain discrete molecules but instead are composed of particles called ions. Ions are atoms or groups of atoms that are electrically charged. These charged particles have what we call a valence–the electrical charge on that element or ion. An ionic compound is composed of a positive part (typically a metal) and a negative part (typically a nonmetal). In ordinary table salt (sodium chloride–NaCl), the sodium atom (a metal) gives up an electron to the chlorine atom (a nonmetal). The sodium atom is now an ion because it has an electrical charge. Since it has one less electron, it has a charge of +1. The chlorine atom becomes a chloride ion and gains one electron, therefore, making it a charge of -1. Because opposite charges attract, the sodium and the chloride ions attract each other and form an ionic bond. The formula unit of NaCl is therefore Na^+ and Cl^- ions. In writing and naming a binary ionic compound such as NaCl, the metal (Na) comes first, and the nonmetal (Cl) comes second. The full name of the metal is used and -ide is added to the nonmetal as a suffix. NaCl is therefore called sodium chloride.

The metals in groups IA and IIA and aluminum in group IIIA always have only one oxidation number (+1, +2, and +3, respectively). Naming binary ionic compounds containing these metals is straightforward. The oxidation states of the metals need not be specified. For example, LiCl is lithium chloride, and MgO is called magnesium oxide. Notice that the full names of the metals (lithium and magnesium) are given, and the suffix "-ide" is added to the names of the nonmetals (chlorine and oxygen).

Ionic compounds generally are very hard, brittle, and have very high melting points. They are solids at room temperature. When they are solid, they do not conduct electricity; when they are melted or put into a liquid solution, they can conduct electricity. This is because their electrical ions can move freely in a liquid state.

Although metals like sodium and calcium form one ionic type (Na^+ and Ca^{2+}), respectively, some metals may form more than one ion because of multiple oxidation states. These metals are usually transition elements. Alkali metals and alkaline earth metals, like sodium and calcium, respectively, have only one type. For example, $FeCl_2$ contains Fe^{2+} ions while $FeCl_3$ contains Fe^{3+} ions. In such a case, the charge on the metal must be specified.

Two systems are commonly used to designate the particular oxidation state of the metal:

THE STOCK METHOD: Currently, this is the most common method used. In this method the oxidation state of the metal is listed with Roman numerals in parentheses after the name of the element. For example, the compound CuF is named copper (I) fluoride, and the compound CuF_2 is named copper (II) fluoride.

THE CLASSICAL METHOD: In this older method, the name of the metal is modified with the suffixes "-ous" (for the lower oxidation number) and "-ic" (for the higher oxidation number) to distinguish between the two. Using this method, the compound CuF would be called cuprous fluoride, and CuF_2 would be called cupric fluoride.

Some ionic compounds contain polyatomic ions. As an example, NH_4NO_3 contains the polyatomic ions NH_4^+ and NO_3^-. They are assigned special names to name the compounds containing them. Many polyatomic anions contain oxygen atoms. They are called oxyanions. When two oxyanions have the same element but a different number of oxygen atoms, the name of the one with fewer oxygen atoms ends in "-ite" while the one with more ends in "-ate." For example, sulfite (SO_3^{2-}) and sulfate (SO_4^{2-}). When more than two oxyanions make up a series, "hypo-" and "per-" are used as prefixes to name the members with the fewest and the most oxygen atoms, respectively.

The following table lists some common ions and their charges:

Valences of Positive One

Ammonium, NH_4^+	Silver, Ag^+
Cuprous, Cu^+	Sodium, Na^+
Lithium, Li^+	

Hydrogen, H^+ is often found as H_3O^+ called the "hydronium ion"

Valences of Positive Two

Barium, Ba^{2+}	Ferrous, Fe^{2+}
Cadmium, Cd^{2+}	Lead, Pb^{2+}
Calcium, Ca^{2+}	Magnesium, Mg^{2+}
Chromous, Cr^{2+}	Mercuric, Hg^{2+}
Cobalt, Co^{2+}	Stannous, Sn^{2+}
Cupric, Cu^{2+}	Zinc, Zn^{2+}

Valences of Positive Three

Aluminum, Al^{3+}	Chromic, Cr^{3+}
Antimony, Sb^{3+}	Ferric, Fe^{3+}

Valences of Positive Four

Stannic, Sn^{4+}	Zirconium, Zr^{4+}

Valences of Negative One

Acetate, $C_2H_3O_2^-$	Fluoride, F^-
Bicarbonate, HCO_3^-	Hydride, H^-
Bisulfate, HSO_4^-	Hydroxide, OH^-
Bisulfite, HSO_3^-	Hypochlorite, ClO^-
Bromide, Br^-	Iodide, I^-
Chlorate, ClO_3^-	Nitrate, NO_3^-
Chlorite, ClO_2^-	Nitrite, NO_2^-
Chloride, Cl^-	Perchlorate, ClO_4^-
Cyanide, CN^-	Permanganate, MnO_4^-

Valences of Negative Two

Carbonate, CO_3^{2-}	Peroxide, O_2^{2-}
Chromate, CrO_4^{2-}	Sulfate, SO_4^{2-}
Dichromate, $Cr_2O_7^{2-}$	Sulfide, S^{2-}
Oxalate, $C_2O_4^{2-}$	Sulfite, SO_3^{2-}

Valences of Negative Three

Phosphate, PO_4^{3-}	Phosphite, PO_3^{3-}

Naming a compound with a polyatomic ion is simple. No changes are made to either component.

Example:

$$(NH_4)_2SO_4$$

This compound is called ammonium sulfate. This is because the polyatomic ions keep their own name when combined. The NH_4 is from the ammonium ion and the SO_4 is from the sulfate ion.

This also works when a monoatomic ion and a polyatomic compound are combined:

$$Ba(C_2H_3O_2)_2$$

This compound is called barium acetate. As before, both the cation and the anion kept their former names.

$$NH_4F$$

The ammonium, as a polyatomic ion, keeps its name. The flourine, as a monoatomic anion, must change its name to fluoride. The final name is ammonium fluoride.

58

These are the rules for naming covalent compounds:
- The first element in the formula is named first, using the full element name.
- The second element is named using the suffix "-ide."
- Prefixes are used to denote the numbers of atoms present.
- The prefix "mono-" is only used to name the second element. For example, CO is carbon monoxide, not monocarbon monoxide.

Prefixes **Examples**

Prefix	Number Indicated	Compound	Name
mono-	1	NO	Nitrogen monoxide
di-	2	N_2O	Dinitrogen monoxide
tri-	3	NO_2	Nitrogen dioxide
tetra-	4	N_2O_3	Dinitrogen trioxide
penta-	5	N_2O_4	Dinitrogen tetraoxide
hexa-	6		
hepta-	7		
octa-	8		
nona-	9		
deca-	10		

Note: There are exceptions to this system of naming binary molecular compounds. Some compounds are referred to by their common names. For example, the compound H_2O is called water, and the compound NH_3 is called ammonia.

Naming Acids

Acids are a group of compounds given special treatment in naming. Acids are compounds that give off hydrogen ions when dissolved in water. The formulas of acids are of the general form of HX, where X is a monatomic or polyatomic anion. For example, HCl and HNO_3 are acids.

The acids can be named using three rules that focus on the ending of the anion (X) portion of the acid.
- When the anion (X) ends in "-ide," the acid name begins with the prefix "hydro-." The anion has the suffix "-ic," and it is followed by the word acid. For example, there is hydrochloric acid (HCl), hydrofluoric acid (HF), hydrobromic acid (HBr).
- When the anion ends in "-ite," the acid ends with the suffix "-ous." For example, in HNO_2, the anion is nitrite; therefore, the acid is called nitrous acid.
- If the anion ends in "-ate," the acid ends with the suffix "-ic." As an example, in HNO_3, the anion is nitrate; therefore, the acid is called nitric acid. Other examples are H_2SO_4, sulfuric acid, $HClO_4$, perchloric acid, and H_3PO_4, phosphoric acid.

Salts

Salts are made when you react acids and bases. The "-ic" suffix of a binary acid becomes "-ide" in its salt. The reaction of hydro<u>chloric</u> acid and <u>sodium</u> hydroxide yields sodium chloride.

The "-ic" suffix of a ternary acid becomes "-ate" in its salt. The reaction of <u>sulfuric</u> acid and <u>sodium</u> hydroxide yields sodium sulfate.

The "-ous" suffix of a ternary acid becomes "-ite" in its salt. The reaction of <u>nitrous</u> acid and <u>sodium</u> hydroxide yields sodium nitrite.

Hydrates

Some compounds will add water molecules to their structure when they crystallize. This water is called water of hydration. An example is $Na_2CO_3 \cdot 10H_2O$ (sodium carbonate decahydrate). The presence of water in these molecules may lead to some differences in properties between different hydrated forms like crystal structure and density, but does not generally lead to significant changes in chemical properties.

6

Chemical Reactions

Generally, when a chemical change occurs, a change in energy for the system occurs. If heat is absorbed or taken up in a reaction, the reaction is endothermic. If heat is given off by the reaction, the reaction is exothermic. For a reaction to occur, a certain amount of energy (called the activation energy) must be put into the reactants. Activation energy is the minimum energy the reactants must have for the reaction to occur. This explains why reactions that are extremely exothermic still may need energy added to the mixture to start the reaction. The higher the activation energy required, the less likely a reaction is to occur spontaneously.

A reactive material is one that can undergo a chemical reaction under certain specified conditions. Generally, the term "reactive material" is used to refer to a substance that can undergo a violent or abnormal reaction in the presence of water or just under normal ambient conditions.

A chemical reaction is a process that results in the interconversion of chemical species. Exothermic reactions give off heat and can be the most dangerous. A separate source of heat is needed to maintain endothermic reactions. Removing the heat from an endothermic reaction slows and eventually stops the reaction.

Rates of Chemical Reactions

The rate at which the reaction occurs depends on the following general factors:

- Surface area of reactants–The larger the surface area (finer the particle), the faster the reaction. Chunks of coal burn. Coal dust explodes.
- Physical state of reactants–A reaction requires that the reactants mix with each other at the molecular level. This means that the faster the molecules move and mix, the faster the reaction can occur. Therefore, gases react faster than liquids that react faster than solids.
- Concentration of reactants–The higher the concentration of the reactants, the faster the reaction can occur.
- Temperature–As a general rule of thumb, the reaction rate doubles for every 10°C (18°F) increase in temperature.
- Pressure–Higher pressure implies a higher concentration of molecules per given volume, thus the higher the pressure, the faster the reaction will occur.

Types of Chemical Reactions

Many results of a HAZMAT incident involve the inadvertent mixing of chemicals. Knowing the compatibility of the materials being mixed is important. If they are incompatible, the results of the mixing could range from the formation of an innocuous gas or liquid to a violent explosion involving very toxic reaction products. Unknown materials must be identified before compatibilities can be determined. Judging the compatibility of more than two reactants is very difficult and requires extensive knowledge of chemistry. The following list illustrates what could happen when some incompatible materials are combined.

- Generation of heat–Mixing acids and water
- Fire–Brake fluid + calcium hypochlorite
- Explosions–Aluminum powder + methylene chloride
- Toxic gas production–Bleach + acid = chlorine
- Flammable gas production–Calcium carbide + water = acetylene gas
- Formation of more toxic substance than either reactant–Chlorine + ammonia = chloramine (household bleach and ammonia cleaner)
- Formation of shock- or friction-sensitive compounds–Ethers + oxygen = peroxide
- Dispersal of toxic dusts and mists–Burning phosphorus
- Violent polymerization–Heating methacrylic acid in a closed container
- BLEVE–Boiling Liquid Expanding Vapor Explosion

Decomposition

$$NH_4NO_3 \rightarrow 2H_2O + N_2O$$
$$+ \text{ heat, light, and sound}$$

Single replacement reactions

$$2Na + 2H_2O \rightarrow H_2 + 2NaOH + heat$$
(spontaneously ignites the flammable hydrogen gas)

Double replacement reactions

$$H_2SO_4 + 2NaOH \rightarrow Na_2SO_4 + 2H_2O$$
$$+ \text{ large amounts of heat, very violent}$$

7

Corrosives

Acids and Bases

Acids and bases were first identified as specific types of compounds due to their behavior in aqueous solutions. An acid is a substance that produces H_3O^+ (H^+) when it is dissolved in water. It is a proton donor and an electron pair acceptor or a species that donates protons, for example, HCl, NH_4^+, and $AlCl_3$.

A base is a substance that produces an OH^- when it is dissolved in water, a proton acceptor, or an electron donor, for example, NaOH, KOH, CH_3^-, or NH_2^-.

Below are examples of strong and weak acids.

Strong and Weak Acids

Strong Acids	Weak Acids
HCl	NH_4^+
H_2SO_4	HCN
HNO_3	HF
$HClO_4$	HNO_2

Overall this is the largest class of compounds transported. It includes the acids, bases or caustics, and several other classes of compounds. They all give off large amounts of heat when diluted with water. Never add water to an acid or a base unless you have large amounts of water and are far away from the mixture. It will react violently. When acids and bases are mixed, extreme amounts of heat are given off. This heat is sufficient to cause steam formation instantaneously and will cause splattering of the materials. These materials are usually corrosive to skin in any amounts and will cause anything from irritation to third degree burns. Depending on the metal and the compound, the rate of corrosivity may be years or a matter of seconds. The inorganic acids and bases are generally more corrosive than most organic acids and bases. However, some organic acids and bases are sufficiently corrosive to steel and flesh to be a significant hazard.

64

Hazards

The acids work by destroying living tissue through the large amount of heat from dilution and neutralization of the acid, and by chemical reactions with the tissue. Acids may be explosive, polymerizable, oxidizers, water reactive, toxic, flammable (by themselves or through hydrogen generation), very reactive, or unstable. Hydrogen gas is given off as acids attack metal. Acids have a sour taste when ingested.

The caustics or bases actually dissolve tissues by reacting with and decomposing the fats in a process called saponification. Bases may be explosive, polymerizable, oxidizers, water reactive, toxic, flammable (by themselves or through hydrogen generation) very reactive, or unstable. They have a general feel of being slick and slimy.

Concentrated Acids

SULFURIC ACID (H_2SO_4, 77 to 100 percent): Sulfuric acid is the most important acid produced and, by volume or weight, the largest produced and used chemical in the world. It is also one of the strongest acids. It is water-reactive in higher concentrations due to its heat of dilution. You would need 100 times more water than acid to make a safe and cool dilution of this material. At room temperature it does not fume or have an odor. The mist is very toxic and highly hazardous and corrosive. It is normally a water white material that is much heavier than water, but in all appearances looks like water. It has an oily appearance and may be colored blue or green with dissolved metals. It weighs more than 12 lbs/gal. The vapor pressure of sulfuric acid is negligible. Old or impure material is frequently a different shade of brown, although pure material with small amounts of organic materials dissolved in it can also be brown. It can be shipped in any size container. Depending on the strength of the acid it can have a relatively high freezing point and will expand in the container if frozen. For example, 93 percent acid freezes at -31°F while 98 percent acid freezes at 29°F. It will cause third-degree burns if not washed off the skin. It is extremely corrosive to the eyes. It will dissolve the entire human body, given enough time. Sulfuric acid reacts violently with water; the stronger the acid strength, the more violent the reaction. It will react with many organic compounds and may produce fire. It will react violently with alkaline solutions. In fact, sulfuric acid reacts with most materials.

Emergency Response: Dike large spills. Prevent entry into sewers, waterways, or low areas. Absorb with sand, clay, or diatomaceous earth. Recover liquid if large amounts.

Common Shipping Designations
- 60 degree = 77.7 percent as sulfuric acid with ~23 percent water
- 66 degree = 93.2 percent
- 1.835 electrolyte = 93.2 percent–also called "battery acid"

NITRIC ACID (HNO_3): Typically shipped as 70 percent solution. Nitric acid is extremely corrosive and will attack most metals. It is a very powerful oxidizer. It is transparent to yellow/orange in color. The yellow color indicates that it has decomposed slightly. Nitric acid is used to manufacture many things such as explosives, fertilizers, pesticides, and pharmaceuticals. It is very toxic; very small amounts or very dilute solutions will turn your skin yellow.

Large amounts cause severe and painful burns. When nitric acid attacks metal, large clouds of nitrogen oxides are given off. Care must be taken to prevent contact between nitric acid and any combustible such as paper, wood, cloth, etc. The reaction between nitric acid and organic material may lead to products that are explosive or very easily ignited. The effects of inhaling nitrogen oxides are usually delayed and sometimes fatal.

Emergency Response: Dike large spills. Prevent entry into sewers, waterways, or low areas. Absorb with sand, clay, or diatomaceous earth. Recover liquid if large amounts. Do not use any oxidizable materials as absorbents.

HALOGEN ACIDS (HF, HCl, HBr, HI): Overall, these acids react the same in the anhydrous forms, creating large clouds of acidic gas when they escape their containers. They love warm, moist areas on the human body and will become quite corrosive in these areas. The burns are quite painful. Inhalation will cause serious damage to the nasal cavity and lungs, and can lead to chemical emphysema and death.

HYDROFLUORIC ACID (HF, 10 to 48 percent in water): A colorless liquid. It is extremely corrosive and will attack glass and metals. It will penetrate the skin, causing severe burns. HF is only neutralized by the calcium in the bone or by calcium gluconate used as an external salve and administered intravenously. Diluting HF is not sufficient to reduce the hazards to an acceptable level. Exposure to concentrations as low as 1 percent can cause severe burns, and extensive body exposure to low concentrations have been fatal. It has a sharp, pungent, and irritating odor.

HYDROGEN FLUORIDE (HF, anhydrous hydrofluoric acid): A colorless, fuming liquid (67°F). It fumes on contact with air. It weighs about 8.5 lbs/gal. It has a vapor pressure of 17.6 psi. The fumes are very dense and heavy (vapor density of 3.0). It has a sharp irritating odor (0.04 ppm). It is extremely toxic (TWA 3 ppm). HF will react with sweat and mucous membranes (nasal passages, lungs, etc.) to give off heat. It attacks glass and most metals. It has a very high heat of dilution. This should be considered more hazardous than aqueous HF. It is an extremely hazardous liquid and vapor and causes severe skin and eye burns. It can be absorbed through skin in toxic amounts. The vapor injures respiratory tracts and causes severe damage. Burns are slow healing and very painful. At greater than 50 percent concentration, burns are immediate and severe. At 20 to 50 percent concentration, burns can be delayed 1 to 8 hours. At less than 20 percent concentration, burns are delayed up to 24 hours. Hydrogen fluoride is the only material that will cause decalcification of bone. Natural neutralization may take days. Any exposures to eyes cause loss of sight. It requires special medical treatment immediately.

Emergency Response: Water fog vapor, water spray (caution-violent), or neutralization with limestone and lime. Fluoride salts are toxic also.

HYDROCHLORIC ACID (HCl, 10 to 37 percent in water): A colorless to pale yellow liquid. Above 32 percent it fumes on contact with air. It is very corrosive to metals. It will cause burns to skin and have a sharp, pungent, and irritating odor. It is also known as muriatic acid. Hydrochloric acid is incompatible with most metals, yielding hydrogen and chlorine gas on contact with oxidizers. It will react with sulfides and cyanide salts to give hydrocyanic acid gas and hydrogen sulfide. It will react with formaldehyde to generate bischloromethyl ether (a known carcinogen). It is highly reactive with alkaline materials.

Emergency Response: Dike spills to prevent material from entering sewers, waterways, or low areas. Recover liquid. Absorb small spills with sand or neutralize with soda ash or limestone.

HYDROGEN CHLORIDE (HCl, anhydrous hydrochloric acid): A colorless to yellow fuming liquefied gas (-121°F). It produces large, white, dense clouds when it gets out of its container. It has a large vapor pressure of 603 psi. The vapor is dense at 1.3. Dry anhydrous HCl is nonreactive and noncorrosive. When wet, it is extremely corrosive and will attack most metals. It is very toxic (TWA 5 ppm). It has a very sharp, pungent, and extremely irritating odor. Vapor is rapidly absorbed by body moisture. Vapor can injure the respiratory tract and cause lung damage. Prolonged exposure may cause dental erosion.

Emergency Response: Water fog the vapor cloud. DO NOT PUT WATER on liquid pools.

HYDROBROMIC ACID (HBr, 48 percent): A colorless to red liquid. It is extremely corrosive to most metals. It has been known to dissolve the steel from under chrome-plated tools, leaving only the chrome plating. It will cause burns to the skin and has a sharp, pungent, and irritating odor.

HYDROGEN BROMIDE (HBr, anhydrous hydrobromic acid): A colorless to pale yellow/red fuming liquefied gas (-88°F). It produces large clouds of white to reddish vapor when it escapes its container. When wet, it is extremely corrosive and will attack most metals. It is very toxic (TWA 3 ppm) and has a sharp, pungent, and extremely irritating odor.

HYDRIODIC ACID (HI, 57 percent in water): A colorless to yellow or red liquid. It is very corrosive to metals and skin. It has a sharp, pungent odor.

PERCHLORIC ACID ($HClO_4$): The strongest mineral acid and is the most corrosive. It is a colorless, odorless liquid and is one of the most powerful oxidizing agents. It will form perchlorate esters with cellulose and cause instantaneous combustion. The reaction between perchloric acid and wood is extremely hazardous. Putting water on the resulting fire is only a temporary fix; the material will spontaneously ignite again when it dries. It is more powerful as an oxidizing agent than nitric acid and is extremely dangerous when around combustible material. Metal salts of perchloric acid are very shock-sensitive and tend to explode violently. Perchloric acid is toxic and will cause severe burns.

PHOSPHORIC ACID (H_3PO_4): A colorless liquid or transparent solid depending upon strength and purity. It is not as corrosive as other acids, but it will cause burns when left in contact with skin.

Tactical Considerations for Acids

- Get help on the way. You will need extra resources.
- Set up decon. Use soda ash or sodium bicarbonate solutions for decontamination.
- Use PPE required by the amount of material spilled (Level A, B, or C). Check permeability and compatibility.
- Approach cautiously. Stay upwind from spill or leak.
- Have fog nozzles available with adequate water supplies. Foam may be used on some acids.
- Have plenty of neutralizing agents available for the spill.
- Have a vacuum truck or pumping systems available to pick up spilled material.
- If you plan to neutralize the acid, plan to use about two pounds of caustic material (soda ash, lime, limestone, sodium bicarbonate) for each pound of acid. Be prepared to check pH often. Stir the acid mix constantly to get the best neutralization. Neutralization will get extremely hot. Expect temperatures of the solution to be 200 to 400°F. Your end pH should be between 4 and 8.

Fuming Acids

OLEUM: Oleum is the term used to describe fuming sulfuric acid. It is 100 percent sulfuric acid that has additional sulfur trioxide (SO_3) dissolved in it. It comes in various strengths such as 20 percent oleum that is 20 percent sulfur trioxide and 80 percent sulfuric acid. It is normally a turbid, off-white liquid that fumes profusely. The vapor density is 2.76. The higher the strength, the more fuming that occurs. The SO_3

escaping from the liquid forms sulfuric acid mist and creates clouds of dense white fumes. The clouds are extremely acidic and very toxic. It is extremely water-reactive and will explode violently upon contact with water (through the generation of steam). Beware of contact with skin. The skin is literally fried on contact, causing third-degree burns instantaneously. Severe respiratory tract injury and lung damage occur from inhalation. Prolonged exposure may cause dental erosion. Oleum is a strong oxidizer and may produce fires with organic material. It reacts with most materials.

Emergency Response: Dike large spills. Prevent entry into sewers, waterways, or low areas. Absorb with sand, clay or diatomaceous earth (will continue to fume). Water fog or foam may be used to reduce to a nonfuming state. Fluorocarbon oil or hollow glass beads may be used to reduce fuming.

Oleum Physical Property Data

Strength	% H_2SO_4	Specific Gravity	Weight lbs/gal	Freezing Point °F	Boiling Point °F
20% oleum	104.5	1.915	16.0	23	288
25% oleum	105.62	1.934	16.1	48	268
30% oleum	106.75	1.952	16.3	66	250
65% oleum	114.63	1.992	16.6	36	137

SULFUR TRIOXIDE (SO_3): Sulfur trioxide is a clear, colorless, oily, fuming liquid. As shipped, it may contain a slight haze and be off-white to light brown liquid. It is very heavy and weighs 15.4 lb/gal. It has a boiling point of 112.6°F (gamma form). It exists in three forms: alpha(α), beta(β) and gamma(γ). The melting points of these three forms are 144.1°F(α-form), 90.5°F(β-form), and 62.2°F(γ-form) respectively. Sulfur trioxide has a very high vapor pressure and escapes from the liquid, forming sulfuric acid mist and creating clouds of dense, white fumes that have a sharp, irritating odor. The clouds are extremely acidic and very toxic. It is extremely water-reactive and will explode upon contact with water (through the generation of steam). Sulfur trioxide is a strong oxidizer. Material causes immediate burns. Severe respiratory tract injury and lung damage may occur. Prolonged exposure may cause dental erosion. Material is extremely corrosive.

Emergency Response: Dike large spills. Prevent entry into sewers, waterways, or low areas. Absorb with sand, clay, or diatomaceous earth (will continue to fume). Water fog and foam may be used to reduce to nonfuming sulfuric acid. It is highly reactive and can ignite combustible materials.

CHLOROSULFONIC ACID (CSA, $ClSO_2OH$): Chlorosulfonic acid is a clear, straw-colored liquid with a sharp, penetrating, pungent odor. It is a very strong acid. It weighs about 14.6 lb/gal. The vapor density is 2.4. It contains both HCl and SO_3. It fumes on contact with air. It reacts violently with water, evolving large quantities of dense white fumes containing HCl and sulfuric acid. Heating to boiling decomposes the material into chlorine, sulfur dioxide, and water. It is extremely corrosive when wet. CSA is extremely toxic and will react with skin instantaneously, causing serious burns and generating large amounts of heat from the reaction with the skin. The vapor is extremely irritating and may cause delayed lung damage.

Emergency Response: Spills can be absorbed with absorbent clay or treated with water fog, foam, or mineral oil. It can be neutralized with caustic materials, although large amounts of heat are generated. CSA is highly reactive and can ignite combustible materials or may cause spontaneous combustion with materials like sawdust and oily rags.

FLUOROSULFONIC ACID (FSA, FSO$_2$OH): Fluorosulfonic acid is a clear, straw-colored liquid with a very pungent odor. It contains both HF and SO$_3$. It reacts violently with water, evolving large quantities of dense white fumes containing HF and SO$_3$. Heating to boiling decomposes the material into fluorine, sulfur dioxide, and water. It is extremely corrosive when wet. FSA is extremely toxic and will react with skin instantaneously.

FUMING NITRIC ACID: Fuming nitric acid comes in two grades–white fuming nitric, which is a clear oily to pale yellow liquid, and red fuming nitric, which is deep orange/red in color. Red fuming acid will fume on contact with air. White fuming acid will give off small amounts of vapor that will turn red with time. Both emit large amounts of oxides of nitrogen and are very toxic. Both are extremely strong oxidizers. Contact with combustibles may be explosive and will cause fires with most organic materials. They are both very corrosive when wet. Material causes immediate burns on contact. Vapor is extremely irritating. Rapid dehydration of body tissue will occur with the skin turning yellow to orange on contact. Severe respiratory tract injury and lung damage will occur, but may be delayed.

- White fuming nitric acid contains 97.5 percent HNO$_3$, 2 percent H$_2$O, <0.5 percent NO$_X$.
- Red fuming nitric acid contains 85 percent HNO$_3$, <5 percent H$_2$O, and 6 to 15 percentNO$_X$.

Emergency Response: Water fog and water streams may be used to dilute material to nonfuming acid. Do not use foam.

Fuming Nitric Acid Physical Property Data

Strength	% NO$_2$	Specific Gravity	Weight lbs/gal	Freezing Point °F	Boiling Point °F
White	<0.5	1.50	12.5	-60	191
Red	6-15	1.57	13.1	unknown	unknown

PHOSPHORUS OXYCHLORIDE (POCl$_3$): A colorless to pale yellow liquid, phosphorus oxychloride fumes on contact with air. It is very water-reactive and generates hydrochloric acid and phosphoric acid. It has a high boiling point (222°F) with a low vapor pressure (0.7 psi). The vapor is extremely dense–5.3. The liquid weighs about 14 lb/gal. Material will cause burns and ulceration of the skin and eyes. Inhalation may cause irritation of the nose, throat and lungs with coughing, discomfort, shortness of breath, and pulmonary edema. Symptoms may be delayed. It will react violently with alkaline solutions. It will generate large amounts of heat of reaction. It is incompatible with acetic acid, aluminum, nitric acid, and organic materials. It reacts with most metals to generate hydrogen gas. However, it is not corrosive to nickel.

Emergency Response: Dike large spills. Prevent entry into sewers, waterways, or low areas. Absorb with sand, clay, or diatomaceous earth.

PHOSPHORUS TRICHLORIDE (PCl$_3$): A colorless to pale yellow liquid, phosphorus trichloride has a pungent, irritating odor and fumes on contact with air. It is very water-reactive and generates hydrochloric acid, phosphine (toxic gas), and diphosphine gas (spontaneously combustible), and phosphoric acid. The boiling point of this material is 167°F and it has a vapor pressure of 3 psi. The vapor density is 4.75 and the liquid weighs about 12.5 lb/gal. Material will cause burns and ulceration of the skin and eyes. Inhalation may cause irritation of the nose, throat, and lungs with coughing, discomfort, shortness of breath, and pulmonary edema. Symptoms may be delayed. It will react violently with water. This may lead to flash fires due to spontaneous ignition of diphosphine. It will react violently with alkaline solutions. It will generate large amounts of heat of reaction. It is incompatible with alcohols, acids, amines, aluminum, organic matter.

Emergency Response: Dike large spills. Prevent entry into sewers, waterways, or low areas. Absorb with sand, clay, or diatomaceous earth. If water is used, it requires 100:1.

Tactical Considerations for Fuming Acids

- Get help on the way. You will need extra resources.
- Set up decon. Use soda ash or sodium bicarbonate solutions for decontamination.
- Use Level A suits. Check permeability and compatibility.
- Approach cautiously. Stay upwind from spill or leak.
- Have water supplies available with fog nozzles. Foam may be used on some fuming acids.
- Provide at least two attack lines. Primary hose line for spill dilution and secondary hose line for emergency personnel protection. Use of water will make the incident seem worse until you get the acid to a nonfuming state.
- Keep water use to a minimum. Plan at least one pound of water for each pound of acid you have spilled or could be spilled. Add water slowly with a fog pattern. WATER and ACID make a HOT combination. Get close enough to attack, but not be splashed. STEAM will be given off. CAUTION. Add water until the massive fuming stops and just steam is given off. Do not add water to liquid anhydrous HCl; use water fog to knock down vapors.
- If you plan to neutralize the nonfuming acid, plan to use about one pound of caustic material (soda ash, lime, limestone, sodium bicarbonate) for each pound of acid plus each pound of water used. It takes about two pounds of caustic material for every pound of undiluted acid. Be prepared to check pH often. Stir the acid mix constantly to get the best neutralization. Neutralization will get extremely hot. Expect temperatures of the solution to be 200 to 400°F. Your end pH should be between 4 and 8.

Strong Bases

SODIUM HYDROXIDE (NaOH): Also known as caustic soda or just plain caustic, sodium hydroxide is a white solid (flakes or pellets) that is deliquescent. Deliquescent means that the material will draw water out of the air and dissolve itself into a liquid. It is very soluble in water. It is extremely corrosive to skin and especially the eyes. It liberates large amounts of heat when dissolved in water. It is usually shipped as a 50 percent solution in bulk. It will attack aluminum, lead, tin, and zinc with the production of hydrogen gas. It is toxic when ingested or inhaled.

POTASSIUM HYDROXIDE (KOH): Potassium hydroxide is known as caustic potash. It is a white solid (flakes or pellets) that is deliquescent. It is very soluble in water. It is extremely corrosive to skin and especially the eyes. It liberates large amounts of heat when dissolved in water. It is usually shipped as a 50 percent solution in bulk. It will attack aluminum, lead, tin, and zinc with the production of hydrogen gas. It is toxic when ingested or inhaled.

AMMONIUM HYDROXIDE (NH_4OH): Ammonium hydroxide is ammonia (NH_3) dissolved in water. It is usually 29 percent in concentration. It is a colorless liquid with a pungent, ammonia-like odor. It is extremely corrosive toward skin and eyes. It attacks copper and copper alloys, forming a blue material. It will also attack galvanized surfaces. It is incompatible with salts of silver and zinc (forms explosive compounds).

AMMONIA (NH_3, anhydrous): Ammonia is a colorless, liquefied gas (-28°F) with a very pungent, choking odor (45 ppm). It is toxic (TWA 25 ppm) and flammable (LEL 16 percent, UEL 25 percent). It will form large clouds of gas when it escapes from its container. It is very corrosive to skin in the liquid stage. Ammonia auto-refrigerates and forms pools of liquid ammonia if the leak is large enough. Do not add water to liquid ammonia; use water fog to knock down vapors.

Weak Bases

SODIUM CARBONATE (Na_2CO_3): Also known as soda ash, sodium carbonate is a white, solid material that is basic when wet or dissolved in water.

SODIUM BICARBONATE ($NaHCO_3$): Sodium bicarbonate is also a white, solid material, more commonly known as baking soda. It is slightly basic when dissolved in water.

CALCIUM HYDROXIDE ($Ca(OH)_2$): Calcium hydroxide is known as caustic lime or slaked lime. It is not very soluble in water, but it is basic when dissolved. It produces a very high pH when dissolved.

Cleaning Up Spills of Acids or Bases

Acids can be neutralized with weak bases such as soda ash, sodium bicarbonate, and calcium hydroxide. Care must be used when using the carbonates, because a large amount of bubbling can occur that causes splattering. Other neutralizing agents can be the strong bases and limestone.

Bases can be neutralized with weak acids like acetic acid (vinegar) or sodium phosphate and by use of the stronger acids. Strong bases can be neutralized by the weak base sodium bicarbonate.

Be very careful when neutralizing spills. Large amounts of heat can be generated if the material is added very quickly or not mixed properly. Take care not to overshoot the neutral end point. Good mixing or agitation is essential. Monitoring the pH is critical in getting the right amount of material for neutralization.

8

Oxidizing Agents

Inorganic Oxidizers

Oxidizing agents are materials that support combustion through the supply of oxygen or other chemical means. They are unpredictable and can react violently without warning. If they should become contaminated, they can be as dangerous as explosive materials. They can also start chemical reactions, liberating heat and toxic gases. Addition of acid or caustic to even a weak oxidizer can produce a very strong oxidizing solution. Be very careful if any oxidizer contacts a base or acid in the presence of a combustible material.

Recognition of oxidizers can be accomplished by looking at the common suffixes and prefixes in the chemical names. The common suffixes are "-ites" and "-ates." The common prefixes are "hypo-" and "per-." Common inorganic oxidizing materials are listed below.

BROMATES: Emit toxic bromine fumes when heated to decomposition and are usually toxic when ingested.

CHLORATES: Emit toxic chlorine fumes when heated to decomposition and are toxic when ingested.

CHLORITES: Bleaching agents that react like hypochlorites. When heated to decomposition they are explosive.

CHROMATES: Do not present significant fire hazards, but are extremely toxic.

HYPOCHLORITES: Bleaching agents that release chlorine monoxide when exposed to fire. When exposed to moist air or wetted, they generate chlorine gas.

INORGANIC PEROXIDES: Hydrogen peroxide, sodium peroxide, and calcium peroxide generate oxygen and can be sensitive to shock. All but hydrogen peroxide are water-reactive.

NITRATES: Yield oxygen and large amounts of toxic nitrogen oxides when heated. Sodium nitrate is very hygroscopic. Old bags of material are very dangerous because sodium nitrate absorbs the water from the air as it sets and increases its combustibility. Sodium nitrate is also known as Chile saltpeter, while potassium nitrate is known as saltpeter.

NITRITES: Less reactive than nitrates but may form highly toxic and reactive by-products by reacting with other nitrogen-containing compounds forming "azo-compounds" and nitrosamines. Some azo compounds are unstable and are sensitive to shock. Some nitrosamines are known to cause tumors in test animals.

PERBORATES: Accelerate fires.

PERCHLORATES: May explode if heated. Most solid perchlorate salts are sensitive to shock.

PERMANGANATES: Can ignite if mixed with corrosives or may explode if in contact with sulfuric acid. These materials may ignite if mixed with some organic materials such as alcohols and amines, causing a flame that is very difficult to extinguish until the chemical reaction between the permanganate and the organic is complete.

9

Water- and Air-Reactive Materials

Types of Water- and Air-Reactive Materials

HYDRIDES: Hydrides are compounds of metals and hydrogen. Lithium hydride, sodium hydride, potassium hydride, lithium aluminum hydride, borane, and diborane (gas) are examples of hydrides. They are irritants, toxic, and are flammable solids and gases. They are water-reactive and will burn when placed in the open air. The fires have to be extinguished with Class D fire extinguishers due to the reactivity of the materials. When they burn or react with water, they generate highly basic materials like sodium hydroxide.

CARBIDES: These classes of materials contain a metal and carbon only. They are water-reactive and generate a flammable gas and the corresponding base. Calcium carbide generates acetylene and calcium hydroxide. Aluminum carbide generates methane and aluminum hydroxide. Magnesium carbide generates propyne and magnesium hydroxide.

NITRIDES: This class of materials contains a metal and nitrogen only. They react with water to give a base and ammonia. They are usually quite pyrophoric (self-ignites in air). Examples are magnesium nitride, generating ammonia, and magnesium hydroxide; and lithium nitride, generating ammonia and lithium hydroxide. Lithium nitride is very pyrophoric.

PHOSPHIDES: These materials contain only a metal and phosphorus. They are very toxic and generate phosphine gas and a base when wet. Phosphine (PH_3) is very toxic (TWA 0.3 ppm) and pyrophoric. Phosphine has a fish- or garlic-like odor. Examples of phosphides are aluminum phosphide and calcium phosphide. Phosphine gas is very flammable, even under conditions where it is not in high enough concentration to be pyrophoric.

CHLORIDES (Production of HCl Gas): These materials contain a metal and chlorine. They are all water reacting, most of them are fuming, and all are very toxic. They generate hydrogen chloride gas when they get wet. Some are explosive when mixed with water. Examples are:
- Aluminum chloride (anhydrous) is a yellowish-white, fuming, hygroscopic solid.
- Boron trichloride is a colorless, fuming liquid.
- Stannic chloride is a colorless, fuming, very caustic oily liquid. Significant heat is given off when mixed with water.
- Titanium tetrachloride is a colorless, fuming liquid.

74

- Phosphorus oxychloride is a fuming, oily liquid with a pungent odor. This material also generates phosphoric acid and hydrochloric acid on contact with water or moist air and is extremely corrosive. Phosphorus oxychloride reacts violently with water, but the reaction may be delayed for some minutes. After mixing, phosphorus oxychloride forms a separate layer below the water until the heat of the reaction at the interface between the two layers causes violent boiling.
- Phosphorus pentachloride is a yellowish solid that fumes in moist air. This material is also a flammable solid and very corrosive.
- Phosphorus trichloride is a highly reactive, fuming liquid that generates large amounts of HCl on contact with water or moist air.
- Silicon tetrachloride is a colorless, fuming liquid whose fumes cause a feeling of suffocation.
- Sulfur chloride is an amber to yellowish-red, oily, fuming liquid that decomposes on contact with water to give HCl and SO_2.
- Sulfuryl chloride is a colorless, fuming liquid with a very pungent odor. It also produces HCl and SO_2 when exposed to moist air.
- Thionyl chloride is a reddish-yellow, fuming liquid and is a strong skin irritant whose fumes cause a feeling of suffocation.

10
Toxicity

Toxicology

The science of toxicology is based on the principle that there is a relationship between a toxic reaction (the response) and the amount of poison received (the dose). An important assumption in this relationship is that there is usually a dose below which no response occurs or can be measured. A second assumption is that once a maximum response is reached any further increases in the dose will not result in any increased effect.

True allergic reactions do not show this type of dose-response relationship. Allergic reactions are special kinds of changes in the immune system and are not really toxic responses. The difference between allergies and toxic reactions is that a toxic effect is directly the result of the toxic chemical acting on cells. Allergic responses are the results of a chemical stimulating the body to release natural chemicals, that are directly responsible for the effects seen. Thus, in an allergic reaction, the chemical acts merely as a trigger, not as the bullet.

For all other types of toxicity, knowing the dose-response relationship is a necessary part of understanding the cause-and-effect relationship between chemical exposure and illness. Keep in mind that the toxicity of a chemical is an inherent quality of the chemical and cannot be changed without changing the chemical to another form. The toxic effects on an organism are related to exposure.

The toxicity of a compound depends on many things: the structure of the molecule, its physical state (solid, liquid, gas), the route of exposure (ingestion, inhalation, skin or eye absorption), and the actual amount of material or dose that enters the bloodstream.

There are a number of measures of toxicity and types of published toxicity data. Published toxicity values are normally based on either animal feeding or exposure studies. They could also be based on estimates of toxicity made by comparing compounds with similar structures with compounds whose toxicity is known. Published data is almost always a measure of the acute or short-term toxic effects of exposure to a known concentration of the compounds. Longer-term effects of exposure to a single dose or the effects of multiple exposures to low levels of exposure are more difficult to quantify, and this data may not be easily available to the First Responder.

Compounds that are known carcinogens (or which are believed to be carcinogens based on their similarity to known cancer-causing agents) will be labeled with a carcinogen label (C). However, the vast majority of compounds in commerce before the 1980s have never been tested to determine whether they cause cancer or other long-term effects.

Terms

The National Institute for Occupational Safety and Health (NIOSH) defines a number of general dose-response terms as does OSHA. The common published data on toxicity include the following terms and definitions.

PERMISSIBLE EXPOSURE LIMIT (PEL): OSHA's exposure limit that cannot be exceeded during any 8-hour work shift of a 40-hour work week.

THRESHOLD LIMIT VALUE (TLV): The airborne concentrations of substances and representative conditions under which it is believed that nearly all workers may be repeatedly exposed day after day without adverse health effects.

TIME-WEIGHTED AVERAGE (TWA): Time-weighted average concentration for a normal 8-hour work day and a 40-hour work week to which nearly all workers may be repeatedly exposed day after day without adverse effect.

SHORT-TERM EXPOSURE LIMIT (STEL): The concentration to which workers can be exposed continuously for a short period of time without suffering from 1) irritation, 2) chronic or irreversible tissue damage, or 3) narcosis of sufficient degree to increase the likelihood of accidental injury, impaired self rescue, or materially reduced work efficiency. It is the 15-minute TWA exposure which should not be exceeded at any time during a workday.

THRESHOLD LIMIT VALUE-CEILING (TLV-C): The concentration that should not be exceeded during any part of the working exposure.

TOXIC DOSE LOW (TD_{Lo}): The lowest dose of a substance introduced by any route, other than inhalation, over any given period of time, and reported to produce any toxic effect in humans or to produce tumorigenic or reproductive effects in animals.

TOXIC CONCENTRATION LOW (TC_{Lo}): The lowest concentration of a substance in air to which humans or animals have been exposed for any given period of time that has produced any toxic effect in humans or produced tumorogenic or reproductive effects in animals.

LETHAL DOSE LOW (LD_{Lo}): The lowest dose, other than LD_{50}, of a substance introduced by any route, other than inhalation, which has been reported to have caused death in humans or animals.

LETHAL DOSE FIFTY (LD_{50}): A calculated dose of a substance which is expected to cause the death of 50 percent of an entire defined experimental animal population. It is determined from the exposure to the substance by any route other than inhalation. As a general rule of thumb, significant damage is done at as little as 10 percent of the published LD_{50}. A published LD_{50} can be misleading since it is based on animal tests and different animal species respond differently to various chemicals. The choice of a test animal may affect the results, leading one to believe that a compound is more or less toxic to humans than the actual toxicity.

LETHAL CONCENTRATION LOW (LC_{Lo}): The lowest concentration of a substance in air, other than LC_{50}, which has been reported to have caused death in humans or animals.

LETHAL CONCENTRATION FIFTY (LC_{50}): A calculated or tested concentration of a substance in air, exposure to which for a specified length of time is expected to cause the death of 50 percent of an entire defined experimental animal population.

SKIN NOTATION: Listed substances followed by the designation skin refer to the significant contribution to exposure by the cutaneous route (skin, mucous membranes, or eyes) either with contact with vapors or, of greater significance, by direct contact with the substance.

IMMEDIATELY DANGEROUS TO LIFE OR HEALTH (IDLH): A condition that poses a threat of exposure to airborne contaminants when that exposure is likely to cause death, or immediate or delayed permanent adverse health effects, or prevent escape from such an environment. These concentrations are based on animal test data or on the flammability levels for less toxic material. IDLH values are typically used to evaluate when an evacuation of the area surrounding an incident is appropriate.

A significant issue with LD_{50}, LC_{50}, and IDLH published values is the fact that they are measures of acute toxicity only. Longer term health effects (including cancers from exposure to some chemicals) are not defined by this published data. Often, the long-term effects of exposure to a given chemical are not known. Compounds which are introduced into commercial manufacture today require extensive toxicity testing, including long-term feeding studies to define chronic effects. However, toxicity testing is very expensive. It is estimated at between $1-2 million (US) per compound, depending on the compound's properties. The law does not require this extensive testing on materials which were already in commercial manufacture before the passage of the laws in the 1970s and 1980s. While some acute toxicity data will usually be listed for a material, do not assume that complete testing has been done. Unless a Material Safety Data Sheet (MSDS) or other published source specifically reports that this testing has been done and that the material is free from long-term effects, it is not possible to be sure that a complete test has been conducted.

One of the more commonly used measures of toxicity is the LD_{50}. The LD_{50} (the lethal dose for 50 percent of the animals tested) of a poison is usually expressed in milligrams of chemical per kilogram of body weight (mg/kg). A chemical with a small LD_{50} (like 5 mg/kg) is very highly toxic. A chemical with a large LD_{50} (1,000 to 5,000 mg/kg) is practically nontoxic. The LD_{50} says nothing about nonlethal toxic effects though. A chemical may have a large LD_{50}, but it may produce illness at very small exposure levels. Saying that chemicals with small LD_{50}s are more dangerous than chemicals with large LD_{50}s is incorrect; they are simply more toxic for short-term acute toxicity. The danger, or risk of adverse effect of chemicals, is mostly determined by how they are used, not by the inherent toxicity of the chemical itself.

The LD_{50}s of different poisons may be easily compared. However, it is always necessary to know which species was used for the tests and how the poison was administered. The route of exposure is important, since the LD_{50} of a poison may vary considerably based on the animal species and the way exposure occurs. Some poisons may be extremely toxic if swallowed (oral exposure) and not very toxic at all if splashed on the skin (dermal exposure). If the oral LD_{50} of a poison were 10 mg/kg, 50 percent of the animals who swallowed 10 mg/kg would be expected to die. The LD_{50} is determined mathematically, and in actual tests using the LD_{50}, it would be unusual to get an exact 50 percent response. In one test the mortality might be 30 percent and in another 70 percent. Averaged out over many tests, the numbers would approach 50 percent, if the original LD_{50} determination was valid.

Besides acute toxicity and the danger of imminent death and/or the ability of a compound to cause cancer, there are a number of additional toxicity concerns and terms that should be understood.

78

EMBRYOTOXIN: A material which may not significantly harm an adult but can cause significant toxic effects, including death to a child in the womb.

MUTAGEN: The ability of a compound to cause changes in the structure of the DNA used to encode your genes. Mutagens may cause changes which may not be observed for several generations but can lead to inherited medical conditions in children or grandchildren. All compounds that are carcinogens are mutagens. It is not necessarily true that all mutagens also cause cancer; this has not been proven.

REPRODUCTIVE HAZARD: May cause changes in reproductive organs or capability. These changes may include atrophy of the organs, decreased sperm count, or significant changes in male or female fertility.

SYNERGIST: A compound or mixture of compounds which increases the relative toxicity of one or more other compounds. This increased toxicity is compared with what the toxicity would be without the synergist. This may be due to the synergist increasing the amount of the toxic material absorbed by the body or to another effect such as reducing or increasing heart rate or respiration. Situations where such effects are observed are called "synergistic."

TARGET ORGAN: An organ or organs that are specifically or selectively damaged by a toxin. Examples include toxins that selectively attack the liver, kidneys, central nervous system, eyes, or lungs. Knowing which target organs are attacked by a given compound makes the selection of personal protective equipment (PPE) easier.

TERATOGEN: A material that causes birth defects in newborns.

TUMOROGEN: The ability of a compound to cause tumors. This is different from a carcinogen in that the tumors may not be cancerous. However, many carcinogens are also tumorogens.

Exposure

Once an individual is exposed to a chemical, a variety of events may occur. The chemical may not penetrate deeply into the body. In this case, its effect will be local, or at the site of contact. The chemical may get into the bloodstream and travel throughout the body and may produce toxic effects involving various parts of the body. Often, specific organs are sensitive to particular chemicals and so are the most affected.

If a chemical is to have more than a local effect, absorption is the first step that must occur. Absorption may be defined as the movement of a chemical into the bloodstream. After some time, the chemical moves via the bloodstream and is distributed throughout the body. This process of movement into the tissues and organs is called distribution. Once the chemical is absorbed into the body, three other processes are possible: metabolism, storage, and excretion. Many chemicals are metabolized or transformed via chemical reactions in the body. These altered chemicals are called metabolites. Sometimes, chemicals or their metabolites are distributed and stored in specific organs. Storage may reduce metabolism and therefore increase the persistence of that chemical in the body. The various excretory mechanisms (exhalation, perspiration, urine, or feces) rid the body of the toxin over time.

For some chemicals, elimination may be a matter of days or months; for others, the elimination rate is so low that they may persist in the body for a lifetime and cause deleterious effects. Most chemicals share all these fates, i.e., some portion of the absorbed chemical will be metabolized, another fraction excreted, and a third part stored. The portion or percent metabolized, stored, or excreted depends on many factors.

Poisons work by changing the speed of different body functions, increasing them (for example, increasing the heart rate or sweating), or decreasing them (for example, decreasing the rate of breathing); people poisoned by parathion (an insecticide) may experience increased sweating because of a series of changes in the body. The first step is the biochemical inactivation of an enzyme. This biochemical change leads to a cellular change (in this case an increase in nerve activity). The cellular change is then responsible for physiological changes, which are the symptoms of poisoning seen or felt in particular organ systems (in this case the sweat glands). The basic progression from biochemical to cellular to physiological effects occurs in most cases of poisoning.

Depending on the specific biochemical mechanism of action, a poison may have very widespread effects throughout the body, or may cause a very limited change in physiological functioning in a particular region or organ. Parathion causes a very simple inactivation of an enzyme which is involved in communication between nerves. However, the enzyme which parathion inactivates is very widespread in the body, and thus the varied effects on many body systems are easily detectable.

Certain factors must be involved that lead to some chemical exposures being beneficial, others being harmful, and still others causing no measurable effects.

Dose

The most important factor that influences toxicity is the dose, or amount of chemical that enters the body. Every chemical is toxic at a sufficient dose. The dose of a chemical plays a major role in determining toxicity. Generally, there is no effect at low doses, but as the dose is increased, a toxic response may occur. The higher the dose, the more severe the toxic response that occurs.

The dose of a poison is going to decide how much effect it produces. The following example illustrates this principle. Suppose ten goldfish are in a ten-gallon tank and one ounce of 100-proof whiskey is added to the water every five minutes until all the fish get drunk and swim upside-down. Probably none would swim upside-down after the first two or three shots. After four or five, a very sensitive fish might. After six or eight shots another one or two might. With a dose of ten shots, five of the ten fish might be swimming upside-down. After fifteen shots, there might be only one fish swimming properly and it too would turn over after seventeen or eighteen shots.

The effect measured in this example is swimming upside-down. Individual sensitivity to alcohol varies, as does individual sensitivity to other poisons. There is a dose level at which none of the fish swim upside-down (no observed effect). There is also a dose level at which all the fish swim upside-down.

A dose-response curve relates the extent of the toxic response to the size, or amount, of the dose. For purposes of this text, the effect of a single exposure to a chemical will be examined.

Dose-Response Curve

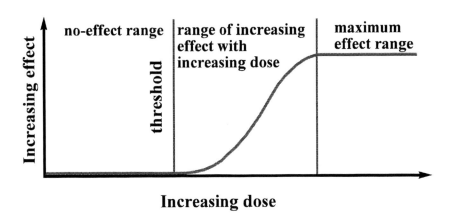

As shown, there is no response at low doses, and the response (or toxic effect) becomes more severe as the dose increases. At a high enough dose, the chemical can be fatal.

The dose relationship curve shows that exposure to a chemical does not always result in toxic effects and that an individual must be exposed to high enough doses for a toxic response to occur. Even higher doses are required for severe toxic effects to occur. The dose-response relationship is different for every chemical and may vary for each individual. Various factors account for this variability.

Dose-Response Chart For Hydrogen Cyanide

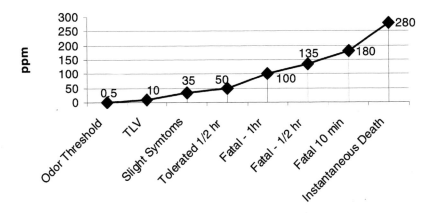

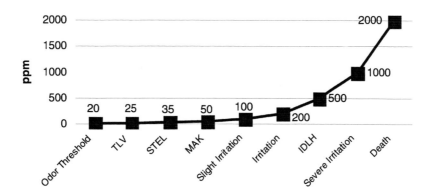

Dose-Response Chart For Ammonia

Properties of the Individual Chemical

Different chemicals vary tremendously in their toxic potential. Some are safe, even in large amounts, while others are very dangerous in extremely small amounts. The fact that chemicals differ in their chemical structures accounts for this variation in toxicity. The ways that a chemical interacts with the body–the amount excreted, how it is metabolized, the rates at which it is absorbed–all depend on the structure of the chemical. Small differences in structure are often associated with large differences in toxicity. For example, the two chemicals shown below vary only by the placement of two bromine (Br) atoms, but one of these chemicals is much more toxic than the other.

High Toxicity-LD$_{50}$ 600 mg/kg
+ mutagen, teratogen, carcinogen

Low Toxicity-LD$_{50}$ 21,500 mg/kg

In other words, it takes a much larger dose of the second chemical to produce the same toxic effect produced by a small amount of the first chemical. Thus, small differences in chemical structure may result in large differences in toxicity.

Measurements of Quantity

Usually, a given amount of a toxic agent will elicit a given type and intensity of response. The dose-response relationship is a fundamental idea in toxicology and the basis for measurement of the relative harmfulness of a chemical. In toxicology studies, the dose given to test organisms is expressed in terms of the quantity administered.

QUANTITY PER UNIT MASS: Usually expressed as milligram per kilogram of body weight (mg/kg).

QUANTITY PER UNIT AREA OF A SKIN SURFACE: Usually expressed as milligram per square centimeter (mg/cm^2).

VOLUME OF SUBSTANCE IN AIR PER UNIT VOLUME OF AIR: Usually expressed as microliters of vapor or gas per liter of air by volume (ppm). Particulates and gases can also be given as milligrams of material per cubic meter of air (mg/m^3).

One of the goals of the science of toxicology is to predict a chemical's toxic effects on humans. Toxicity is a general term used to show adverse effects produced by poisons. These adverse effects can range from slight symptoms like headaches or nausea to severe symptoms like coma, convulsions, and death. Before a chemical is released for sale or use, it must undergo toxicity tests to determine possible adverse effects. These effects fall into three basic categories–acute toxicity, subacute toxicity, and chronic toxicity. The two types most often referred to are acute and chronic.

ACUTE TOXICITY: Occurs after a single exposure to a chemical (or a limited number of exposures) and is seen immediately (within minutes or hours).

CHRONIC TOXICITY: Occurs after repeated long-term exposures, and effects are seen months or years after the initiation of exposure.

Most toxic effects are reversible and do not cause permanent damage, but complete recovery may take a long time. However, some poisons cause irreversible (permanent) damage. Poisons can affect just a particular organ system, or they may produce generalized toxicity by affecting a number of systems. Usually the type of toxicity is subdivided into categories based on the major organ systems affected.

Because the body only has a certain number of responses to chemical and biological stressors, it is often difficult to sort out the signs and symptoms and determine the actual cause of human disease or illness. Often, it is impossible to detect whether an illness was caused by chemical exposure or by a biological agent (like a flu virus). A history of exposure to a chemical is one important clue in helping to establish the cause of illness, but such a history does not constitute conclusive evidence that the chemical was the cause. To establish this cause-and-effect relationship, it is important that the chemical be detected in the body (such as in the blood stream), at levels known to cause illness. If the chemical produces a specific and easily detected biochemical effect (like the inhibition of the enzyme acetylcholinesterase), the resulting biochemical change in the body may be used as conclusive evidence.

Acute Toxicity

Since testing potentially hazardous material in humans is not appropriate, toxicity tests are conducted using experimental animals, especially rats and mice. One of the more common measures of acute toxicity is the LD_{50} measured in rats or mice.

The lower the LD_{50} the more acutely toxic the chemical. The higher the LD_{50}, the less acutely toxic the chemical. Thus, the LD_{50} is a measure of the relative toxicity of different chemicals, e.g., nicotine is much more acutely toxic than aspirin.

LD_{50} values determined for experimental animals can be used to estimate LD_{50} values for humans. These estimates are inexact, because they assume that humans are identical to rats, mice, and other species, except for weight. If we use this kind of rough estimate and express doses in common units of measurement, we could make a table of LD_{50}s for humans.

The following table shows the approximate LD_{50} for various chemical substances if fed to humans, LD_{50} for a 160 lb human.

Note that the LD_{50} measures only one toxic effect: death. It does not suggest the dose that will lead to other, less serious, toxic effects. The LD_{50} is also limited because it reflects a single-exposure situation. It is not used to describe toxicity due to repeated exposures to the same substance, or to a mixed exposure, where the individual is exposed to more than one substance at a time.

84

ACUTE TOXICITY

Chemical	LD_{50} (mg/kg)
sucrose (table sugar)	29,700
ethyl alcohol	14,000
vinegar (acetic acid)	3,310
sodium chloride (table salt)	3,000
vitamin A	2,000
vanillin	1,580
malathion	1,375
aspirin	1,000
chloroform	800
2,4-D	375
ammonia	350
copper sulfate	300
carbaryl	250
caffeine	192
phenobarbital	162
ethylene dibromide	146
sodium nitrite	85
arsenic (arsenic acid)	48
aflatoxin B1	7.0
sodium cyanide	6.4
strychnine	2.5
nicotine	1.0
sarin	0.1
VX	0.014
dioxin (TCDD)	0.001
botulinum toxin	0.000001

HUMAN TOXICITY

Chemical	LD$_{50}$
sucrose (table sugar)	5 lb bag
ethyl alcohol	5 pints
vinegar (acetic acid)	1.2 gallon
sodium chloride (table salt)	1 cup
vitamin A	several hundred pills
vanillin	several gallons
malathion	½ cup
aspirin	150 tablets
chloroform	2.5 tbs
2,4-D	½ cup
ammonia	3 pints household
copper sulfate	4 tsp blue viking
carbaryl	4 tsp Sevin
caffeine	15 gal coffee
phenobarbital	400 tablets
ethylene dibromide	1 tsp Bromofume
sodium nitrite	1 tsp (200 lbs salad)
arsenic (arsenic acid)	2 tsp Zotox
aflatoxin B1	swimming pool
sodium cyanide	garden pea
strychnine	pinch
nicotine	1 pack cigarettes
sarin	a smell
VX	a touch
dioxin (TCDD)	24,000,000 fish
botulinum toxin	cannot be seen

Chronic Toxicity

Although a large variety of toxic effects can occur after repeated exposure over a long time, one is of particular concern: cancer. Because of the seriousness of this effect, scientists attempt to figure out if chemicals can cause very small increases in the incidence of this disease, e.g., one additional cancer victim in one million people. Because cancer develops over a long time, and scientists wish to detect it at very low incidences, testing for this effect is very time-consuming and expensive. This simply means that it is possible to study only a few chemicals in a few different species of animals. Because scientists are looking for a low incidence, they would either have to test a very large number of animals or use an extremely high dose that could produce a high incidence in a small number of animals, e.g., 10 cancers in 50 animals. The cost of using millions of animals is prohibitive, so studies are performed using very high doses. These tests provide information only about the top (high-dose) part of the cancer dose-response curve. They do not show what the incidence of cancer is at lower doses–doses corresponding to commonly occurring levels in the environment. To estimate what might happen at low doses in humans, scientists make many assumptions and calculate the risk from these assumptions and the laboratory animal results.

Occasionally, large numbers of humans have been inadvertently exposed to a toxic chemical, so some information about human responses is available. Unfortunately, figuring out the exact amount of exposure or even the type and number of substances to which individuals were exposed is often difficult. Since chemicals are so much a part of daily life, everyone is exposed to a variety of chemicals, complicating the interpretation of the studies. However, epidemiological investigations, as these human population studies are called, can sometimes be very helpful. The link between cigarette smoking and lung cancer and other diseases was established because of epidemiological evidence. This type of evidence has also proven useful in cases in which people were exposed to a single chemical that produced unusual toxic effects. An example is the occupational exposure to vinyl chloride, which was associated with a relatively high percentage of workers exhibiting a very rare form of liver cancer. Results of epidemiological studies are difficult to interpret and generally cannot be used to show that specific chemicals cause cancer or other toxic effects in humans. Often, epidemiological evidence is used in conjunction with results of studies conducted on laboratory animals to show that effects which occur in animals can also occur in humans.

Other types of tests are being developed to study chronic toxicity, but most still need refinement. Better tests will probably be available in the future. In addition, scientists are working hard to gain a basic understanding of how chemicals produce their toxic effects. If researchers can learn enough about how chemicals cause their effects in living systems, they may be able to predict toxicity from a basic knowledge of the chemical and of the differences between creatures, e.g., rats versus humans. Once this occurs, using the assumptions that introduce large uncertainties into human risk assessments will no longer be necessary.

Individual Susceptibility

When an individual is exposed to a dose of a chemical, a number of personal factors will influence the severity of the toxic effect, if any, which occurs. Sensitivity to a chemical often depends on the age of the individual. In addition, it depends on the history of that individual, since previous exposures to toxic chemicals (or even nontoxic ones) can affect later reactions to the same or new chemicals. These variables and other personal factors will be discussed in the remainder of this section.

The susceptibility of individuals to toxic chemicals is often greatest when they are very young or quite old. This is true partly because metabolism and excretion in the very young or very old are much less efficient, so these age groups are less efficient at detoxifying and eliminating hazardous chemicals. Thus, it may take a smaller amount of poison to harm an infant, much less than the amount that would adversely affect a healthy adult.

Similarly, individuals with good nutrition and health are more resilient, so they can better metabolize and excrete toxic substances. Certain diseases may increase toxic effects because they affect the organs most important to metabolism and excretion. Both liver and kidney diseases fall into this category.

Because of hormonal differences, and perhaps different body composition, certain chemicals may affect males more than females, or vice versa.

Finally, inherited differences among people can affect the way the body reacts to toxic substances. A good example is the broad range of responses people have to bee stings: some have a violent reaction, while others show only slight effects.

Many factors affect the reaction of an organism to a toxic chemical. The specific response elicited by a given dose varies depending on the species being tested and variations that occur among individuals of the same species.

Duration and Frequency of Exposure

There is a difference in type and severity of effects depending on how rapidly the dose is received (duration) and how often the dose is received (frequency). If a dose is administered slowly, so that the rate of elimination or the rate of detoxification keeps pace with the intake, it is possible that no toxic response will occur. The same dose could produce an effect with rapid administration. An exposure to high concentrations of a material for a short period can lead to injury or death. Exposure for long durations to a small quantity or frequent exposures to small amounts can also lead to injury or death. Organophosphorous pesticides are excellent examples of this. A large dose in a short time (seconds) can be just as fatal as a small exposure over several hours.

Route of Exposure

Biological results can be different for the same dose, depending on whether the chemical is inhaled, ingested, applied to the skin, or injected. Natural barriers impede the intake and distribution of material once in the body. These barriers can attenuate the toxic effects of the same dose of a chemical. The effectiveness of these barriers is partially dependent upon the route of entry of the chemical.

Environmental Factors

Environmental factors may contribute to the response for a given chemical. For example, such factors as air pollution, work place conditions, living conditions, personal habits, and previous chemical exposure may act in conjunction with other toxic mechanisms.

88

Chemical Combinations

Some combinations of chemicals produce different effects from those attributed to each individually.

SYNERGISTS: Chemicals that, when combined, cause a greater than additive effect. For example, hepatotoxicity is enhanced because of exposure to both ethanol and carbon tetrachloride.

POTENTIATION: A type of synergism where the potentiator is not usually toxic in itself, but has the ability to increase the toxicity of other chemicals. Isopropanol, for example, is not hepatotoxic. Its combination with carbon tetrachloride, however, increases the toxic response to the carbon tetrachloride.

ANTAGONISTS: Chemicals that, when combined, lessen the predicted effect. There are four types of antagonists.

Functional–Produces opposite effects than the same physiologic function. For example, phosphate reduces lead absorption in the gastrointestinal tract by forming insoluble lead phosphate.
Chemical–Reacts with the toxic compound to form a less toxic product. For example, chelating agents bind up metal such as lead, arsenic, and mercury.
Dispositional–Alters absorption, metabolism, distribution, or excretion. For example, some alcohols use the same enzymes in their metabolism.
Receptor–Occurs when a second chemical either binds to the same tissue receptor as the toxic chemical or blocks the action of a receptor and by that reduces the toxic effect. For example, atropine interferes with the receptor responsible for the toxic effects of organophosphate pesticides. Another dispositional antagonist is Antabuse which, when administered to alcoholics, inhibits the metabolism of acetaldehyde, giving the patient a more severe, prolonged hangover.

Other items to consider besides toxicity:

- Acute effects
- Chronic effects
- Corrosivity
- Mutagen
- Teratogen
- Carcinogen
- Inhalation
- Skin notation
- Chemical properties
- Skin sensitizer
- Physical properties
- Asphyxiants
- Irritants
- Dermatitis
- Anaesthetics
- Neurotoxins
- Nephrotoxins
- Hepatotoxins
- Hematopoietic
- Dermatitis

To look at the toxicology of organic chemicals we will look at the two-carbon-compound ethane as a base molecule. We will change the functional groups and add different substituents to the base molecule to see how toxicity is effected.

From looking at the LD_{50} data presented in the Human Toxicity table, you should draw the conclusion that everything can harm you. Remember Paracelcus and his statement in the 15th century, "Everything is a poison. The only thing that differentiates a poison from a remedy is the dose." All chemicals are poisonous to some extent. Even compounds as "nontoxic" as table salt or sugar can have significant toxic effects (including death) at high enough doses. The more complex a chemical is the more likely it is to have some short–term or long-term toxic effect.

Relative Toxicity to Humans and Other Species

Pesticides, by their nature, are intended to kill or inhibit the growth of some undesirable species. While some pesticides are very toxic to humans, many pesticides are designed to affect processes that humans do not have. For example, interfering with the transition from caterpillar to moth could kill the moth population with little or no toxicity to humans or other species that do not have this metabolic process. For this reason, pesticide compounds and formulations may have very low levels of human toxicity and at the same time have a significant impact on the environment. Quantities of pesticide that would have little or no toxicity for a human being could effectively sterilize a stream for many miles downstream, killing fish, insects, and benthic life. Similarly, the amount of some herbicides that would have little effect on human life could kill all plant life in the area of a spill. For this reason it is important to consider both human toxicity and also potential impact on the environment when evaluating decontamination and remediation techniques.

While it is possible to chemically react and detoxify many compounds using simple decontamination procedures with bleach or ammonia, many pesticides do not react rapidly enough under "normal" decontamination conditions to significantly reduce the toxicity or biological activity of the active ingredient in the pesticide in the timeframe of a typical HAZMAT response. Some of the factors that affect this include:

- Relative solubility in water versus organic solvents.
  - Many pesticides are poorly soluble in water and water-based decontamination solutions may be ineffective because there is little or no mixing of the decon solution and the active pesticide. Some pesticides are formulated with organic inerts which make them difficult to decontaminate with aqueous decontamination solutions.
- Inherent stability to chemical attack and environmental degradation.
  - Many pesticides (as well as many other organic compounds) will only react slowly with acid or base and may not be attacked by standard alkaline or hypochlorite decontamination solutions. Similarly, while many pesticides degrade rapidly in the environment, some pesticides are designed to be persistent in the environment and may be present in significant concentrations a year or more after application.
- Adsorbtion onto soil particles or absorbtion into the organic-rich soil and stream bottoms may affect toxicity and environmental damage.
  - Many pesticides will bind tightly to the soil, especially where there is a significant amount of organic matter present such as in humus soil or at the bottom of slow moving creeks and wetlands. While this may be useful for dry decontamination of personnel and equipment or decontamination with an organic solvent, it can create significant problems with site remediation.

Environmental Data

Data on the toxicity and environmental fate of pesticides (and other organic compounds as well) is found in a variety of forms and in numerous different places.

Toxicity Data–Acute Toxicity

Material Safety Data Sheets (MSDS) will typically give the mammalian toxicity data in terms of LD_{50} values. An MSDS for a pesticide may also contain information on toxicity to other species. Typically, an MSDS for a nonpesticide will not include data on environmental degradation or toxicity to other species. Where an MSDS does list toxicity it may provide data on the acute (short-term) toxicity to fish, birds, and insects. This may be given in the form of:

- **LC_{50}** - The LC_{50} is the concentration in water or air that will kill 50 percent of a given species within a defined time period. You will typically see this data reported as follows:

  Fish LC_{50} (96 hr) carp 0.04 mg/l or LC_{50} (96 hr) bluegill 0.65 mg/l

  Daphnia LC_{50} (48 hr) <0.1mg/l or LC_{50} (48 hr) 0.96 micrograms/l

LC_{50} is also used for feeding studies and may be reported as follows:

  8-day dietary study LC_{50} for mallard ducks >5000 mg/kg diet

LC_{50} is also used to report toxicity when inhalation is a significant route of exposure. For example, the inhalation LC_{50} (4 hr) for rats is 4.3 mg/l

- **LD_{50}** is used to report acute dose data and is the type of data most available on an MSDS. Unlike LC_{50} which is the measure of the concentration of a toxicant in the environment, LD_{50} is a measure of the actual dose of the toxic material delivered to the subject animals which causes death in 50 percent of the animals in a given time period. It is most often seen as follows:

  LD_{50} (oral) rat 650 mg/kg or LD_{50} percutaneous for rabbit 217 mg/kg

It is important to note that while some pesticides are extremely toxic to many different species, some pesticides have very specific toxicity for only a few species. For example:

  Azinphos methyl is a highly toxic insecticide (Signal Word DANGER) with an LD_{50} for mammals of 9-20 mg/kg, high toxicity to fish (LC_{50} (96 hr) for trout of 0.02 mg/L) and very high toxicity for daphnia and other aquatic invertebrates (LC_{50} (48 hr)=0.0011 mg/L).

By contrast:

  Carbaryl (Signal Word WARNING), a widely used insecticide, has significantly lower acute toxicity for mammals (LD_{50} for rats 500-800 mg/kg), for birds (LD_{50} 1000-3000 mg/kg depending on the species), and for fish (LC_{50}=1.3-10 mg/l depending on species). However, carbaryl is extremely toxic to insects (1 gram is enough to kill 1 million bees) and to aqueous invertebrates (LC_{50} for daphnia=0.006 mg/l).

Environmental Decomposition and Degradation Rates

There are a number of sources of information about the normal rate of degradation of an organic compound in the environment. These include such reference works such as *The Pesticide Manual*, published by the British Crop Protection Council; *Handbook of Environmental Data on Organic Compounds,* by Verschueren; and the series of *Fate and Exposure Data,* published by the Noyes Data Corporation. In addition, some degradation data may be available from the MSDS.

Degradation in the environment may occur as the result of microbial action, because of hydrolysis or air oxidation or by reaction caused by exposure to sunlight. Data may also exist for the effect of pH and temperature on degradation rate, although this data may only be available through the manufacturers of the active ingredient.

Environmental degradation data is typically given as either a kinetic half-life ($k_{1/2}$) or as an environmental half life (DT_{50}). Both values are measures of how long a particular compound lasts in the environment. It is important to note that a compound may be present at significant levels for many half-lives depending on its degradation rate and its relative toxicity. For example, with a half-life of 1 month; half of the initial dose is still present after 1 month, one quarter of the initial dose is still present at 2 months, one eighth is present at 3 months and there is still one 64th or 1.5 percent of the original dose still present at 6 months.

Kinetic half-life ($k_{1/2}$) is typically used when the data on decomposition rate is generated in a laboratory and frequently specifies the pH of the kinetics run. Kinetic half-life data normally only measures the rate of hydrolysis of the sample in water.

For example:

- $k_{1/2}$(pH=7) = 6.5 days
- $k_{1/2}$ (pH=9.5) = 3.4 hrs

Environmental half-life is normally determined from soil or water analysis and reflects degradation from many different modes include hydrolysis, air oxidation, biological activity, and photolysis by sunlight. This is normally reported as DT_{50}.

For example:

- DT_{50} (soils) = 0.9-9 days
- DT_{50} (water) <1 day
- Photolytic DT_{50} on soil surface 23.8 days

There are still numerous formulations that include inorganic compounds containing copper, arsenic, and mercury which are used as fungicides, insecticides, seed treatments, and to protect plant grafts. These compounds may decompose in the environment, but because of the inherent toxicity of the constituent atoms, the reaction products may remain very toxic. For example, while copper, arsenic, or mercury compounds may change oxidation states or change the substituents attached to them (such as from mercuric chloride to mercuric oxide), the toxicity associated with the elements does not change and only decreases by slowly being redistributed in the environment and thus diluted. No environmental decomposition data will be found for such compounds.

92

Other Useful Environmental Data

There are several physical constants which are found with published environmental data that are useful in determining the fate of organics and in choosing the most effective decontamination and remediation approaches.

The Octanol-Water Partition Coefficient (K_{ow})

Octanol is a long-chain alcohol which is slightly soluble in water and which forms a separate layer on water. The distribution of an organic between the water layer and the octanol layer is a measure of the relative solubility of the component in water versus oils and lipids, or fats. For example,

- K_{ow}= [concentration X]octanol/[concentration X]water

The octanol-water partition coefficient is used as a measure of whether a compound will tend to bioaccumulate, i.e., build up in the food chain or in a particular organism's fat. The octanol-water coefficient is also a good measure of whether the active ingredient in an oil-based formulation will stay in the oil or distribute into water.

Octanol-water partition coefficients can range from less than 1 for a compound, which is very water soluble, to hundreds of thousands or millions for organic compounds which are soluble in oil but not water soluble. For this reason K_{ow} data is sometimes given as a logarithmic number such as

- $\log K_{ow}$ = 6.93 instead of K_{ow} = 8,500,000.

The Soil-Water Distribution Coefficient (K_d)

The soil-water distribution coefficient is a measure of the tendency of a compound to bind to the surface of soil rather than stay dissolved in the water. There is little data reported for this coefficient because the value tends to vary significantly depending on the amount of organic matter in the soil.

Adjusted Distribution Coefficient (K_{oc})

More commonly used is the adjusted distribution coefficient (K_{oc}) which takes into account the proportion of organic carbon in the soil. Published K_{oc} numbers may range from 3 to 5 to tens or hundreds or thousands. High K_{oc} values indicate that the component in question will tend to bind with the soil and will tend to accumulate where the highest soil organic carbon load is found–such as in marshland or slow-moving stream bottoms.

Remember to treat all chemicals with respect. However, we do not mean to say to wear Level A protection at every response. You have to look at the chemical's toxicity, vapor pressure, boiling point, skin absorption data, long-term health effects, and inhalation data to make a valid risk assessment. If a material boils at 250°F and has a skin absorption problem, you would not need to wear Level A and probably could get by with Level C. Just evaluate all options, using all the data you can find. Examples can be found in the following table.

Two-Carbon Derivatives

Name	Boiling Point (°F)	TLV	LD$_{50}$	IDLH	Odor Threshold	Other
Ethane	-86				899	Asphyxiant
Ethylene	-103					Asphyxiant
Acetylene	84	5000				Asphyxiant
Ethyl benzene	136	100	3500	2000	140	Teratogen
Ethyl chloride	12	1000	14600	20000		
Vinyl chloride	14	5	3463		260	Carcinogen
Ethyl bromide	38	200	1350			Carcinogen
Ethylenedichloride	84	10	670	1000	100	Carcinogen
Ethylenedibromide	131	20	108	400		Carcinogen
Trichloroethane	74	350	836	1000	100	Carcinogen
Ethyl alcohol	78	1000	7060		10	Teratogen
Ethylene glycol	198	50	4700			Kidney
Ethyl ether	35	400	1215	19000	0.8	
Acetic acid	118	10	3310	1000	1	
Trichloroacetic acid	198	1	400			
Acetyl chloride	51	5	3310	100	1	
Acetamide	221		7000			Carcinogen
Dimethylacetamide	166	10	4300	47	400	Liver
Ethyl acetate	77	400	5620	10000	1	
Vinyl acetatc	73	10	2920		0.12	Carcinogen
Ethyl acrylate	100	5	800	2000	0.0002	Carcinogen
Acetaldehyde	21	100	661	10000	0.21	Carcinogen
Ethylamine	17	10	400	4000		
Diethylamine	56	10	540	2000	0.14	
Triethylamine	90	10	460	1000		
1,2 Diaminoethane	117	10	500	2000	10	
Ethanolamine	170	3	1700			
Acetonitrile	82	40	2730	4000	40	
Nitroethane	114	100	1100	1000	163	
Diethylsulfate	210		880			Carcinogen
Ethyl mercaptan	94	0.5	682	2500	0.001	
Diethylsulfide	92		5930			
Ethylene oxide	11	10	72	800	50	Carcinogen

11
Organic Chemistry

Organic chemistry is the chemistry of carbon and carbon-containing compounds. All carbon compounds, except a few inorganic carbon compounds, are organic compounds. Inorganic carbon compounds include the oxides of carbon, the bicarbonates and carbonates of metal ions, hydrogen cyanide, the metal cyanides, the metal carbides, and a few others. Compounds that contain metal-carbon bonds are typically referred to as organometallic compounds. Organometallic compounds are generally pyrophoric and hydrolytically unstable compounds.

The Nature of Organic Chemistry
There are more than ten million organic compounds characterized, that make up the foods we eat (made of carbohydrates, lipids, proteins, and vitamins), furs and feathers, hide and skins, and the organisms from which they came. Organic compounds also include the building blocks for plastics, synthetic and natural fibers, dyes and drugs, insecticides and herbicides, ingredients in perfumes and flavoring agents, and petroleum products.

The name organic chemistry came from the word organism. Before 1828, all organic compounds had been obtained from living organisms or their remains. The belief then was that the synthesis of organic compounds from inorganic compounds in the laboratory was impossible. All efforts had failed, and scientists became convinced that some "vital force" the living organisms had was necessary to make an organic compound. The synthesis of urea from inorganic substances in 1828 led to the disappearance of this vital force theory.

Organic Families and Their Functional Groups
Studying such large numbers of organic compounds requires organization. By custom and use, organic compounds are sorted into families consisting of compounds with similar structures and chemistry defined by "functional groups." Functional groups are small structural units within molecules at which most of the compound's chemical reactions occur. Compounds with the same functional groups will typically undergo the same kinds of chemical reactions regardless of how large or small the molecule is.

Representing Chemical Compounds–Condensed Structures
To save space and time, condensed structures may be used to simplify the drawing and writing of structural formulas of organic compounds. C-H bonds are understood, and CH_3 means that three hydrogen atoms are bonded to a carbon atom.

96

For example:

CH$_3$ is understood to be

$$
\begin{array}{c}
\text{H} \\
| \\
\text{H}-\text{C} \\
| \\
\text{H}
\end{array}
$$

CH$_3$CH$_2$OH is understood to be

$$
\begin{array}{c}
\text{H} \quad \text{H} \\
| \quad\quad | \\
\text{H}-\text{C}-\text{C}-\text{O}-\text{H} \\
| \quad\quad | \\
\text{H} \quad \text{H}
\end{array}
$$

Hydrocarbons, compounds that contain only carbon and hydrogen, are considered to be the parents of all other compounds. Or, put another way, all other organic molecules are considered to be modifications of the parent hydrocarbon. Hydrocarbons are typically divided into two classes: aliphatic and aromatic. The term aliphatic originally meant fatty and aromatic meant fragrant. These terms no longer apply in their original meaning. Aliphatic now means straight and branch chain compounds and those cyclic compounds that resemble the straight and branch chain compounds. Aromatic compounds are benzene and compounds that resemble benzene in chemical behavior.

The basis of organic chemistry is structural theory. We can separate all organic compounds into several families based on similarity of structure. When we classify compounds of the basis of structure, simultaneously we find that we have classified the compounds as to their physical and chemical properties. A particular set of properties is thus characteristic of a particular kind of structure.

Within a family of compounds variations in properties exist. All members of the family may react with a particular reagent or other chemical, but some may react more readily or more violently than others. Within a single compound there may be variations in properties, one part of a molecule being more reactive or undergoing "different chemistry" than another part. These variations in properties correspond to variations in structure.

The various classes of chemical compounds will be discussed in different sections. Some of the different aliphatic families are: alkanes, alkenes, alkynes, dienes, halogenated hydrocarbons, alcohols, ethers, carboxylic acids, aldehydes, ketones, esters, and amines. Some of the families of aromatic hydrocarbons are: anilines, phenols and a host of substituted benzenes. During this discussion we will talk about the "hydrocarbon" backbone that can be abbreviated as R or R'. This backbone is nothing more than some carbon atoms strung together. If we looked at a model of a hydrocarbon it would branch and look like a backbone or spine. We will also talk about isomers. An isomer is defined as a compound with the same molecular formula as another compound, but with a different structure.

It is useful to have a kind of shorthand when writing organic equations. The symbol R$_x$ stands for the word radical and in organic chemistry will represent parts of a molecule other than the functional group where chemistry is occurring. It is used to simplify equations or to summarize reactions where the chemistry of concern is that of the functional group, and the nature (chain length for the carbon chain, etc.) does not really matter. For example, we can write an equation in the form:

$$RNH_2 + HCl \rightarrow RNH_3^+ + Cl^-$$

This is the reaction between organic amines and hydrogen chloride or hydrochloric acid. In this case it does not make any difference in the description of the reaction if the organic compound reacting is methylamine (CH_3NH_2), ethylamine ($CH_3CH_2NH_2$), or any similar compound. The R takes care of any alkane group in which you may substitute for that group. It takes care of all the equations, including methylamine, ethylamine, propylamine, butylamine, etc. It gives a simpler view of how one group or class of molecules behave in a specific reaction and not just the reaction of a single molecule (like methylamine).

We will discuss functional groups or substituents after the discussion on alkanes for better understanding. Generally, all organic materials will react with strong oxidizers, some faster than others. Also as a rule all organic materials are flammable, combustible, or decompose with heat. Organic chemicals have different levels of toxicity; some are downright deadly, while others are used as food additives. We will discuss the toxicity aspect regarding classes of compounds in later sections of this text.

NOMENCLATURE (NAMING)
Each organic compound and each class of compounds have a name made up of several parts: a part that tells how long the longest chain of carbons is, modifiers that tell what else is on the chain besides hydrogen and an ending that tells which subgroup of organics to which the molecule belongs. For example, the ending "-ane" specifies that the molecule is an alkane. We will discuss the nomenclature or naming of each type of compound as we discuss the different types of organic molecules.

In the following sections we will discuss the classes of molecules or the organic chemical families of molecules based on functional groups. We will start out with the simplest and work our way to more complicated and more energetic molecules.

Alkanes

Alkanes are organic compounds that contain only carbon and hydrogen. All of their names end in "-ane" indicating that they are members of the group of alkanes. They are also known as paraffins. The most common simple alkanes are methane CH_4, ethane C_2H_6 (CH_3CH_3), propane C_3H_8 ($CH_3CH_2CH_3$), and butane C_4H_{10} ($CH_3(CH_2)_2CH_3$). For the straight chain alkanes the only thing that changes in the structure of the molecule is the number of (CH_2) groups in the chain.

The principle industrial source of alkanes is petroleum and natural gas. Natural gas is separated to form Liquefied Natural Gas (LNG) which is almost pure methane and Liquefied Petroleum Gas (LPG) which is a mix of pure propane/butanes.

Petroleum Distillation Fractions

Fraction	Distillation Temperature, °C	Carbon Number
Gas	Below 20	C_1-C_4
Petroleum ether	20-60	C_5-C_6
Ligroin (light naphtha)	60-100	C_6-C_7
Natural gasoline	40-205	C_5-C_{10}, and Cycloalkanes
Kerosene	175-325	C_{12}-C_{18}, and Aromatics
Gas oil	Above 275	C_{12} and Higher
Lubricating oil	Nonvolatile liquids	Long Chains Attached to Cyclic Structures
Asphalt or petroleum coke	Nonvolatile liquid	Polycyclic Structures

Crude oil (paraffin-base petroleum) contains many different alkanes from very short chain hexanes (C_6H_{14}), which are liquid even at very cold temperatures, to very long-chain alkanes (C_{20}-C_{34}) that have high melting points and appear to be waxes or even hard solids at ambient temperatures. The petroleum refining process first separates the material based on boiling points; lower boiling compounds are removed by distillation (heating the crude oil to boil off the more volatile compounds and condensing them back into different liquid fractions). The lower boiling compounds are used as fuel (automotive gasoline, aviation fuel, home heating oil, and fuel oil for industrial boilers). Some higher boiling components are used as lubricating oils and wax such as paraffin wax (melting point 50-70°C).

In petroleum refining most of the higher boiling materials are subjected to high temperature and catalysts in a process called cracking. This converts larger higher-boiling alkanes into smaller alkanes and alkenes (another class of molecules we will discuss shortly) to increase yields of the smaller more valuable molecules used as fuels.

Large organics + Heat + Catalyst –> Smaller organics + Hydrogen gas

Catalytic reforming converts alkanes and cycloalkanes into aromatic hydrocarbons.

Alkanes for the most part are nonreactive unless subjected to high temperature (this does not include burning). They will react with chlorine and bromine in the presence of ultraviolet light or heat (250° to 400°C) to generate halogenated hydrocarbons (a separate class which will be discussed in a later section). All alkanes will burn with generally yellow fire and produce only small amounts of black smoke. Alkanes will react with strong oxidizers very slowly.

Note: In the real world you will encounter temperatures for physical properties like melting point and boiling point listed in both degrees F and C. Typically all physical properties are given in °C, while flash points are given in °F.

PHYSICAL PROPERTIES OF ALKANES

Except for very small alkanes, the boiling point rises 20 to 30°C for each carbon that is added to the molecule. This 20 to 30°C rise in boiling point for each additional carbon will hold true for the other families of organic compounds as well. All alkanes are less dense than water. Generally all alkanes are nearly insoluble in water. Measured solubilities are roughly 300 to 400 ppm at 25°C and atmospheric pressure. The first four alkanes are gases, the next 13 are liquids, and those that contain more than 18 carbons are solids at normal room temperature.

Common Alkane Hydrocarbons

Name	Formula	Melting Point °C	Boiling Point °C	Flash Point °F	LEL %	UEL %	Toxicity
Methane	CH_4	-183	-162	Gas	5.0	15.0	Asphyxiant
Ethane	CH_3CH_3	-172	-88.5	Gas	3.0	12.5	Asphyxiant
Propane	$CH_3CH_2CH_3$	-187	-42	-148	2.1	9.5	PEL 1000
n-Butane	$CH_3(CH_2)_2CH_3$	-138	0	-76	1.6	8.4	PEL 800
n-Pentane	$CH_3(CH_2)_3CH_3$	-130	36	-40	1.5	7.8	PEL 600
n-Hexane	$CH_3(CH_2)_4CH_3$	-95	69	-7	1.1	7.5	PEL 50
n-Heptane	$CH_3(CH_2)_5CH_3$	-90.5	98	25	1.0	6.7	PEL 400
n-Octane	$CH_3(CH_2)_6CH_3$	-57	126	56	1.0	5.6	PEL 300
n-Nonane	$CH_3(CH_2)_7CH_3$	-54	151	88	0.9	2.9	PEL 200

ISOMERS

Isomers are molecules that have the same molecular formula, but different structures. The "normal" structure is the straight chain isomer and is usually denoted by an "n" in front of the name. This molecule is considered the "parent" molecule and the isomers are considered modifications of this parent.

There are five hexanes, nine heptanes, and 75 decanes. These molecules are considered branched-chain variants of the normal or straight chain parent with prefixes such as "iso-," "neo-," "sec-," and "tert-" and have common names such as isopentane or neopentane. Having prefixes for every individual isomer is impractical, so a system has been developed by the International Union of Pure and Applied Chemistry (IUPAC) which gives a unique name to every compound. In this system the isomers are considered variations of the longest straight chain with shorter substituent groups, sometimes called radicals, replacing some hydrogens on the straight chain. These substituents are named simply by taking the name for the number of carbons in the substituent, dropping the "-ane" and adding "-yl." Thus methane becomes methyl and ethane becomes ethyl.

ALKANE ISOMERS

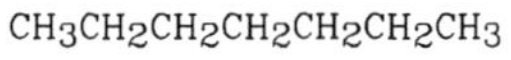

$CH_3CH_2CH_2CH_2CH_2CH_2CH_3$

n-HEPTANE

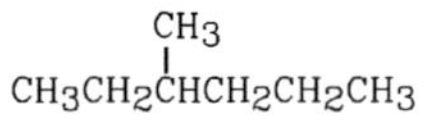

$CH_3CH_2\overset{\underset{|}{CH_3}}{C}HCH_2CH_2CH_3$

3-METHYLHEXANE

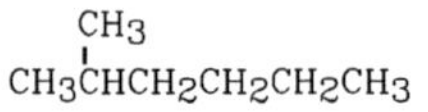

$CH_3\overset{\underset{|}{CH_3}}{C}HCH_2CH_2CH_2CH_3$

2-METHYLHEXANE

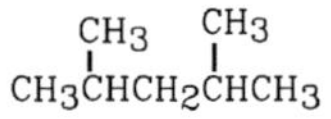

$CH_3\overset{\underset{|}{CH_3}}{C}HCH_2\overset{\underset{|}{CH_3}}{C}HCH_3$

2,4-DIMETHYLPENTANE

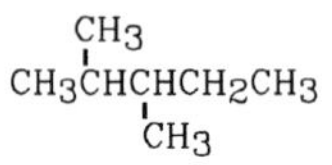

$CH_3\overset{\underset{|}{CH_3}}{C}H\overset{\underset{|}{CH_3}}{C}HCH_2CH_3$

2,3-DIMETHYLPENTANE

$CH_3\overset{\underset{|}{CH_3}}{C}CH_2CH_2CH_3$ $_{\underset{CH_3}{|}}$

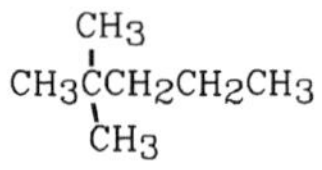

2,2-DIMETHYLPENTANE

Therefore, we see names such as methylpropane (isobutane), 2-methylbutane (isopentane), etc. If more than one group (i.e., methyl) is present, then the prefixes "di-," "tri-," "tetra-," etc. are used to show that there are 2, 3, or 4 of a given substituent. The ending "-ane" shows that these are alkanes. The name pentane or hexane says that there are 5 or 6 carbons in the longest chain. The substituent name (methyl in this case) says that at least one of the hydrogens on the longest chain has been replaced by a CH_3. The numbering tells you where these methyl radicals or substituents are placed. While the common name for a molecule does not necessarily tell you what the actual structure is and may be different in different countries, the IUPAC name is internationally recognized and unique for each molecule.

The "branched-chain" isomers have a lower boiling point than their straight chain counterparts. The more branches, the lower the boiling points.

Common Alkane Isomers

Name	Formula	Melting Point °C	Boiling Point °C	Flash Point °F	LEL %	UEL %	Toxicity
n-Butane	C_4H_{10}	-138	0	-76	1.6	8.4	PEL 800
Isobutane	C_4H_{10}	-159	-12		1.8	8.4	
Pentane	C_5H_{12}	-130	36	-40	1.5	7.8	PEL 600
Isopentane 2-Methyl Butane	C_5H_{12}	-160	28	-60	1.4	8.3	
Neopentane 2,2-Dimethylpropane	C_5H_{12}	-17	9.5		1.4	7.5	
Hexane	C_6H_{14}	-95	69	-7	1.1	7.5	PEL 50
Isohexane 2-Methylpentane	C_6H_{14}	-154	60	20	1.0	7.0	TWA 500
3-Methylpentane	C_6H_{14}	-118	63	19	1.2	7.0	TWA 500
2,2-Dimethylbutane	C_6H_{14}	-98	50	-54	1.2	7.0	TWA 500
2,3-Dimethylbutane	C_6H_{14}	-129	58	-20	1.2	7.0	TWA 500

Materials that are gases at ambient temperatures do not have flashpoints. Flashpoint is a measure of the flammable vapors above the liquid phase. If the material is normally a gas, a liquid phase is not present. These gases are extremely flammable. Some materials that are normally gases, but which are shipped as cryogenic liquids, will have flash points listed. If a material is a gas, assume that its flash point is very low (propane, for example). Methane and ethane will cause asphyxiation before they become toxic.

When blank spaces are found in a table, no data can be found. When you encounter missing data, a judgment has to be made. If you can find a similar compound or a parent compound with the same generic formula, then you can assume that the chemicals you are looking at will have similar properties and toxicity.

Alkenes (Olefins)

Alkenes are compounds that are similar to the parent alkane except they contain fewer hydrogens. They contain a structural feature called a carbon-carbon "double bond" which gives them different chemical properties from the alkanes. They are sometimes called unsaturated hydrocarbons or olefins. The ending -ene in their name shows that they have at least one double bond in their longest chain. The most common of these compounds have both a common name and IUPAC name. The IUPAC name is similar to that of alkanes except that the ending -ene shows a double bond along with a number to show where in the chain the double bond occurs. Other prefixes may be used such as E-, Z- cis-, or trans- to show specific geometry around the C=C double bond. The common names for the simpler alkenes are used frequently in commerce; ethene is usually called ethylene and propene is usually called propylene for most industrial uses.

ALKENE ISOMERS

cis-2-butene   TRANS-2-BUTENE

The industrial source of alkenes is the cracking of petroleum. The smaller alkenes are obtained from fractional distillation of the "cracked" petroleum. Higher alkenes that cannot be removed by distillation remain as components of gasoline.

Alkenes react readily and rapidly with chlorine and bromine at room temperature; they may react so fast that an explosion could occur. At elevated temperatures this reaction is explosive. Alkenes will also react with gaseous hydrochloric acid, hydrobromic acid, and hydriodic acid. These reactions are generally slow, but could be explosive under the wrong conditions. The reaction products are halogenated hydrocarbons, which are typically more toxic than the "parent" alkenes. Halogenated hydrocarbons are molecules where one or more of the hydrogens on the "parent" molecule has been replaced with a bromine, chlorine, etc.

Alkenes + Halogens –> Halocarbons or Alkyl Halides

If the above acids are aqueous acids, then the reaction products include alcohols. Cold sulfuric acid will also react with alkenes to form a compound that, upon addition of water and heat, forms alcohols.

Alkenes + Aqueous Acids –> Alcohols

Under hot sulfuric acid conditions (above 70°C), alkenes may dimerize to form hydrocarbons.

$$\text{Alkenes} + H_2SO_4 \rightarrow \text{Dimers and Polymers}$$

Dimers and polymers are compounds where two or more or the alkenes become "building blocks" for larger molecules.

Alkenes will react rapidly with oxidizers to form glycols and other alcohols. Reaction may be rapid enough for spontaneous combustion to occur.

All alkenes will burn. They burn with a hotter fire than alkanes and generally produce a little more black smoke.

Alkenes are the basis for the plastics industry. Polymerization to form "polyolefins" is always a consideration when dealing with these materials. This polymerization can be extremely violent. More details can be found in the plastics section of this chapter.

The physical properties of alkenes are similar to those of alkanes. They are insoluble in water and are less dense than water.

Common Alkene Hydrocarbons

Name	Formula	Melting Point °C	Boiling Point °C	Flash Point °F	LEL %	UEL %	Toxicity
Ethylene	$CH_2=CH_2$	-169	-102	GAS	2.7	36.0	Asphyxiant
Propylene	$CH_2=CHCH_3$	-185	-48	-162	2.0	11.1	Asphyxiant
1-butene	$CH_2=CHCH_2CH_3$	-185	-6.5	-112	1.6	10.0	Asphyxiant
1-pentene	$CH_2=CH(CH_2)_2CH_3$		30	0	1.5	8.7	
1-hexene	$CH_2=CH(CH_2)_3CH_3$	-138	64	20	1.2	6.9	
Cis-2-butene	$CH_3CH=CHCH_3$	-139	4	-100	1.7	9.0	
Trans-2-butene	$CH_3CH=CHCH_3$	-106	1	-100	1.8	9.7	
Isobutylene	$CH_2=C(CH_3)_2$	-141	-7		1.8	9.6	
Cis-2-pentene	$CH_3CH=CHCH_2CH_3$	-151	37	-4	1.5	8.7	
Trans-2-pentene	$CH_3CH=CHCH_2CH_3$	-180	36	-4	1.5	8.7	
3-Methyl-1-butene	$CH_2=CHCH(CH_3)_2$	-135	25	20	1.5	9.1	
2-Methyl-2-butene	$CH_3CH=C(CH_3)_2$	-123	39	20			Asphyxiant
2,3-Dimethyl-2-butene	$(CH_3)_2C=C(CH_3)_2$	-74	73	-4			

Alkynes and Dienes

Alkynes are compounds that contain a carbon-carbon triple bond. Their chemical and physical properties are similar to alkenes. The simplest members of this class are compounds such as ethyne (acetylene) C_2H_2 [CH≡CH], propyne (methylacetylene) C_3H_4 [CH$_3$C≡CH], 1-butyne (ethylacetylene) C_4H_6 [HC≡CCH$_2$CH$_3$], and 2-butyne (dimethylacetylene) C_4H_6 [CH$_3$C≡CCH$_3$].

Dienes are compounds that have two carbon-carbon double bonds, so they have essentially the same properties as alkenes. The simplest members of this group are compounds such as 1,3-butadiene C_4H_6 [CH$_2$=CHCH=CH$_2$], 1,4-pentadiene C_5H_8 [CH$_2$=CHCH$_2$CH=CH$_2$], and 2,3-dimethyl-1,3-butadiene C_6H_{10} [CH$_2$=C(CH$_3$)C(CH$_3$)=CH$_2$].

The alkynes have common names based on acetylene. For example, propyne is usually called methylacetylene, 2-butyne is usually called dimethylacetylene and 1-butyne is called ethylacetylene. The key is to remember that acetylene is an alkyne.

The principal industrial use of alkynes is as acetylene for welding or cutting torches. Acetylene is produced by the addition of water to calcium carbide and the gas collected is dissolved under pressure in acetone. Calcium carbide is produced by reacting coke (made from coal) and calcium oxide (made from limestone) together at 2000°F. The other industrial source of acetylene is from the high temperature partial oxidation of methane.

Other alkynes are used as intermediates in the synthesis of more complex molecules. However, most alkynes are used on the sites where they are produced due to their tendency to polymerize, therefore there is little bulk shipment of alkynes.

The principal industrial source of dienes is from the cracking process in the petroleum industry. A pure alkane or alkene is subjected to heat and catalysts to produce the desired diene. The diene is then purified by distillation.

Reactions of alkynes and dienes are very similar to those of alkenes. They undergo the same types of reactions, except that their reaction is usually much faster. They react with halogens and hydrogen halides to produce halogenated hydrocarbons. These reactions happen extremely fast and may be violent.

Alkynes react with acid and water to produce either aldehydes or ketones. Alkynes will also react with different metal salts to produce metal acetylides that are extremely shock sensitive and explosive in nature.

Alkynes and dienes react explosively with oxidizers. They are all extremely flammable and burn with a yellow sooty fire.

Alkynes and dienes under the right conditions can also polymerize with explosive force. Alkynes tend to polymerize explosively if they are exposed to too much pressure (meaning high concentration) or are heated at too high of a temperature. Acetylene over 20 psi explodes in the pipe without any other initiating force or activation. Acetylene used for welding is normally shipped with a solvent (acetone) added to the cylinder to prevent polymerization.

Diene and alkyne isomers are named similarly to the alkenes and alkynes with endings of -yne or -diene showing the presence of a "triple bond" or two "double bonds" and numbers designating the position of the bond.

Triple Bond

HC≡CH	CH₃C≡CH	CH₃C≡CCH₃
Acetylene	Methyl Acetylene	Dimethyl Acetylene
Ethyne	1-propyne	2-butyne

The physical properties of alkynes and dienes are very similar to those of alkenes. They are more soluble in water than either alkanes or alkenes. Acetylene is completely soluble in water. They are less dense than water.

Common Alkynes and Dienes

Name	Formula	Melting Point °C	Boiling Point °C	Flash Point °F	LEL %	UEL %	Toxicity
Acetylene Ethyne	HC≡CH	-82	-75	0	2.5	82	TLV 5000
Propyne	HC≡CCH₃	-101	-23		1.7		
1-Butyne	HC≡CCH₂CH₃	-122	9	30			
2-Butyne	CH₃C≡CCH₃	-24	27	-4	1.4		
1-Pentyne	HC≡C(CH₂)₂CH₃	-98	40	-4	1.4		
2-Pentyne	CH₃C≡CCH₂CH₃	-101	55				
1,3-Butadiene	CH₂=CHCH=CH₂	-113	-4.5	-105	2.0	11.5	TLV 10 (C)*
1,3-Pentadiene	CH₂=CHCH=CHCH₃	-87	42	-45	2.0	8.3	
1,4-Pentadiene	CH₂=CHCH₂CH=CH₂	-148	26	39			
Isoprene	CH₂=C(CH₃)CH=CH₂	-146	34	-65	1.5	8.9	

*(C) = Carcinogen

Cyclic Aliphatic Hydrocarbons

Cycloalkanes and cycloalkenes are very similar to the alkenes and alkanes with the exception that these compounds have rings. Instead of being long chains of carbons, the carbons are strung around in a ring formation. The addition of the name "cyclo-" denotes that these are cyclic hydrocarbons. The six-carbon cyclic isomer of hexane is called cyclohexane.

Petroleum is a natural source of cycloalkanes and these compounds are known by the petroleum industry as naphthenes. Industrial sources of individual cyclic compounds include hydrogenation of aromatic hydrocarbons to produce cycloalkanes.

The reactions are the same as those of the corresponding alkanes and alkenes. There are many more isomers possible with "cyclo-" hydrocarbons because the ring forms a natural source of isomer formation: the isomer with two substituents on the same side of the ring is a different molecule from the one where the substituents are on opposite sides of the ring. "Cis" and "trans" are also used to designate having substituents on the same side or opposite sides of the plane of the ring.

Cis and Trans

cis   trans

Physical and chemical properties are again very similar to those of the alkanes and alkenes. The only real differences in physical properties are that the boiling points and densities are higher. The fire characteristics are the same.

Common Cyclic Hydrocarbons

Name	Formula	Melting Point °C	Boiling Point °C	Flash Point °F	LEL %	UEL %	Toxicity
Cyclopentane	C_5H_{10}	-94	49	-20	1.1	8.7	TLV 600
Cyclopentene	C_5H_8	-93	46	-20			
Cyclohexane	C_6H_{12}	6.5	81	-4	1.3	8.0	TLV 300
Cyclohexene	C_6H_{10}	-104	83	<21	1.1		TLV 300
Methylcyclopentane	C_6H_{12}	-142	72	<20	1.0	8.3	
Cis-1, 2-dimethylcyclohexane	C_8H_{16}	-50	124	61	1.0		
Trans-1, 2-dimethylcyclohexane	C_8H_{16}	-88	119	51	1.0		
1,3-Cyclopentadiene	C_5H_6	-85	42	77			
1,3-Cyclohexadiene	C_6H_8	-98	80.5	73			

Aromatic Hydrocarbons

Aromatic hydrocarbons are organic compounds that have a ring structure that is different from the aliphatic ring compounds. These compounds are based on the structure of benzene and compounds that have the similar chemical properties of benzene are all called "aromatic." The names of these compounds do not always have the same endings like alkanes and alkenes. Typically the pure aromatic compounds have the same "-ene" ending that alkenes have. Examples are benzene (C_6H_6) and toluene (C_7H_8) (also known as methyl benzene). Common names for aromatic hydrocarbons are used more often than the official IUPAC names. Common names such as toluene for methylbenzene, xylene for dimethylbenzene, cumene for isopropylbenzene and styrene for phenylethene or phenylethylene are used frequently in commerce. Phenyl is a common substitute for the name benzene substituent C_6H_5-.

The principal sources of aromatic hydrocarbons are petroleum products and coal. When coal is made into coke there is a liquid by-product formed called coal tar. This coal tar is very rich in aromatic hydrocarbons that are purified by distillation or by catalytic reforming. The chemical modifications of petroleum products, such as catalytic reforming, account for most of the aromatic hydrocarbon production.

106

Aromatic hydrocarbons do not undergo the same reactions as the aliphatic hydrocarbons. Most reactions of aromatic hydrocarbons require the presence of a catalyst and go by a different reaction route than aliphatics. Aromatics are much less reactive than alkanes, alkenes, or alkynes for most reactants.

Aromatic molecules will react with fuming sulfuric acid and nitric acids. The reaction with nitric acid produces nitroaromatic compounds that can be explosive in nature. Many nitro compounds are also toxic by skin adsorption and are persistent in the environment.

Aromatics will react slowly with strong oxidizers.

Aromatics will react with halogens slowly to produce halogenated compounds in the presence of a catalyst such as metal or metal oxides (like rust).

Aromatic hydrocarbons burn with a hot flame and lots of black sooty smoke.

Aromatic hydrocarbons can be attached to an aliphatic chain or have aliphatic "substituents." These compounds with both aromatic and aliphatic character are called aryl molecules and the different parts of the molecule (aromatic and aliphatic) can each undergo the reactions normally expected of aromatic or aliphatic molecules.

The isomers of aromatic hydrocarbons usually have an "ortho (o-)," "meta (m-)," or "para (p-)" in front of the name. These terms are sometimes abbreviated by the first letter of the term. For example, there are three isomeric xylenes (dimethylbenzenes), which are designated o-xylene, m-xylene, and p-xylene. They all have the chemical formula C_8H_{10}.

The physical properties of aromatic hydrocarbons are similar to the hydrocarbons we have already looked at. They are insoluble in water and are usually less dense than water. The boiling points increase with molecular weight and show the usual 20 to 30°C increase for each carbon. Aromatic hydrocarbons can be very toxic. They can also be carcinogens. Typically these molecules are more toxic than the other organic materials we have talked about so far.

Ortho, Meta, and Para

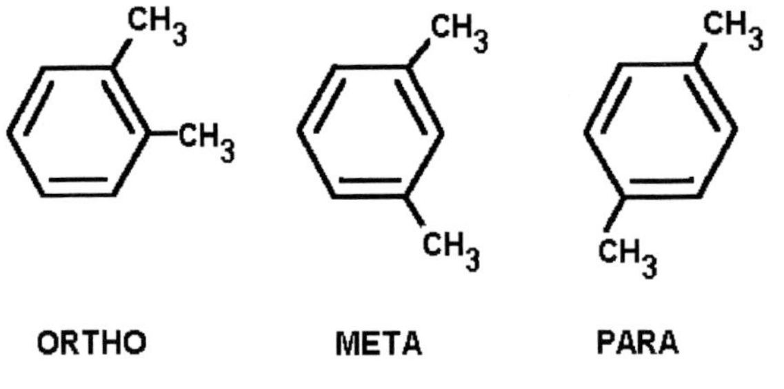

ORTHO   META   PARA

Common Aromatic Hydrocarbons

Name	Formula	Melting Point °C	Boiling Point °C	Flash Point °F	LEL %	UEL %	Toxicity
Benzene	C_6H_6	5.5	80	12	1.2	7.8	TLV 10 (C)*
Toluene	$C_6H_5CH_3$	-95	111	40	1.1	7.1	TLV 100
o-Xylene	$1,2\text{-}C_6H_4(CH_3)_2$	-25	144	90	0.9	6.7	TLV 100
m-Xylene	$1,3\text{-}C_6H_4(CH_3)_2$	-48	139	81	1.1	7.0	TLV 100
p-Xylene	$1,4\text{-}C_6H_4(CH_3)_2$	13	138	81	1.1	7.0	TLV 100
Mesitylene	$1,3,5\text{-}C_6H_3(CH_3)_3$	-45	165	122			TLV 25
Ethylbenzene	$C_6H_5CH_2CH_3$	-95	136	70	0.8	6.7	TLV 100
Cumene	$C_6H_5CH(CH_3)_2$	-96	152	96	0.9	6.5	TLV 50
p-Cymene	$CH_3C_6H_4CH(CH_3)_2$	-70	177	117	0.7	5.6	
Biphenyl	$C_6H_5\text{-}C_6H_5$	70	255	235	0.6	5.8	TLV 0.2
Naphthalene	$C_{10}H_8$	80	218	190	0.9	5.9	TLV 10
Diphenylmethane	$C_6H_5CH_2C_6H_5$	26	263	266			
Styrene vinylbenzene	$C_6H_5CH{=}CH_2$	-31	145	88	0.9	6.8	TLV 50 (C)*
Phenylacetylene	$C_6H_5C{\equiv}CH$	-45	142				

*(C) = Carcinogen

Halogenated Hydrocarbons

Halogenated hydrocarbons contain chlorine, fluorine, bromine, or iodine plus the hydrocarbon structure. They are also known as alkyl halides or aryl halides and usually named for the halide they are associated with. For example, chlorine-containing hydrocarbons have names such like methylene chloride (dichloromethane) (CH_2Cl_2); bromine-containing hydrocarbons have names such as cyclohexyl bromide ($C_6H_{11}Br$); fluorine-containing hydrocarbons have names such as vinyl fluoride ($CH_2{=}CHF$). There are many common names in commercial use.

The industrial source of halogenated hydrocarbons is the direct chlorination or bromination of the corresponding hydrocarbon. The fluorinated compounds are usually made from substituting a fluorine atom for a chlorine atom on a chlorinated hydrocarbon.

Alkyl and aryl halides are fairly unreactive. They will react with strong bases and metals such as sodium quite vigorously.

The isomers of the alkyl and aryl halides are named similarly to the corresponding hydrocarbons. Aromatic chlorinated hydrocarbons can be a problem due to their toxicity and environmental stability. Ones you have heard about are polychlorinated biphenyls (PCBs) or polybrominated biphenyls (PBBs).

Cloroprene is a halogenated alkene shipped extensively to make polymers. It can also be called 2-chlorobutadiene. It is a very reactive molecule. It can air oxidized or be heated to polymerize violently. It is also very flammable and will produce toxic materials on combustion.

108

The physical properties of the alkyl and aryl halides are very similar. They are water insoluble. They have much higher boiling points than alkanes of the same number of carbons. For a given alkyl group, the boiling point increases with increasing atomic weight of the halogen. So fluoride would have the lowest boiling and an iodide would have the highest boiling point for halo-derivatives of the same parent alkane or aromatic. Increasing the number of halogens on the molecule increases the boiling point. When these materials burn, they give off large amounts of the acid gases HCl, HBr, HI, and HF. Other by-products can be phosgene and its related compounds. Heavily halogenated hydrocarbons are not flammable. Many of these materials do not have flash points, but have flammable or explosive ranges. Materials like carbon tetrachloride and the Halon® products have been used as fire extinguishment materials. The larger molecules with these halogens are used as fire retardants. The densities of the halogenated materials are almost always greater than one, with the exceptions of the small mono-substituted chlorides and fluorides like methyl chloride (chloromethane). These materials are usually toxic and need to be handled properly. Many of these materials are carcinogens. Toxicity tends to increase with the size of the halogen. In other words, I > Br > Cl > F in toxicity.

Halogenated hydrocarbons are extremely good solvents for oils and grease. Halogenated hydrocarbons penetrate the skin easily and may cause significant toxicity by skin adsorbtion. Many halogenated hydrocarbons are used as refrigerants.

Common Halogenated Hydrocarbons

Name	Formula	Melting Point °C	Boiling Point °C	Flash Point °F	LEL %	UEL %	Toxicity
Methylchloride chloromethane	CH_3Cl	-97	-24	GAS	7	19	TLV 50
Methylbromide bromomethane	CH_3Br	-94	4	NONE	10	16	TLV 5 (C)*
n-Propylchloride 1-chloropropane	$CH_3CH_2CH_2Cl$	-123	46	65	2.6	11	
n-Propylbromide 1-bromopropane	$CH_3CH_2CH_2Br$	-110	71	78	4.6		
Isopropylchloride 2-chloropropane	$CH_3CHClCH_3$	-118	35	-31			
Isopropylbromide 2-bromopropane	$CH_3CHBrCH_3$	-89	59	67			
Methylene chloride dichloromethane	CH_2Cl_2	-97	40	NONE	14	22	TLV 50 (C)*
Dibromomethane	CH_2Br_2	-52	97	NONE			
Chloroform trichloromethane	$CHCl_3$	-63	61	NONE			TLV 10 (C)*
Bromoform tribromomethane	$CHBr_3$	8.3	150	NONE			TLV 0.5
Carbon tetrachloride tetrachloromethane	CCl_4	-23	77	NONE			TLV 5
Carbon tetrabromide tetrabromomethane	CBr_4	89	190	NONE			TLV 0.1
Fluorobenzene	C_6H_5F	-42	85	9			
Chlorobenzene	C_6H_5Cl	-45	132	75	1.3	7.1	TLV 10
Bromobenzene	C_6H_5Br	-31	156	124	6	36.5	

*(C) = Carcinogen

Comparison of DuPont Refrigerants

Name	Formula	CAS	Boiling Point (°F)
Freon® 11	CCl_3F	75-69-4	75
Freon® 12	CCl_2F_2	75-71-8	-22
Freon® 112	CCl_2FCCl_2F	76-12-0	199
Freon® 112A	CCl_3CClF_2	76-11-9	197
Freon® 113RC	CCl_2FCClF_2	76-13-1	118
Freon® 114	$CClF_2CClF_2$	76-14-2	39
Freon® 115	$CClF_2CF_3$	76-15-3	-38
Freon® 116	CF_3CF_3	76-16-4	-109
Freon® 13	$CClF_3$	75-72-9	-115
Freon® 14	CF_4	75-73-0	-198
Freon® 22	$CHClF_2$	75-45-6	-41
Freon® 23	CHF_3	75-46-7	-116
Freon® E1	$CF_3CF_2CF_2OCHFCF_3$	3330-15-2	105
Halon® 1301	$CBrF_3$	75-63-8	-72
Halon® 1211	$BrClF_2C$	353-59-3	27
Suva® 134A	CH_2FCF_3	811-97-2	-16
Suva® 23	CHF_3	75-46-7	-116
HFC 125	CHF_2CF_3	354-33-6	-55
HFC 318	$(CF_2)_4$	115-25-3	21
HFC 134	CHF_2CHF_2	359-35-3	-3
HFC 134A	CH_2FCF_3	811-97-2	-16
HFC 143A	CH_3CF_3	420-46-2	-53
HFC 152a	CH_3CHF_2	75-37-6	-13
HFC 227EA	CF_3CHFCF_3	431-89-0	-32
HFC 23	CHF_3	75-46-7	-116
HFC 236FA	$CF_3CH_2CF_3$	690-39-1	31
HFC 32	CH_2F_2	75-10-5	-61

Alcohols

Alcohols are compounds that contain a hydroxyl (-OH) group. This can be shown generally as ROH where R is any alkyl or substituted alkyl group. Alcohols are among the most useful molecules for industrial synthesis and exist in large numbers of varieties in nature. They were among the first organic chemicals sold commercially. Therefore, there are a number of different common names associated with many of these compounds which are still used extensively. In the simplest "common names" they are named for their alkyl group. For example, CH_3OH is known as methyl alcohol or methanol, CH_3CH_2OH is known as ethyl alcohol or ethanol, CH_2OHCH_2OH is known as ethylene glycol or dihydroxy ethane or 1,2-ethanediol. Unfortunately, other common names are used for these same compounds and may appear on shipping papers. Methanol is also known as "wood alcohol." Ethanol is sometimes called "grain alcohol."

Other names sometimes used for some alcohols include terms like "hydrins" or "carbinols." They may also contain other functional groups such as: a double bond ($H_2C=CHCH_2OH$) like allyl alcohol; a cyclic ring such as cyclohexanol; a halogen ($ClCH_2CH_2OH$) in 2-chloroethyl alcohol (common name ethylene chlorohydrin). There can also be primary alcohols {1°} like butyl alcohol, secondary alcohols {2°} like sec-butyl alcohol, or tertiary alcohols like tert-butyl {3°} alcohol.

Primary, Secondary, and Tertiary Alcohols

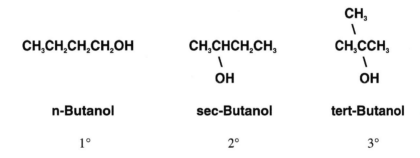

The key to identifying that these molecules are alcohols is the "-ol" ending in their names. Aromatic alcohols are known as phenols and will be discussed later.

The industrial source of alcohols is the hydration (adding water) of alkenes, fermentation of carbohydrates (sugars), oxidation of alkanes, the reduction of aldehydes, or the oxo process of adding carbon monoxide and hydrogen to alkenes.

Alcohols may react differently depending on their original structure. This may affect the speed of the reaction. Alcohols react with strong acids such as HI, HBr, HCl, and H_2SO_4. They can undergo substitution reactions to replace the hydroxy group with another atom or group of atoms or undergo elimination reactions to form alkenes and polymers. Depending upon reaction conditions, the same alcohol may undergo both substitution and addition reactions while leading to a complex mixture of reaction products. They can also react with phosphorus halides to make halogenated hydrocarbons.

112

Alcohols also react with metals like sodium, potassium, and powdered aluminum. The resulting compounds (known as alkoxides) are extremely basic and are usually very reactive. For example, methanol and sodium form sodium methoxide, which has some of the characteristics of both methanol and sodium hydroxide. The process of forming the alkoxide salt with a metal also generates hydrogen gas which is an additional safety hazard due to the highly flammable nature of this gas.

$$CH_3OH + Na \rightarrow CH_3O^- \ Na^+ + \frac{1}{2}H_2$$

Alcohols also react with organic acids to form a class of compounds known as esters (which will be discussed in a later section).

Secondary and primary alcohols will also react with oxidizers to form aldehydes and ketones (under transportation conditions this reaction usually results in a fire).

Alcohols have different physical properties from any of the other classes of compounds we have discussed previously.

All of the compounds discussed before had low solubilities in water (300-500 ppm); alcohols are much more soluble in water. In fact, the lower alcohols are completely soluble or "miscible" with water. This is because alcohols are "polar" and the hydrocarbons are "nonpolar." Usually, the bigger the alcohol chains, the less soluble it becomes in water. Methanol, ethanol, iso-propanol, and propanol are all miscible, while n-butyl alcohol is only 8 percent soluble in water; n-pentyl alcohol is only 2 percent, and n-hexyl alcohol is only about 1 percent soluble in water.

Both melting points and boiling points for the alcohols are unusually high compared with the corresponding alkanes and alkenes. This is also due to the polarity of the alcohols and the fact that the alcohols can "self-associate" with other alcohol molecules.

Comparison of Alkane and Alcohol Physical Properties

Compound	Molecular Weight	Melting Point °C	Boiling Point °C
Ethane C_2H_6	30	-172	-88.5
Methanol CH_3OH	32	-97	65
Propane C_3H_8	44	-187	-42
Ethanol C_2H_5OH	46	-115	78
Butane C_4H_{10}	58	-138	0
n-Propanol C_3H_7OH	60	-126	97

The boiling points show the usual increase with increasing carbon number and the usual decrease with branching. Small alcohols typically burn with a clear blue flame depending on the size of the hydrocarbon chain. The larger alcohols will produce black smoke and soot.

Common Alcohols

Name	Formula	Melting Point °C	Boiling Point °C	Flash Point °F	LEL %	UEL %	Toxicity
Methyl Alcohol	CH_3OH	-97	65	52	6.0	36	TLV 200
Ethyl Alcohol	CH_3CH_2OH	-115	78	48	3.3	25	TLV 1000
n-Propyl Alcohol	$CH_3CH_2CH_2OH$	-126	97	59	2.1	13.7	TLV 200
n-Butyl Alcohol	$CH_3(CH_2)_2CH_2OH$	-90	118	95	1.4	11.2	TLV 50
n-Pentyl Alcohol	$CH_3(CH_2)_3CH_2OH$	-78.5	138	120	1.1	10	
Isopropyl Alcohol	$CH_3CHOHCH_3$	-86	83	60	2.5	12	TLV 400
Ethylene Glycol	$HOCH_2CH_2OH$	-13	197	>230	3.2	15.3	TLV 50
Cyclohexanol	$C_6H_{11}OH$	24	161	154	1.2	12.3	TLV 50
Allyl Alcohol	$CH_2=CHCH_2OH$	-129	97	72	2.5	18	TLV 2
Benzyl Alcohol	$C_6H_5CH_2OH$	-15	205	213			
Triphenylcarbinol	$(C_6H_5)COH$	163	360				

Ethers

Ethers are compounds of the general formula R-O-R. They are usually named by identifying the organic portion of the compound followed by the word ether. For example, CH_3OCH_3 is known as methyl ether or dimethyl ether; $CH_3CH_2OCH_2CH_3$ is known as diethyl ether or ethyl ether; $C_6H_5OCH_3$ is known as phenyl methyl ether or by the common name anisole. If a group does not have a simple name, the compound may be named as an "alkoxy" derivative. For example, $HOCH_2CH_2OCH_2CH_3$ is known as 2-ethoxyethanol, a material that contains both an alcohol and an ether group. If the ether is cyclic, the common name is almost always used. Examples are 1,4-dioxane, furan, and tetrahydrofuran. Do not confuse dioxane with dioxin; although they sound similar, they are totally different.

1,4-DIOXANE   FURAN   TETRAHYDROFURAN

The industrial source of ethers is usually through the dehydration (removal of water) of alcohols. They are used chiefly as solvents, but dimethyl ether is also used as a propellant for aerosol sprays, both for water soluble and nonwater soluble materials.

Ethers are comparatively unreactive compounds. However, on exposure to air most ethers slowly form unstable peroxides. Although present in only low concentrations, these peroxides are very dangerous. They can cause violent explosions or fires due to their shock-sensitive nature. Some peroxides are so sensitive that the act of screwing off the lid off a bottle may set them off. Vinyl ethers are notorious for their reactivity and are significant fire, explosion, and polymerization hazards. Be extremely cautious around these materials.

114

Diethyl ether was the first anesthetic used for surgery in the 1800s and was used to anaesthetize surgical patients in the United States until the 1960s. It is still used in some parts of the world for surgery. Caution must be used whenever ethers are present to prevent exposure with the potential loss of consciousness in exposed personnel.

Ethers are either symmetrical and have the same groups on each side or unsymmetrical and have different groups on each side. The isomers are similar to the corresponding hydrocarbon isomer grouping. The term methoxy also indicates that there is an ether present in the molecule.

The ethers have some very different physical properties, depending on how may oxygen molecules are present and how long the hydrocarbon chain is. Some ethers, like dimethyl ether, are partially water soluble (30 percent); ethyl ether is only 6 percent soluble, but 1,4-dioxane and tetrahydrofuran are completely soluble.

Ethers are typically very flammable and have lower flash points and boiling points than you would expect. They typically burn with a clearer flame and less smoke than other organic materials. The vapors can travel long ways and flash back to the source of ignition.

Common Ethers

Name	Formula	Melting Point °C	Boiling Point °C	Flash Point °F	LEL %	UEL %	Toxicity
Methyl ether	CH_3OCH_3	-141	-24	GAS	3.4	27	
Ethyl ether	$CH_3CH_2OCH_2CH_3$	-116	35	-40	1.8	48	TLV 400
n-Propyl ether	$CH_3(CH_2)_2O(CH_2)_2CH_3$	-123	89	40	1.3	7	
Butyl methyl ether	$CH_3(CH_2)_3OCH_3$	-115	70	14			
Isopropyl ether	$(CH_3)_2CHOCH(CH_3)_2$	-85	69	9	1	21	TLV 250
1,4-Dioxane	$C_4H_8O_2$	11.8	101	54	2	22	TLV 25 (C)*
Furan	C_4H_4O		32	-32	2.3	14.3	
Tetrahydrofuran	C_4H_8O	-108	67	1	1.8	11.8	TLV 200
Anisole	$C_6H_5OCH_3$		154	125			
Phenyl ether	$C_6H_5OC_6H_5$	28	259	>230	0.8	1.5	TLV 1

*(C) = Carcinogen

Aldehydes and Ketones

Aldehydes are compounds of the general formula RCHO; ketones are compounds of the general formula RCOR'. The R groups can be either aliphatic or aromatic. Both compounds contain the carbonyl group (C=O) and are collectively called carbonyl compounds. The aldehydes are named by identifying the R and adding an "-al" at the end or by identifying the corresponding carboxylic acids by replacing the "-ic" by "-aldehyde." For example, CH_2O is known as formaldehyde or methanal; CH_3CHO is known as acetaldehyde or ethanal; CH_3CH_2CHO is known as propionaldehyde or propanal.

SPECIAL NOTE: The use of the "-al" ending in the IUPAC name to designate an aldehyde can be a significant problem for the First Responder. In some parts of the United States, the speech patterns make it difficult to distinguish between the pronunciation of ethanol (also called ethyl alcohol) and ethanal (also called acetaldehyde). Since these compounds have substantially different hazards and require different personal protective equipment, it is critical the material be identified correctly. Names ending in "-ol" or "-al" need to be spelled out to make certain that the right compound is being identified, so as not to confuse one material with another.

The simplest ketone has the common name acetone. For most other aliphatic ketones we name the two groups attached to the carbonyl carbon, and follow these names by the word ketone. If the carbonyl group is attached to a benzene ring, the ketone is named as a "-phenone." The IUPAC names use the longest chain of the parent structure and replace the "-e" of the corresponding alkane with "-one" along with a number to designate the position of the carbonyl group. For example, CH_3COCH_3 is known as acetone or propanone; $CH_3CH_2COCH_3$ is known as methyl ethyl ketone (MEK) or butanone; $CH_3CH_2COCH_2CH_3$ is known as ethyl ketone or 3-pentanone; $C_6H_5COCH_3$ is known as acetophenone.

The primary industrial source of aldehydes and ketones is the oxidation of other organic compounds like alkenes, alkynes, and alcohols. Primary alcohols give aldehydes, and secondary alcohols give ketones by oxidation.

Aldehydes and ketones react vigorously with oxidizers. Aldehydes are the most easily oxidized materials. When they oxidize, they form their corresponding acids. Ketones will produce different acids depending on the structure of the original ketone. Ketones will also react with halogens to form chlorinated materials which will be more toxic than the starting material.

RCHO + Oxidizer –> RCOOH + By-products

RCOR + Oxidizer –> RCOOH + By-products

Cyanide will also react with aldehydes and ketones to form products called cyanohydrins.

Cyanohydrins are used extensively in industrial synthesis (especially as intermediates in plastics and pharmaceutical products) and are shipped in bulk by all transportation modes. The most common of the cyanohydrins is acetone cyanohydrin which is used to make the monomer that goes into Plexiglas®, among other things. This material is less toxic than the original cyanide, but it will decompose upon exposure to water to form hydrogen cyanide and the original ketone.

Aldehydes and ketones will react with strong bases like sodium hydroxide to undergo several different types of reactions. Many different products are possible, but alcohols are general one of the products. The reaction between aldehydes and ketones and a strong base is exothermic and may be violent!

The smaller aldehydes and ketones are more soluble in water. The small 2- to 3-carbon carbonyls are very soluble in water. The larger ones (7 carbons and above) are insoluble in water. These materials are polar compounds. They have lower boiling points than the alcohols and carboxylic acids of the same size, but they have much higher boiling points than the alkanes and ethers. Aldehydes and ketones have low flash points and are very flammable. These materials burn with a bluish flame. The smaller molecules have very little black smoke or soot production.

Common Aldehydes and Ketones

Name	Formula	Melting Point °C	Boiling Point °C	Flash Point °F	LEL %	UEL %	Toxicity
Formaldehyde Methanal	H_2CO		-3	GAS	7	70	TLV 0.3 (C)*
Acetaldehyde Ethanal	CH_3CHO	-125	21	-40	4	60	TLV 100 (C)*
Propionaldehyde Propanal	CH_3CH_2CHO	-81	48	-16	2.6	17	
Butyraldehyde Butanal	$CH_3(CH_2)_2CHO$	-96	75	12	1.4	12.5	
Acrolein Ethenal	$CH_2=CHCHO$	-87	53	-2	2.8	31	TLV 0.1
Benzaldehyde	C_6H_5CHO	-10	195	188			
Acetone	CH_3COCH_3	-94	56	1	2	13	TLV 750
Methyl Ethyl Ketone 2-Butanone	$CH_3COCH_2CH_3$	-87	80	26	1.8	10.1	TLV 200
Methyl Isobutyl Ketone 4-Methyl Pentanone	$CH_3COCH_2CH(CH_3)_2$	-80	117	56	1.2	8	TLV 50
Cyclohexanone	$C_6H_{10}O$	-47	155	116	1.1	9.4	TLV 25
Acetophenone	$C_6H_5COCH_3$	19	202	180			

*(C) = Carcinogen

Carboxylic Acids

Carboxylic acids are organic compounds that contain the carboxyl group R-COOH or $R-CO_2H$ attached to a hydrocarbon frame. They are called weak acids since they do not dissociate completely or give up acid protons easily, but they can still cause acid burns to exposed skin.

There are large numbers of carboxylic acids which are found in nature (including many different acids found in our own bodies). These acids were among the first molecules studied and given names in the 1800s. Unfortunately, many common names for the acids are still in widespread use and there are no "systems" relating common names to structure as there is in the IUPAC system. Therefore "common nomenclature" for carboxylic acids is complex.

The IUPAC names for carboxylic acids are straightforward; the longest chain including the acid group is named as if it were an alkane; the ending "-e" is dropped and replaced with "-oic acid." Thus, the 2-, 3-, and 4- carbon acids are named ethanoic acid, propanoic acid, and butanoic acid. Other straight chain acids are named similarly. When the carboxylic acid functional group is attached to an aromatic ring, the name benzoic acid is used. The acids are like all other organic compounds and can contain other functional groups. These are named and are given a positional number like any other class of molecule. Some naturally occurring carboxylic acids have more than one carboxylic acid functional group. In the IUPAC system these are identified by the endings "-dioic" acid or "-trioic" acid.

The key to common acid names is the word acid in the name. There is no "system" to common names and, unfortunately, common names are used extensively. The first six simple carboxylic acids have the common names of formic, acetic, propionic, butyric, valeric, and caproic acids. The first five of dicarboxylic acids (which are all naturally occurring compounds) are oxalic, malonic, succinic, glutaric, and adipic acids. When encountering a compound named as an acid, refer to reference works or an MSDS to identify the actual structure of the compound.

The industrial source of simple straight-chain acids is usually the oxidation of another compound such as a hydrocarbon or alcohol into the acid. Many more complex acids can be derived from natural sources like animal fats or vegetable oils.

The carboxylic group undergoes a number of important reactions. The reaction with basic materials such as sodium hydroxide or metals results in salt formation. The name for the salt of an acid uses the name of the cation followed by the name of the acid with the ending "-ic acid" changed to "-ate." For example, CH_3COONa is known as sodium acetate; $HCOONH_4$ is known as ammonium formate. The IUPAC names are similar; the sodium salt of ethanoic acid is sodium ethanoate, etc.

$$RCOOH + NaOH \rightarrow Na^{+ -}OOCR + H_2O$$
$$\text{Salt}$$

The reaction of carboxylic acids with inorganic chlorides like thionyl chloride, phosphorus trichloride, and phosphorus pentachloride results in the carboxylic acid chloride. This group of molecules is sometimes called "acyl halides" and is used extensively in industrial organic synthesis and shipped commercially.

$$RCOOH + P\text{-}Cl_5 \rightarrow RCOCl + \text{by-products}$$

Reactions with alcohols and acids result in ester formations. The hydrocarbon side chains react like any other hydrocarbon chain.

$$RCOOH + ROH \rightarrow RCOOR + H_2O$$

The pH of the carboxylic acids in water varies with the structure and substitution on the acid molecule. They can be very acidic with pHs as low as 0.5 to pHs of 5.

118

The physical properties of the acids are similar to the alcohols in some ways. The first four aliphatic acids are totally water soluble. The five-carbon acid is partly soluble and the larger acids are insoluble. The aromatic acids are extremely insoluble in water. Acids are soluble in ethers, alcohols, and other polar organic liquids. The acids are very high boiling compared with other organic materials of the same carbon number. The odors of the smaller acids are very distinct. Formic acid is very sharp and biting and is responsible for the sting in insect bites. Acetic acid is the smell of vinegar, while propionic acid smells like old very dirty gym socks. Butyric acid smells like very rancid butter. Valeric and caproic acid smell even worse. Caproic acid was first isolated from rotting goat fat and is the compound that gives this material its characteristic pungent odor. The larger acids have very little odors due to their low volatility.

The aromatic acids are all solids. They have high melting points, very high boiling points (> 250°C), and they are not water soluble to any appreciable extent at pH=7.

These materials will burn. The smaller acids can have lower flash points than expected. They will usually burn with a yellow soot-filled flame.

Common Carboxylic Acids

Name	Formula	Melting Point °C	Boiling Point °C	Flash Point °F	LEL %	UEL %	Toxicity
Formic acid methanoic acid	HCO_2H	8	100	156	18	57	TLV 5
Acetic acid ethanoic acid	CH_3CO_2H	16	117	104	4	19.9	TLV 10
Propionic acid propanoic acid	$CH_3CH_2CO_2H$	-23	141	125	2.9	12.1	TLV 10
Butyric acid butanoic acid	$CH_3(CH_2)_2CO_2H$	-6	162	170	2	10	
Acrylic acid propenoic acid	$CH_2=CHCO_2H$	13	139	130	2	13.7	TLV 2
Methacrylic acid 2-Methyl propenoic acid	$CH_2=C(CH_3)CO_2H$	16	163	170			TLV 20
Glycolic acid hydroxyethanoic acid	$HOCH_2CO_2H$	75					
Benzoic acid	$C_6H_5CO_2H$	122	249	250			

Derivatives of Carboxylic Acids

Closely related to the carboxylic acids and to each other are a number of chemical families known as functional derivatives of carboxylic acids. A functional derivative here means that you have replaced part of the acid group with something else. Here we will talk very briefly about acid chlorides (RCOCl), anhydrides (RCO-O-OCR), amides ($RCONH_2$), and esters (RCO-OR'). These compounds all contain the acyl group R-C=O.

Street Smart[TM] Chemistry

Acid halides are named for the corresponding acids. The "-ic acid" is dropped and "-yl chloride" (or bromide or fluoride) is added. For example, CH_3COCl is acetyl chloride using common nomenclature and ethanoyl chloride in the IUPAC system. Acid halides are very reactive and may react violently with water. They will also react with caustic, ammonia, alcohols, amines, thiols, and other organic acids. These reactions can be very violent and generate a large amount of heat and vapors. Hydrochloric acid is a usual by-product.

Anhydrides are also named for the corresponding acid. The acid is dropped and anhydride added. For example, $(CH_3CO)_2O$ is acetic anhydride. The IUPAC name is similar, ethanoic anhydride. When the two acids are different from each other, both are named, for example, acetic propionic anhydride, which would be ethanoic propanoic anhydride in the IUPAC system.

Anhydrides react very similarly to acid halides. They react rapidly and vigorously with caustic, ammonia, alcohols, amines, thiols, and water. An organic acid is a usual by-product. Anhydrides are used as raw materials for some commercial processes and as intermediates in the synthesis of polyesters and polyamide textile fibers.

Amides and esters are fairly nonreactive with other organic materials. The amides are typically used as solvents in industry or, less commonly, as reaction intermediates.

Acrylate and methacrylate esters are used in the polymers business. These monomers can polymerize violently under the wrong conditions. More details can be found in the polymers section of this chapter.

IUPAC nomenclature for amides is also easy; the "-ic acid" ending is dropped and "-amide" is added. For example, CH_3CONH_2 is commonly called acetamide and the IUPAC name is ethanoamide.

Similarly, IUPAC nomenclature for esters is done by using the name of the alcohol followed by the acid name. Again the "-ic acid" is dropped and the ending "-ate" is added. For example, $CH_3CO\text{-}OCH_3$ is known as methyl acetate or methyl ethanoate in the IUPAC system.

A mention of special esters has to be made. Fats are special esters. They are used in everyday life by everybody. The most important ones are those occurring naturally in animal and vegetable fats. Liquid fats are called oils. Such materials as corn oil, coconut oil, cottonseed oil, palm oil, soy bean oil, and butter are made up largely of esters of carboxylic acids. These esters are derived from just one alcohol, glycerol, $HOCH_2CHOHCH_2OH$, and so are known as glycerides. These fats are sources for the production of pure acids, manufacture of many different types of detergents, and drying oils for paint.

All of the functional derivatives of carboxylic acids are very polar materials. The boiling points of the acid chlorides, anhydrides, and esters are about the same as the corresponding aldehyde or ketone. The amides are very high boiling materials. The border line for water solubility for esters is three to five carbons and five or six carbons for the amides.

Acid chlorides have a very sharp irritating odor due at least partly to the reaction with water in air to produce HCl. The acid chlorides are generally fuming materials due to this reaction.

Amides have little or no odor.

Liquid anhydrides also have a very sharp odor where solids have little odors.

Esters have very pleasant, characteristic odors. They are used in perfumes and artificial flavors. You have probably smelled iso-amyl acetate. It is used as the material for respirator fit testing and is better known as banana oil.

The acid chlorides and anhydrides are very toxic due to their reactivity with the body. They form acids in the body and do severe damage to moist tissue. The chloroformate family is a common ester/acid chloride used in industry.

The amides are typically very toxic to the liver.

The industrial source of these materials is from the reaction of the carboxylic acid with another chemical to produce the final product.

Common Carboxylic Acid Derivatives

Name	Formula	Melting Point °C	Boiling Point °C	Flash Point °F	LEL %	UEL %	Toxicity
Acetyl chloride ethanoyl chloride	CH_3COCl	-112	52	40	7.3	19	
Chloroacetyl chloride 2-chloroethanoyl chloride	$ClCH_2COCl$	-22	105	NONE			TLV 0.05
Benzoyl chloride	$C_6H_5CO_2Cl$	-1	198	156	1.2	4.9	
Acetic anhydride ethanoic anhydride	$(CH_3CO)_2O$	-73	139	130	2.7	10.3	PEL 5
Formamide methanoamide	$HCONH_2$			310			TLV 10
Acetamide ethanoamide	CH_3CONH_2	80					
Methylformamide N-methyl methanoamide	$HCONHCH_3$		180	210			
Dimethyforamide N, N-dimethyl methanoamide	$HCON(CH_3)_2$	-61	153	136	2.2	15.2	TLV 10
Dimethyacetamide N, N-dimethyl ethanoamide	$CH_3CON(CH_3)_2$	-20	165	158	1.8	11.5	TLV 10
Methyl acetate methyl ethanoate	$CH_3CO_2CH_3$	-98	57.5	15	3.1	16.0	TLV 200
Ethyl acetate ethyl ethanoate	$CH_3CO_2CH_2CH_3$	-84	77	26	2.2	11.5	TLV 400
Vinyl acetate ethenyl ethanoate	$CH_3CO_2CH=CH_2$	-93	72	20	2.6	13.4	TLV 10
Methyl acrylate methyl propenoate	$CH_2=CHCO_2CH_3$	-75	80	44	2.1	14.5	TLV 10
Methyl methacrylate methyl-2-methyl propenoate	$CH_2=C(CH_3)CO_2CH_3$	-48	100	50	2.1	12.5	TLV 100
Benzyl acetate	$CH_3CO_2CH_2C_6H_5$	-51	206	216			
Ethyl benzoate	$C_6H_5CO_2CH_2CH_3$	-34	212	184			
Methyl chloroformate	$ClCO_2CH_3$		71	64			AEL 0.5
Ethyl chloroformate	$ClCO_2CH_2CH_3$	-81	93	36			AEL 0.5

Organic Sulfur Compounds

Sulfonic Acids and their Derivatives
Another group of important organic acid is the family of sulfonic acids. These acids are derived from sulfur trioxide. They are named by adding "-sulfonic acid" to the name of the compound to which the $-SO_3H$ group is attached. Most sulfonic acids are aromatic, for example, $C_6H_5SO_3H$ is benzenesulfonic acid. These should not be confused with the sulfates which are derivatives of sulfuric acid.

The industrial process for the manufacture of sulfonic acids is the direct sulfonation of the aromatic material with fuming sulfuric acid. The acid chloride is usually manufactured from the treatment of the aromatic compound with chlorosulfonic acid. This material is known as a sulfonyl chloride. Sulfonyl chlorides and sulfonamides are very important intermediates in the manufacture of agricultural chemicals and pharmaceuticals.

Sulfonic acids are very strong acids. These materials will react with any basic material to form salts.

$$RSO_3H + NaOH \rightarrow RSO_3^- Na^+ + H_2O$$

Sulfonyl chlorides are very reactive and can react explosively with water generating dense clouds of hydrochloric acid. They will also react with alcohols to form sulfonic esters and with amines to form sulfonamides.

$$RSO_2Cl + ROH \rightarrow RSO_2OR + HCl$$

Sulfonic acids are very water soluble. This group is introduced into large organic molecules like dyes and drugs for this reason–i.e., to make the large molecule more water soluble. Sulfonic acids are very deliquescent (they pick up water from the air and form a puddle). They usually have low volatility. If heated, the sulfonic acid will usually decompose before it boils. Sulfonyl chlorides may react with atmospheric moisture to form large clouds of toxic fumes. They have a very sharp odor. Sulfonamides are solids.

Sulfates
In terms of volume of materials shipped, the principle organic derivatives of sulfuric acid are dimethylsulfate (DMS), $(CH_3)_2SO_4$, and diethylsulfate (DES), $(CH_3CH_2)_2SO_4$. The industrial source of these materials is the reaction of the respective alcohol and sulfuric acid to form the sulfate ester. These materials are heavy oily corrosive liquids. They react with water or body fluids to decompose into sulfuric acid. These materials are readily absorbed through the skin. They are water white with no odor. Once in the body these materials decompose and then will eat their way out of the body. It may take up to 24 hours for this to occur so there is a delay between the exposure and the appearance of visible burns. Both materials are highly toxic. DMS is a carcinogen and DES is a mutagen. Both compounds are considered inhalation hazards.

Sulfides and Mercaptans
Sulfides are organic compounds of the general structure R-S-R' and are also known as thioethers. An example of a sulfide is methyl sulfide.

The sulfur analog of carbon dioxide, carbon disulfide or CS_2, is sometimes used as a solvent and can be encountered as the decomposition by-product of some agricultural products.

Mercaptans have the general structure R-SH and are also known as thiols. An example of a mercaptan is methyl mercaptan (CH_3SH) which is the odorant in natural gas. ALL mercaptans have very powerful odors and many are shipped labeled "stench." The powerful scent of skunk is a mixture of small sulfur compounds.

Sulfide and mercaptan compounds are extremely toxic, smell very bad, are very flammable, and will give off large amounts of sulfur dioxide when they burn. They react similarly to alcohols and ethers.

Amines

Amines have the general formula RNH_2 (primary), R_2NH (secondary), or R_3N (ternary) where R is any alkyl or aryl group. They are usually named by identifying the alkyl or aryl part of the molecule followed by the word amine. You may see the term amino for more complicated amines. For example, CH_3NH_2 is methyl amine; $(CH_3)_2NH$ is dimethyl amine; $(CH_3)_3N$ is trimethyl amine; $CH_3NHCH_2CH_3$ is methylethylamine; $C_6H_5NH_2$ is known as aniline; $CH_3C_6H_4NH_2$ is known as toluidine.

The industrial source of amines is from the reaction of ammonia and alcohols, reduction of other nitrogen containing materials like nitrobenzene to form aniline, or reaction of organic acids with ammonia, heat, and hydrogen.

Amines are strong bases. Methyl amines are considered corrosive. They react with acids to form salts. Primary and secondary amines will also react with acid chlorides, anhydrides, some halogenated compounds, and some metal compounds. Some of these metal amine complexes can be sensitive to shock and will explode violently.

There are many combinations of amines. One, two, or three carbon groups can be attached to the amine. Some of these complexes are very difficult to name. Recognize that there is an amine present by the key words amino or amine. There can also be an amine salt. These are usually named by replacing the "-amine" with ammonium-like dimethylammonium chloride. They will be solids under normal conditions and are very water soluble. Another form of an amine is the quaternary ammonium salt. This molecule has four groups around the nitrogen.

There is one diamine and its derivatives that is used industrially in large quantities. This material is hydrazine and the many different derivatives of hydrazine. Hydrazine has two nitrogen atoms connected together, H_2N-NH_2. This material is very reactive. Hydrazines are used in cleaners and industrial descalars. If hydrazine and hydrogen peroxide are mixed, a hypergolic (igniting spontaneously on contact) explosive reaction occurs. This mixture of hydrazine and peroxide was once used as a rocket fuel.

Like ammonia, amines are polar compounds. They have higher boiling points than nonpolar compounds of the same molecular weight, but lower boiling points than alcohols or carboxylic acids. Amines are fairly water soluble until you get to about six carbons on the molecule. The small amines like methylamine smell like ammonia; at about three or more carbons they have a very "fishy" odor. Most amines have very low odor thresholds. Aliphatic amines are very corrosive to the skin. Burns are caused almost immediately and are very painful. Aromatic amines are generally very toxic and are readily absorbed through the skin with often fatal results. Aromatic amines on exposure to air, will change color from clear to dark brown. They may pass through different stages of oxidation and be any color.

Common Amines

Name	Formula	Melting Point °C	Boiling Point °C	Flash Point °F	LEL %	UEL %	Toxicity
Methylamine	CH_3NH_2	-93		GAS	4.9	20.8	TLV 10
Dimethylamine	$(CH_3)_2NH$	-93	7	GAS	2.8	14.4	TLV 10
Trimethylamine	$(CH_3)_3N$	-117	2.9	20	2.0	11.6	TLV 10
Ethylamine	$CH_3CH_2NH_2$	-81	16	GAS	2.5	14	TLV 10
n-Propylamine	$CH_3(CH_2)_2NH_2$	-83	48	-35	2.0	10.4	
Isopropylamine	$(CH_3)_2CHNH_2$	-101	33	-26	2.0	10	TLV 5
n-Butylamine	$CH_3(CH_2)_3NH_2$	-49	78	6	1.7	9.8	TLV 5
Cycohexylamine	$C_6H_{11}NH_2$	-17	134	90			TLV 10 (C)*
Benzylamine	$C_6H_5CH_2NH_2$	10	184	140			
Hexamethylenediamine	$NH_2(CH_2)_6NH_2$	42	204	178	0.7	6.3	
Aniline	$C_6H_5NH_2$	-6	184	158	1.3	11	TLV 2 (C)*
Methylaniline	$C_6H_5NHCH_3$	-57	196	174			TLV 0.5
Dimethylaniline	$C_6H_5N(CH_3)_2$	1	193	145	1	7	TLV 5
o-Phenylenediamine	$NH_2C_6H_4NH_2$	103	256				TLV 0.1 mg/m^3

*(C) = Carcinogen

Other Nitrogen-Containing Materials

Nitriles and cyanohydrins are derivatives of hydrogen cyanide. Nitriles have the general formula R-CN and cyanohydrins have the general formula R-(COHCN)-R'. For example, acetonitrile (CH_3CN) and acrylonitrile ($CH_2=CHCN$) are commonly shipped in bulk. They have other common names also like methylcyanide or vinylcyanide. The smaller nitriles are water soluble. They are very toxic materials. Acetonitrile is an excellent solvent. Acrylonitrile is a monomer used in the manufacture of plastics.

Cyanohydrins such as acetone cyanohydrin ($CH_3COHCNCH_3$) are used as intermediates in the manufacture of other compounds. They are manufactured from a ketone or aldehyde by the addition of hydrogen cyanide. These materials will react with water to form HCN gas and the ketone or aldehyde. They are very toxic. Neutralization of these materials is accomplished by the addition of caustic and hypochlorite. This treatment effectively destroys the toxicity of the cyanide.

Aminonitriles (replacement of the hydroxy group with an amine group on cyanohydrins) are also an important building block chemical. These materials are very toxic. They may contain high levels of ammonium cyanide which is a volatile material at room temperature and which is as poisonous as hydrogen cyanide.

Nitro organic molecules contain the NO_2 group. Examples are nitromethane (NO_2CH_3) and nitrobenzene ($NO_2C_6H_5$). These materials are extremely flammable materials. The more nitro groups present, you have the more dangerous they are. The most famous of the nitro materials is trinitrotoluene or TNT. The material is very explosive and is used in the manufacture of dynamite and other explosives. These materials are very toxic. Nitromethane is an excellent solvent and is used in "Super Glue" solvents and removers. It is also used as a fuel in high-speed race cars.

Common Nitrogen-Containing Materials

Name	Formula	Melting Point °C	Boiling Point °C	Flash Point °F	LEL %	UEL %	Toxicity
Acetonitrile	CH_3CN	-48	82	42	4.4	16	TLV 40
Acrylonitrile	$CH_2=CHCN$	-83	77	32	3.0	17	TLV 2 (C)*
Acetone cyanohydrin	$CH_3COH(CN)CH_3$	-19		147	2.3	11	
Nitromethane	CH_3NO_2	-29	100	95	7.3		TLV 100
Nitrobenzene	$C_6H_5NO_2$	5	210	190	1.8	40	TLV 1

*(C) = Carcinogen

Phenols

Phenols are aromatic alcohols or aryl alcohols. They have the general formula Ar-OH, where Ar is phenyl or other aryl group. Phenols differ from other alcohols in having an OH group attached directly to an aromatic ring. These compounds are generally named after the simplest member of the family, phenol (C_6H_5OH). The methyl phenols are known as cresols and the dihydroxy phenols are known by their common names, catechol, resorcinol, and hydroquinone.

PHENOL   o-CRESOL   CATECHOL

The industrial source of some phenols is coal tar or isolation from various plants. Most of the phenols are used in industrial synthesis or by-product recovery.

Phenols are very weak acids. They will react with strong bases to form water soluble salts. Phenols like alcohols will end in "-ol" or even "-ole" depending on their common name. They may be known as essential oils like eugenol or oil of cloves.

Phenols are liquids or low-melting solids. Except for the simplest phenols like phenol or catechol, they have minor solubility in water. Phenol is extremely soluble in water and is often shipped as a 70-90 percent solution. Like amines they are colorless, but are easily oxidized to form colored by-products. Phenols will react with halogens and nitric acid at room temperature in weak concentrations to form more toxic or explosive compounds. Nitro phenols and their salts can be shock sensitive and extremely explosive. Picric acid (trinitrophenol), which was used as a commercial and military explosive, is a good example of a nitro phenol and its dangerous properties. Phenols are readily absorbed through the skin and can be extremely toxic.

Common Phenols

Name	Formula	Melting Point °C	Boiling Point °C	Flash Point °F	LEL %	UEL %	Toxicity
Phenol	C_6H_5OH	41	182	175	1.7	8.6	TLV 5
o-Cresol	$C_6H_5OHCH_3$	33	191	178	1.4		TLV 5
m-Cresol	$C_6H_5OHCH_3$	10	203	187	1	1.4	TLV 5
p-Cresol	$C_6H_5OHCH_3$	33	202	193	1	1.1	TLV 5
2-Chlorophenol	C_6H_5OHCl	8	175	147			

Heterocyclic Compounds

Heterocycles are cyclic molecules which have another atom instead of carbon in the ring. These are compounds like pyrroles (C_4H_4N), furans (C_4H_4O), thiophenes (C_4H_4S), imadazoles ($C_3H_4N_2$), oxazoles (C_3H_3NO), thiazoles (C_3H_3NS), pyrazoles ($C_3H_4N_2$), pyrrolidines (C_4H_9N), pyridines (C_4H_9N), and pyrimidines ($C_4H_4N_2$). This class of compounds also includes the epoxides. Most of these compounds are like materials discussed already. These compounds have ring structures (everything is grouped in a base ring with different arrangements of the carbons and the other ring component).

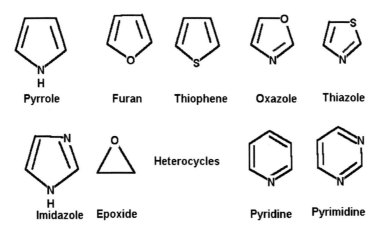

Furans and oxazoles are similar to ethers. They have some of the same characteristics. They are very flammable and are used as solvents.

Pyrroles, imadazoles, pyrazoles, pyrrolidines, and pyridines are very much like the amines. They emit a foul odor and are used as solvents and intermediates. They are all flammable and are usually toxic. Pyrimidines are solids and have a slight odor. They are used as intermediates in different products and are important building blocks for pharmaceuticals and agricultural chemicals.

Thiophenes and thiazoles contain sulfur. They smell so bad that the presence of a leak will be known quickly. They are very toxic and extremely flammable. They are used as intermediates and solvents.

Epoxides such as ethylene oxide and propylene oxide are small cyclic ethers. They are extremely flammable, toxic and will explode with little provocation.

Monomers, Plastics, and Polymers

Plastics
Plastics are a group of materials that belong to a much larger class of materials called polymers. A polymer is a giant molecule made up of thousands of tiny subunits that have the unique property of being able to react with themselves to form larger molecules. The process by which this takes place is called polymerization, and the tiny (relatively speaking) molecules that have this unique property of combining with themselves are called monomers. Both words, monomer and polymer, come from Greek roots; "mono-" meaning one, "poly-" means many, and "-mer" means part. Therefore, monomer means one part, and polymer means many parts. Sometimes, the polymer can be made up of many tens of thousands of the monomer molecules, depending on the type of polymer the manufacturer wants to make. Before getting into the different types of plastics, however, it is important to examine this much larger group of materials called polymers.

There are really two groups of polymers, the first being natural (existing in nature), and the other being synthetic, or manmade. This would seem a mere pittance compared with how much polymerization that Mother Nature regularly contributes. The natural polymers include cellulose, the major ingredient in wood and woody plants, and cotton, which is nearly pure cellulose, leather, silk, wool, and skin. The cellulose from wood is also the major ingredient in paper and all paper products, including cardboard and cardboard products. The DNA in human cells and the proteins that make up muscles and hair are all examples of natural polymers. The volume of polymers and polymeric products that nature manufactures, which man then uses to build shelters, make clothes, and the other comforts demanded by society, are plainly evident.

Synthetic polymers, which will be discussed in detail in this section of the text, are artificial polymers usually designed and manufactured to have specific useful properties, are plainly evident.

Monomers
The monomers are a group of molecules having the unique capability of reacting with themselves (or with similar molecules) to form a giant molecule called a polymer. The process in which this unique reaction occurs is called polymerization.

Street Smart™ Chemistry

Chapter 11/Organic Chemistry

128

Typically, monomers are either easily liquefiable flammable gases, or low flashpoint flammable liquids. As liquefied gases, they are subject to the spectacular Boiling Liquid Expanding Vapor Explosion (BLEVE). As monomers (whether liquefied gases or liquids), they are subject to the equally spectacular explosion called runaway polymerization.

Many of the monomers are unsaturated hydrocarbons, with one or more double bond. The presence of double bonds is what makes monomers reactive and unstable. Under the proper conditions of heat and pressure, and with the proper initiator and/or catalyst, the double bond will open to create a very reactive free radical that will react quickly with any another monomer molecule it encounters. Since the product of this reaction between the free radical and a monomer is another free radical, the result is a chain reaction. This reaction continues adding monomers onto the chain until the process runs out of unreacted monomers or another compound is added to stop the reaction. In industrial polymerization processes the conditions are carefully monitored to control the rate of reaction and the length of the polymer chain (to control the physical properties of the resulting polymer). In a HAZMAT incident, where the polymerization reaction is not carefully controlled, the resulting hazards are significant. Although monomers are not as unstable as the organic peroxides or azo compounds used to start the polymerization reactions, they will react explosively if too much heat energy is allowed to reach them. This type of pressure-releasing explosion, the result of a large amount of material undergoing a chemical reaction uncontrollably and instantaneously, is called runaway polymerization. Significant heat and pressure may be generated and the resulting change in physical state from liquid monomers to a solid polymer will cause very large changes in the volume of the material. The result is often the violent rupture of the vessel (reactor, drum, tank truck or railcar) containing the monomer. Stopping a runaway polymerization is extremely difficult, if not impossible, once it has started.

THE MONOMERS

In this section the most important monomers used in the polymer industry around the world are discussed. There are other monomers which are manufactured and shipped that are typically used in smaller quantities to change the properties of the polymers such as additives that cause the polymer to accept dyes more easily.

ACETALDEHYDE: A colorless, fuming liquid with a pungent fruity odor. It is water soluble and is a skin and respiratory irritant. Its flash point is -40°F, and it boils at 60°F.

ACRYLIC ACID: A monomer of some acrylic plastics. It is a colorless liquid with an acrid odor. It is toxic and corrosive, has a flash point of 130°F, and boils at 304°F.

ACROLEIN: A colorless or yellowish liquid, whose vapors produce a choking sensation. It is a powerful irritant, has a flash point below 0°F, and boils at 95°F. The acrid odor of acrolein is familiar to most firefighters. It is a decomposition product from the effect of fire on some plastics used as thermal insulation or as electrical insulation and is encountered frequently as the unpleasant odor in electrical fires.

ACRYLONITRILE: The monomer of polyacrylonitrile is toxic by ingestion and inhalation and is a carcinogen. It is a colorless liquid that is only partially soluble in water. It has a specific gravity of 0.80 and a flash point of 32°F, and it boils at 139°F. The chemical name for acrylonitrile is vinyl cyanide; when it burns it will liberate hydrogen cyanide gas. It is also one of the monomers of ABS (acrylonitrile butadiene styrene) plastic.

ADIPIC ACID: A solid monomer that has a flash point of 385°F. It is one monomer in the system of producing nylon as well as many adhesives, wall coatings, etc. Adipic acid contains no double bonds and is used to make polyamides and polyesters. Adipic acid will not undergo runaway polymerization reactions.

1,3-BUTADIENE: A colorless gas with a mild aromatic odor. It is easily liquefied and has a boiling point of 24°F. It is one of the monomers for ABS plastic and is flammable.

BUTYLENE: The monomer of polybutylene and one of the LP gases. It is used as a monomer rather than as a fuel. Polybutylene pipe is used extensively in plumbing applications.

CHLOROPRENE: A colorless liquid that is toxic and flammable. It is the monomer of polychloroprene, better known as neoprene elastomers or synthetic rubbers.

EPICHLOROHYDRIN: A colorless liquid that smells like chloroform. It is the monomer of some epoxy resins and phenoxy resins. It is only slightly soluble in water, has a specific gravity of 1.18, a flash point of 93°F, and boils at 207°F. When it burns, it liberates hydrogen chloride.

ETHYL ACRYLATE: Another acrylic monomer which is used extensively in textile treatment, latex paints, surface coatings, and polishes. It is a colorless liquid with a penetrating, acrid odor. It has a flash point of 60°F, and boils at 211°F. It is slightly soluble in water and has a specific gravity of 0.92.

ETHYLENE: The monomer of polyethylene and an easily liquefiable gas. Since it is the thermoplastic monomer used in largest volume, it is the monomer that is shipped around the country in the largest quantities. It is a colorless gas with a sweet odor and taste and an auto-ignition temperature of 914°F. It is also used as a refrigerant, a fruit ripener, and in the production of many other chemicals.

ETHYLENE OXIDE: An extremely hazardous flammable gas used as one of the monomers for epoxy plastics. It is particularly dangerous because of its extremely wide flammability range, from 3 percent to 100 percent. The upper limit means that ethylene oxide will burn with no oxygen present. Spills from a container of ethylene oxide, along with an ignition source, will result in the flames backing up into the tank or cylinder and exploding.

FORMALDEHYDE: The monomer of acetal plastics such as Delrin®. It is a colorless, toxic gas with a strong, pungent odor that is very soluble in water and is highly flammable. It is toxic by inhalation and a strong skin irritant. Its auto-ignition temperature is 806°F. Formaldehyde has also been known to cause allergic responses and to trigger asthma attacks in susceptible persons.

METHACRYLIC ACID: The monomer of some of the acrylic plastics. It is a colorless liquid with an acrid, disagreeable odor and is corrosive and combustible. It has a flash point of 170°F, is soluble in water, and is a strong skin irritant.

METHYL ACRYLATE: The monomer of another of the acrylics; a colorless liquid with an acrid odor. Although methyl acrylate is sometimes polymerized by itself, it is more frequently used in copolymers.

METHYL METHARYLATE: The monomer of polymethyl methacrylate, the most common of the acrylic plastics. Although there are many different manufacturers of polymethyl methacrylate, the most famous trade name for this plastic is Lucite®. Polymethyl methacrylate forms a crystal clear sheet when it is cast that is good enough to be used as glazing material. It has a flash point of 50°F and is slightly soluble in water, with a specific gravity of 0.94, and it is readily polymerizable by heat or light. It is a colorless liquid with an acrid odor.

PHENOL: A toxic, combustible solid that liquefies easily. It is a monomer for phenol-formaldehyde and phenol-furfural resins. Phenol is an aromatic alcohol and does not self-polymerize.

PROPYLENE: The monomer of polypropylene and a colorless, easily liquefiable gas. It has an ignition temperature of 927°F and is a simple asphyxiant.

PROPYLENE OXIDE: A colorless, flammable liquid used as one of the monomers for epoxy plastics.

STYRENE: A colorless, oily liquid with an aromatic odor; the monomer of polystyrene. It is insoluble in water (being a hydrocarbon) and has a specific gravity of 0.9. It has a flash point of 88°F and an auto-ignition temperature of 914°F. It is toxic by ingestion and inhalation.

TETRAFLUOROETHYLENE: A flammable, colorless gas that is the monomer for polytetrafluoroethylene (PTFE) resins. The most widely known of these polymers is Teflon®.

VINYL ACETATE: The monomer of polyvinyl acetate used in thermoset plastics and adhesives. Vinyl acetate is a colorless liquid with a flash point of 30°F and an auto-ignition temperature of 800°F. It is insoluble in water and has a specific gravity of 0.9345. It is toxic by inhalation and ingestion.

VINYL CHLORIDE: The monomer of polyvinyl chloride or PVC. PVC is used extensively in pipes, vinyl siding, and flooring material. It is an easily liquefiable gas that is subject to a BLEVE. It is insoluble in water and has a specific gravity of 0.9121. It is toxic by inhalation, is a suspected carcinogen, and liberates hydrogen chloride when it burns.

VINYLIDENE CHLORIDE: The monomer of polyvinylidene chloride which is widely known as Saran or Saranwrap. Vinylidene chloride is a colorless liquid with a flash point of 14°F that liberates hydrogen chloride when it burns.

TYPES OF SYNTHETIC POLYMERS

Synthetic polymers can also be divided into two groups: rubbers and plastics.

Classes of Plastics

There are two great divisions of plastics: thermoplastic and thermoset.

THERMOPLASTIC: A plastic formed by heat and pressure which, once formed, may be reformed by the further use of heat and pressure. In other words, a processor can change plastic resins and compounds from powder, pellet, or cube form into a finished part by heating and applying pressure.

THERMOSET PLASTICS: May be formed by heat and pressure just once. Any further attempts to reshape a thermosetting plastic will result in thermal degradation (decomposition or even burning) of the product.

131

Whether a particular plastic is thermoplastic or thermosetting depends upon the chemistry of its monomer and on the polymerization process. A plastic may be either a thermoplastic or a thermoset. It cannot be both, although there are groups of chemically similar plastics, such as the polyesters, which include both thermoplastic polyesters and thermosetting polyesters.

ACRYLONITRILE-BUTADIENE-STYRENE (ABS): A thermoplastic terpolymer, or a polymer made by the polymerization of three different monomers. This polymer is produced in grades required by users with properties of the final thermoplastic controlled by changing the proportions of each of the three monomers used. It is an extremely tough plastic used wherever rough treatment can be expected. ABS is very useful in structural parts such as camper bodies and tops, canoes, telephones, refrigerators and other appliances, sanitary ware, pipe, power tools, and interior aircraft parts. Whenever additional properties are needed and they cannot be achieved by altering any of the three monomers, other substances are added to the thermoplastic to impart these properties. When this situation occurs, the resulting thermoplastic material is called a compound. This statement is true of all thermoplastics, not ABS alone. ABS can acquire additional properties, such as flame suppression, color, and antioxidation properties, among many others, by adding in the correct modifier to the compound. Unfortunately, ABS does not weather very well, so its use outdoors is limited, unless it is capped with a thin layer of a weather-resistant thermoplastic laminated over it.

ACETAL: This thermoplastic was once considered an engineering thermoplastic only but is now receiving great acceptance as a decorative thermoplastic that can also be functional. It is a highly crystalline thermoplastic possessing a high degree of hardness, good chemical resistance, strength, and good electrical properties. It is a polymer of formaldehyde and, as such, is a good engineering thermoplastic. It is used in making aerosol containers, pens, butane-filled cigarette lighters, and toys.

ACRYLICS: There are many types of acrylic thermoplastics, but the most popular, and therefore the most common, is the polymer based on methyl methacrylate monomer: polymethyl methacrylate, or PMMA. This thermoplastic possesses excellent optical and weathering characteristics, is tough, resistant to heat and many chemicals, and exhibits low electrical conductivity. Because of their outstanding weathering and optical properties, acrylics are excellent candidates to replace glass in signs and glazing applications. They may be extruded or injection-molded to make what is called molding powder. However, the vast majority are cast in a liquid form onto a moving belt or between glass plates to form sheets. These may then be used as such or may be vacuum- or compression-formed into other shapes. Products made from acrylics include signs, sanitary ware, spas and pools, residential and commercial glazing, automotive lighting lenses, and lighting fixtures.

FLUOROPOLYMERS, or **FLUOROPLASTICS:** A group of plastics characterized by the substitution of fluorine for one or more of the hydrogens on an alkane to form the monomer. There are several monomers that are produced, which, upon polymerization, each produce a unique polymer. As a group, the fluoroplastics offer great resistance to a wide variety of chemical environments and have good electrical resistance, high heat resistance, and extremely low coefficients of friction.

There are several fluoroplastics whose uses are determined according to their suitability for a particular job. The most familiar fluoroplastic is the one used to coat home cookware, polytetrafluoroethylene [PTFE], better known by its trademarked name, Teflon®. The rest of the fluoroplastics family includes polychlorotrifluoroethylene, ethylene-chlorotrifluoroethylene copolymers, fluorinated ethylene-propylene copolymers, perfluoroalkoxy resins, ethylene-tetrafluoroethylene copolymers, polyvinyl fluoride, and polyvinylidene fluoride.

COPOLYMERS: A copolymer is a plastic made by the mixing together of two monomers and the subsequent polymerization of the mixture; some copolymers may be produced by a "grafting" process, a totally different procedure. These polymers may be difficult to pronounce, but they perform extremely important jobs in commerce, ranging from electrical insulation to earthquake protection for tall buildings. Fluoroplastics may be extruded, injection-molded, or may be powder coated, a process in which a layer of fine thermoplastic powder is made to cover the part to be coated. The part is then heated so that the polymer flows evenly over the entire surface of the part.

NITRILES: The nitrile resins are really polyacrylonitrile (PAN), but referring to them by the shorter name is easier. These thermoplastics are known for their outstanding gas transmission properties and are sometimes called homer resins. The reason for the name is because bottles and containers made of nitrile thermoplastics are impervious to the passage of oxygen or carbon dioxide through the walls of the container, thereby serving as a home to either gas. In addition, these thermoplastics possess good resistance to hydrocarbon and chlorinated hydrocarbon solvents, good electrical resistance, and good mechanical properties. The proper chemical name for acrylonitrile monomers is vinyl cyanide. Polyacrylonitrile may be blow-molded or injection-molded.

NYLONS: The family of thermoplastics known as nylon belongs to a group of polymers known as polyamides. The chemistry of the nylons and the specific polymerization processes each participates in is rather long and complicated; will be described, only the general properties of the nylons although it should be realized that there are many different polymers possible, with different specific properties.

Nylons usually have good mechanical and electrical properties, which originally put them in the class of engineering thermoplastics. Their outstanding resistance to wear enables them to continue to be used in many strictly engineering capacities. The fact that they also are strong, stiff, and very tough, makes them useful in substituting for metals in the outer casings of power tools and several other applications. The nylons can be modified by compounding ingredients, by copolymerization, and even by terpolymerization (the polymerization of three monomers to make one thermoplastic). The largest growth area for the nylons today is the automobile, where they may be used in fifty or more different parts. Nylons are also widely used in the electrical industry and consumer goods such as clothing, carpeting, upholstery, household goods, and packaging, and in a myriad of other products. Nylons may be extruded and injection-molded.

POLYCARBONATE (PC): A very important engineering thermoplastic whose strength enables it to be used in some structural applications. It has excellent high impact strength, excellent dimensional stability, good electrical properties, and good heat stability. With its excellent optical properties, it is used as glazing material, in automobile headlights and instrument panels, traffic light housings and lenses, protective covers for street lights, office water cooler bottles, and food containers. Polycarbonates may be extruded into film and sheet, and some small parts are injection-molded.

POLYESTERS: The thermoplastic polyesters are the saturated polyesters, namely, polyethylene terephthalate (PET) and polybutylene terephthalate (PBT). PBT has good chemical, mechanical, and electrical properties and is usually injection-molded. It is used to make electrical switches and connectors, fuse cases, TV tuners, automotive distributor caps and rotors, pump impellers, and other large automotive parts.

PET: The thermoplastic that has replaced glass in large soft drink bottles, mainly because of its light weight, clarity, and its action as a homer to carbon dioxide. It is also very useful in producing film and fiber. Polyester clothing is made from PET fibers, as is the polyester carpeting, upholstery, and polyester cord used in automobile tires. It is also used as a coating over other materials, such as paper, and may be made into photographic and X-ray film. PET may be extruded, injection-molded, blow-molded, or extrusion-coated. In this process the thermoplastic polyester is melted in an extruder and then applied in a thin coat over another material.

POLYETHYLENE: The number one thermoplastic in volume in the world today is polyethylene (PE), and the many variations that can be made from the ethylene monomer have been listed as an example at the beginning of this chapter. PE is used in housewares, packaging, trash bags, milk bottles, and other bottles and containers. It is used also in films for use as vapor barriers in construction or over mulch in agriculture, electrical insulation, in pipe and conduit, and in literally hundreds of other applications. All grades of PE may be extruded, injection-molded, blow-molded, or calendared. Calendaring is a process where the polymer is passed through a series of three or four mill rolls that presses the thermoplastic into a sheet or film. It can also be rotationally cast, a process whereby powdered resin is introduced to a mold that is revolving in all planes and heated. This causes the resin to fuse, partially melt, and flow into all parts of the mold, assuming the shape of the mold's interior. All the various grades of polyethylene added make it, by far, the most widely produced plastic in the world.

POLYPROPYLENE: The monomer of polypropylene (PP) is propylene (propene), which is an alkene-like ethylene (ethene). Consequently, polyethylene, polypropylene, and a small but growing volume thermoplastic called polybutylene (PB) are classed together as the polyolefins. They resemble each other as the finished polymer, and they burn in a similar fashion, but that is the extent of the close resemblance.

Polypropylene is tougher than polyethylene and exhibits good low-temperature impact resistance, and good heat, chemical, and moisture resistance. Processing it is easy. It may be extruded or injection-molded. It is used to make toys, housewares, luggage, furniture, packaging, bottles and containers, tubing, film and sheet, and many automotive parts.

POLYSTYRENE: The third highest thermoplastic in volume behind polyethylene and polyvinyl chloride is polystyrene (PS). It has good optical clarity, dimensional stability, electrical and chemical resistance, and good colorability (all, of course, in the transparent and/or nonfoamed grades). It is available as crystal grade, medium impact polystyrene (MIPS), high impact polystyrene (HIPS), and as a product involving major modifications, adding other monomers before polymerization. It is used in packaging, electrical parts, sheet and film, toys, appliance cabinets, refrigerator inner liners, audio and video cassettes, lids and containers, and countless other items. In its foamed grades, such as foamed hot drink cups, it is a great insulating material, and may be used for that purpose in construction of houses and commercial buildings. Polystyrene may be extruded, injection-molded, and blow-molded.

POLYURETHANE: As with the other polymers previously mentioned (polyesters), there exist both thermoplastic and thermosetting types of polyurethanes; only the thermoplastic polyurethanes will be discussed here. They are usually very flexible, tough, and abrasion resistant. They may be extruded or injection-molded. The thermoplastic polyurethanes are used in clothing, shoes, diapers, athletic equipment and lettering, packaging, and automotive parts.

POLYVINYL CHLORIDE: Although it is the number two thermoplastic in the world with respect to volume, polyvinyl chloride (PVC) is number one when it comes to the number of uses to which it is put. Its monomer is vinyl chloride (VCM), and once the resin is through the polymerization process, PVC may appear in many applications. PVC, as it comes out of the reactor, is useless as a thermoplastic. It is much too hard and brittle and may decompose the very first time anyone tries to extrude or mold it. To convert

134

it into a flexible PVC compound, a plasticizer must be added to make it softer and more pliable. PVC has, as was said before, more uses than any other thermoplastic; these uses include shower curtains, phonograph records, flooring, wall covering, house upholstery, automotive parts, electrical parts and insulation, and pipes and conduits.

THERMOSET PLASTICS: Probably the thermoset plastic produced in largest volume is polyurethane, principally in its use as a foam. In the foam grades, polyurethane is one of the most valuable insulating materials available to us. It is found as an insulation in the walls of our homes, in industrial plants, and in refrigerators and freezers. It is also extensively used as a cushioning material and is present in upholstery in our homes and automobiles and in the mattresses on which we sleep.

Amino resins
Amino resins include the urea-formaldehyde and melamine formaldehyde resins. They are used for adhesives, laminates, coatings, and foam. Molding compounds are used to make sanitary ware, buttons, dinnerware, wiring devices, and appliance parts, while laminating resins are used to make counter tops, table tops, furniture, and wall paneling. The adhesive resins are used to bond together plywood, furniture, particle board, and flooring. Coating resins are used to grease-proof and shrink-proof textiles and to add fire retardancy to other plastics.

Epoxy resins
These have good electrical, thermal, and chemical resistance, low shrinkage, and good impact resistance. They are used mostly for coatings and finishes.

Phenolic resins
These are thermosetting plastics with good heat and chemical resistance, good dielectric properties, surface hardness, and good thermal and dimensional stability. Fillers are added to the resin to give specific properties. Phenolic resins are molded. They are used to make electrical receptacles and switches, automotive components, knobs, appliance parts, utensil handles, casters, rollers, and other load bearing items.

Organic Peroxides

The organic peroxides have the general structure R-O-O-R. They are named by using the radical and peroxide. For example, benzoyl peroxide [$(C_6H_5CH_2)_2O_2$]. Generally, they are used as initiators or catalysts in a polymerization reaction. An initiator is a material that starts a reaction, while a catalyst is a material that controls the speed of a reaction but is not consumed in the reaction.

If there was ever a group of hazardous materials into which people attempt to include as many hazards as possible, it would be the organic peroxides. As the name states, the materials are organic, and anything organic will burn. The presence of the peroxide radical is an intimate source of oxygen, which the organic peroxide will give up readily. Recall that this is a definition of an oxidizing agent. Thus, two legs of the fire triangle are present, and all that is needed is the energy or heat leg. Wanting to appear dissimilar from any other hazardous material, the organic peroxides even have the third leg present; this takes the form of an unstable molecule that can absorb energy from the environment to produce enough energy within the molecule to serve as its own ignition source!

Organic peroxides are generally liquids or white powders, depending on their individual chemistry. The peroxide functional group between two hydrocarbon radicals is extremely unstable; the slightest amount of energy may be enough to cause a violent molecular decomposition with the release of a tremendous amount of energy. What happens is this: the organic peroxide molecules are fairly stable at some low temperature, and they are usually kept at that temperature. Yet if ambient temperatures rise, and the organic peroxide is exposed to the temperature rise, the fragile peroxide linkage begins to disintegrate. This additional energy created and absorbed by the remaining organic peroxide molecules of course speeds up the reaction, which feeds upon itself until the organic peroxide seems almost to explode. It is not really an explosion but has been described by fire fighters as a firestorm. The absorption of energy which speeds up the disintegration of the molecule is known as its SADT, which stands for self-accelerating decomposition temperature. This SADT is a property of every organic peroxide; that is, every organic peroxide has its own SADT, which may be near 0°F or may be higher than 50°F. Whatever it is, when that temperature is reached by some portion of the mass of organic peroxide, decomposition will begin, and it is irreversible. Once the reaction has begun, there is no chance of stopping it; the only hope is that the amount of organic peroxide involved is small, and that the exposures can be protected.

The organic peroxides, as stated, have so many hazards that they do not seem useful to industry, considering all the risks involved. Industry does a pretty good job of handling these hazardous materials, however, and the occasional incident occurs mostly because of an oversight. The hazards of organic peroxides are instability, flammability, high reactivity, potential for explosivity (especially in a fire), potential for corrosion, toxicity, and as oxidizers.

The hazard of a peroxide being unstable may mean that any sudden input of energy may cause the violent decomposition of the peroxide molecules. The organic peroxides are so unstable that even slow inputs of energy may cause decomposition. The user of these materials must guard against any energy in any form reaching them. Heat is the most common form of energy that threatens the organic peroxide molecule, so protection must be provided from the common methods of generating and transferring heat.

Shock is another common form of sudden energy input, so containers must be protected from falling objects and rough treatment. Indeed, one method of disposal of organic peroxides is to have a sharpshooter fire a high-powered bullet into the container from a safe distance.

The flammability of organic peroxides means that they should never be exposed to an ignition source. It may seem redundant to make this statement. Knowing that organic peroxides are so unstable when heated, a situation could arise in which the materials are kept cool but may still be exposed to an ignition source of one sort or another. Flammable materials and oxidizing agents should never be stored next to each other.

The fact that organic peroxides are also oxidizing agents makes the above statement seem ridiculous, which should lead to some clue as to the storage problems of organic peroxides! The reactivity of organic peroxides means that they will enter into chemical reactions very easily. The explosiveness of organic peroxides is related to the speed with which energy is introduced to the material. If it is as rapid as the above-mentioned bullet, or as intense as an approaching flame front, most organic peroxides will explode.

Not all organic peroxides are corrosive, but several are, particularly those that include acid as part of the name. Since it would be a monumental job to classify peroxides as to their relative corrosiveness, treating them all as highly corrosive is best.

The same may be said for the toxicity hazard of the organic peroxides. Some may be extremely toxic, while others may be harmless from this aspect. Concentration of the peroxide is an important consideration in its toxicity.

12

Weapons of Mass Destruction

Introduction

Prior to 1990, the issue of emergency response to a chemical, biological, or radiological attack on a civilian population was not a significant part of standard HAZMAT training. Most planning and preparation throughout the world focused on these topics as part of a scenario involving the use of weapons of mass destruction in a strategic end-of-the-world scenario or in a more limited battlefield environment. Troops were trained to operate against the background of the battlefield use of small tactical nuclear weapons or chemical warfare. Except for an all-out nuclear war, in these scenarios civilian populations, especially urban populations, would not normally be the primary target of these weapons but rather were considered collateral damage from the attack on military forces. International treaties that prohibited the use of these weapons on civilian populations were in place. Substantial numbers of troops in many countries were trained to fight and survive a toxic battlefield. However, civilian responders, especially in the United States, were largely untrained to cope with the need to respond to an intentional use of chemical, biological, or radiological weapons against civilian populations by domestic or foreign terrorists. A number of incidents over the last decade has changed the world and now training in weapons of mass destruction is a necessity. A number of incidents caused this change in view:

- In 1991 during the Gulf War, Iraq fired SCUD missiles at cities in Saudi Arabia and in Israel. Although these missiles were equipped with conventional warheads, after the war it was established that the Iraqi military had both chemical and biological weapons in large quantity.
- In 1994 and 1995 members of the Japanese cult Aum Shinrikkyo, used the nerve agent sarin against Japanese civilians. In the 1995 attack on the Tokyo subway system, there were 12 confirmed deaths, and about 5,500 people sought medical treatment.
- In 1996, Chechen separatists planted a radioactive dirty bomb in a Moscow park consisting of dynamite and radioactive Cs^{137}. This apparently was intended as a warning and the device did not explode.
- In 2001, anthrax was used in the United States in letters sent through the US Postal Service. Although the death toll was relatively low, the disruption to the mail service and to some public buildings was significant and the cleanup costs were enormous.

Although this is a chemistry text, biological, chemical, and radiological warfare agents will be discussed in detail.

138

Biological Hazards

Summary
Biological agents are the oldest of the nuclear, biological, and chemical (NBC) triad and have been used by governments in warfare for over 2,500 years. In addition, use of toxins by nonstate sponsored groups is not new. Terrorist groups have included these weapons into their arsenals. Biological agents are more deadly on a compound per weight basis than chemical agents and occur naturally in the environment. Many of these agents have been refined and could be made more resistant in laboratories. Some of the poisons (toxins) produced by bacteria have been developed for use as biological weapons. Most notable is the botulinum toxin, which can produce death after being ingested or inhaled in minute quantities.

Historical
The use of biological weapons and efforts to make them more useful as a means of waging war have been recorded numerous times in history. Two of the earliest reported uses occurred in the 6th century BC, with the Assyrians poisoning enemy wells with rye ergot, and Solon's use of the purgative herb hellebore during the siege of Krissa. In 1346, plague broke out in the Tartar army during its siege of Kaffa (at present day Feodosia in Crimea). The attackers hurled the corpses of those who died over the city walls; the plague epidemic that followed forced the defenders to surrender, and some infected people who left Kaffa may have started the Black Death pandemic which spread throughout Europe. Russian troops may have used the same plague-infected corpse tactic against Sweden in 1710.

On several occasions, smallpox was used as a biological weapon. Pizarro is said to have presented South American natives with smallpox-contaminated clothing in the 15th century, and the English did the same when Sir Jeffery Amherst provided Indians loyal to the French with smallpox-laden blankets during the French and Indian War of 1754 to 1767. Native Americans defending Fort Carillon sustained epidemic casualties which directly contributed to the loss of the fort to the English.

In this century, there is evidence that during World War I, German agents inoculated horses and cattle with glanders in the U.S. before the animals were shipped to France. In 1937, Japan started an ambitious biological warfare program, located 40 miles south of Harbin, Manchuria, in a laboratory complex code named "Unit 731." Studies directed by Japanese General Ishii continued there until 1945, when the complex was leveled by burning it. A post-World War II investigation revealed that numerous organisms had received Japanese research attention, and that experiments had been conducted on prisoners of war. Slightly less than 1,000 human autopsies apparently were carried out at Unit 731, most on victims exposed to aerosolized anthrax. Many more prisoners and Chinese nationals may have died in this facility; some have estimated up to 3,000 human deaths. In 1940, a plague epidemic in China and Manchuria followed reported overflights by Japanese planes dropping plague-infected fleas. By 1945, the Japanese program had stockpiled 400 kilograms of anthrax to be used in a specially designed fragmentation bomb.

In 1943, the United States began research into the offensive use of biological agents. This work was started, interestingly enough, in response to a perceived German biological warfare (BW) threat as opposed to a Japanese one. The United States conducted this research at Camp Detrick (now Fort Detrick), which was a small National Guard airfield prior to that time, and produced agents at other sites until 1969, when President Nixon stopped all offensive biological and toxin weapons research and production by executive order. Between May 1971 and May 1972, all stockpiles of biological agents and munitions from the now defunct U.S. program were destroyed in the presence of monitors representing the United States Department of Agriculture, the Department of Health, Education, and Welfare, and the states of Arkansas, Colorado, and Maryland. Included among the destroyed agents were Bacillus anthracis, botulinum toxin, Francisella tularensis, Coxiella burnetii, Venezuelan equine encephalitis virus, Brucellosis, and Staphylococcal enterotoxin B. The United States also had a medical defensive program, begun in 1953, that continues today at USAMRIID.

In 1972, the United States and many other countries signed the *Convention on the Prohibition of the Development, Production and Stockpiling of Bacteriological (Biological) and Toxin Weapons and on Their Destruction*, commonly called the *Biological Weapons Convention*. This treaty prohibits the stockpiling of biological agents for offensive military purposes, and also forbids research into the offensive employment of biological agents. The former Soviet Union and the government of Iraq were both signatories to this accord. However, despite this historic agreement among nations, biological warfare research continued to flourish in many countries hostile to the United States. There were also several cases of suspected or actual use of biological weapons. Among the most notorious of these were the yellow rain incidents in Southeast Asia, the accidental release of anthrax at Sverdlovsk, and the use of ricin as an assassination weapon in London in 1978.

Testimony from the late 1970s indicated that the countries of Laos and Cambodia were attacked by planes and helicopters delivering aerosols of several colors. After being exposed, people and animals became disoriented and ill, and a small percentage of those stricken died. Some of these clouds were thought to be comprised of trichothecene toxins (in particular, T2 mycotoxin). These attacks are lumped under the label yellow rain. There has been a great deal of controversy about whether these clouds were truly biological warfare agents: some have argued that the clouds were nothing more than bee feces produced by swarms of bees.

In late April of 1979, an incident occurred in Sverdlovsk (now Yekaterinburg) in the former Soviet Union which appeared to be an accidental release of anthrax in aerosol form from the Soviet Military Compound 19, a microbiology facility. Residents living downwind from this compound developed high fever and difficulty breathing, and a large number died. The final death toll was estimated at the time to be between 200 and 1,000. The Soviet Ministry of Health blamed the deaths on the consumption of contaminated meat, and for years controversy raged in the press over the actual cause of the outbreak. All evidence available to the United States government indicated a massive release of aerosolized anthrax. In the summer of 1992, U.S. intelligence officials were proven correct when new Russian President Boris Yeltsin acknowledged that the Sverdlovsk incident was in fact a large scale accident involving the escape of an aerosol of anthrax spores from the military research facility. In 1994, Meselson and colleagues published an in-depth analysis of the Sverdlovsk incident (Science 266:1202-1208). They documented that all of the 1979 cases occurred within a narrow zone extending downwind in a southerly direction from Compound 19. A total of 77 patients were identified by Meselson's team, including 66 fatalities and 11 survivors.

In August of 1991, the first United Nations inspection of Iraq's biological warfare capabilities was carried out in the aftermath of the Gulf War. On August 2, 1991, representatives of the Iraqi government announced to leaders of United Nations Special Commission Team 7 that they had conducted research into the offensive use of Bacillus anthracis, botulinum toxins, and Clostridium perfringens (presumably one of its toxins). This was the first open admission of biological weapons research by any country in recent memory, and it verified many of the concerns of the U.S. intelligence community publicly. Iraq had extensive and redundant research facilities at Salman Pak and other sites, many of which were destroyed during the war.

In 1995, further information on Iraq's offensive program was made available to United Nations inspectors. Iraq conducted research and development work on anthrax, botulinum toxins, Clostridium perfringens, aflatoxins, wheat cover smut, and ricin. Field trials were conducted with Bacillus subtilis (a simulant for anthrax), botulinum toxin, and aflatoxin. Biological agents were tested in various delivery systems, including rockets, aerial bombs, and spray tanks. In December 1990, the Iraqis filled 100 R400 bombs with botulinum toxin, 50 with anthrax, and 16 with aflatoxin. In addition, 13 Al Hussein (SCUD) warheads were filled with botulinum toxin, 10 with anthrax, and 2 with aflatoxin. These weapons were deployed in January 1991 to four locations. All in all, Iraq produced 19,000 liters of concentrated botulinum toxin (nearly 10,000 liters filled into munitions), 8,500 liters of concentrated anthrax (6,500 liters filled into munitions), and 2,200 liters of aflatoxin (1,580 liters filled into munitions).

The threat of biological warfare has increased in the last two decades, with a number of countries working on offensive use of these agents. The extensive program of the former Soviet Union is now controlled largely by Russia. Former Russian president Boris Yeltsin stated that he would put an end to further offensive biological research; however, the degree to which the program has been scaled back, if any, is not known. Revelations from a senior BW program manager who defected from the Florida State University in 1992 outlined a remarkably robust biological warfare program including active research into genetic engineering, binary biologicals, and chimeras. There is also growing concern that the smallpox virus, eliminated from the face of the earth in the late 1970s and now stored in only two laboratories at the CDC in Atlanta and the Institute for Viral Precautions in Moscow, may have been bargained away by desperate Russian scientists seeking money.

There is intense concern in the West about the possibility of proliferation or enhancement of offensive programs in countries hostile to the western democracies, due to the potential hiring of expatriate Russian scientists. It was reported in January 1998 that Iraq had sent about a dozen scientists involved in BW research to Libya to help that country develop a biological warfare complex disguised as a medical facility in the Tripoli area. In a report issued in November 1997, Secretary of Defense William Cohen singled out Libya, Iraq, Iran, and Syria as countries aggressively seeking nuclear, biological, and chemical weapons.

Rogue nations and terrorist organizations have shown a strong interest in the use of BW because the weapons are inexpensive to produce, difficult to monitor, and can produce illness and death in large numbers of people. About 25 countries are currently suspected of possessing BW, five of which (Iran, Iraq, Libya, Syria, North Korea) have histories of belligerent militant behavior.

There is also an increasing amount of concern over the possibility of terrorist use of biological agents to threaten either military or civilian populations. There have been cases of persons loyal to extremist groups trying to obtain microorganisms which could be used as biological weapons.

By definition, the use of biological weapons or biological warfare (BW) is the use of microorganisms (bacteria, viruses, and fungi) or toxins (poisons produced by living organisms) to produce death or disease in humans, animals, and plants. Few healthcare providers have been trained to recognize or treat victims of a biological agent attack. Nonetheless, the principles of detection, personal protection, infection control, and treatment parallel the standard approach to any natural disease outbreak (such as influenza, Rift Valley Fever, meningitis, and hepatitis).

A single bacterium that divides every 20 minutes can give rise to over one billion organisms in 10 hours. Inhaling 40,000 spores of anthrax (enough to fit on the head of a pin) would result in a death rate of 95 percent. BW can be produced with minimal start-up equipment and supplies and can easily be introduced into a building's ventilation system, released into a busy shopping center from an aerosolized can, or placed into the food system with little or no warning. Called the poor man's nuclear bomb, these agents are appealing to countries with limited resources.

Certainly the threat of biological weapons being used against US military forces is broader and more likely in various geographic scenarios than at any point in our history. Therefore, awareness of this potential threat and education of our leaders and medical care providers on how to combat it are crucial.

General Properties

Despite the inherent differences between the various types of biological agents, bacteria, viruses, and toxins share some common characteristics. Since BW are nonvolatile (do not evaporate), they must be dispersed in aerosols as 1 to 5 micron size particles (1/30,000 of the diameter of a hair follicle), which may remain suspended in the air for hours (depending on certain weather conditions). The primary route of infection or portal of entry would be inhalation (pulmonary). If inhaled, the particles will deposit deep into the small air sacs (alveoli) of the lungs causing disease. Each of these agents can be easily disseminated from industrial sprayers modified to generate the small particle size. The aerosol can also be delivered from an airplane or boat traveling upwind from the intended target.

Warning Properties

There are currently few available monitoring devices that will recognize a BW release, and they are complex and costly. In fact, there are very few initial warning signs of a biological attack. A BW aerosol would most likely be invisible. Within hours or days of the attack, a pattern of injury may result in large numbers of patients with similar signs and symptoms presenting to hospitals or other healthcare facilities. These initial complaints will be characteristic of a flu outbreak and many of the patients will be sent home. Soon, more prominent symptoms will develop, alerting healthcare personnel to the unusual nature of the outbreak. This recognition may be markedly delayed in cases where, for example, the initial release occurred in an airport. Under these circumstances, those infected will unknowingly board their airplanes and travel to every conceivable corner of the world before experiencing any adverse symptoms. This could result in numerous secondary exposures. Subsequently, when the disease progresses to a life-threatening condition, first responders and ER personnel become the front line of assessment, diagnosis, and treatment.

Characteristics of Biological Agents:

- Biological agents show some similarities to chemical agents, but some significant differences will also be noted.
- From a responder's point of view, the biggest difference is time. Unlike chemical agents, most of which have an immediate effect, most biological agents all have a delayed effect ranging from several hours to days, and in some cases weeks. When responding to a biological incident, there may be no immediate casualties or anything significant unless someone witnesses, the actual release or a suspected dissemination device has been located.
- Responders need to understand some of the basic characteristics of potential biological agents and how to protect themselves.

Biological Agents:

- Are not dermally active. Unlike some of the chemical agents (nerve and blister agents), biological agents cannot penetrate healthy unbroken skin. (An exception is T-2 Mycotoxin, which causes skin damage.) To cause disease, most biological agents must be inhaled or ingested. Skin provides a good barrier to most agents, in contrast to some chemical agents which can cause toxic reactions and symptoms if placed on the skin.
- Are nonvolatile. Biological agents will be disseminated as either liquid or solid aerosols, with the biological material being subjected to the environment. Many biological agents are living organisms and adverse temperature and humidity will affect them. Sunlight, particularly ultraviolet rays, will kill many of them. In this environment, most will only last a few hours or days. Because of this, use of biological agents is more likely at night or in enclosed areas.

- By weight are generally more toxic than chemical agents. For example, ricin, one of the toxins mentioned later, is 2 to 3 times more toxic than VX, the most toxic nerve agent, and botulinum, another toxin, is 5,000 to 10,000 times more toxic than VX.
- Are invisible to human senses. They cannot be seen, tasted, heard, felt, or smelled.
- Have a range of effects. Biological agents have a variety of effects depending on the organism and how it affects the victim, the dose received, and the route of entry. This range can run from skin irritation through death.
- Are obtained from nature. Each of the biological agents has a natural host. In some instances, with little training or equipment, a small amount of culture or material can be "grown" into larger quantities which are then placed in a dissemination device.
- Are relatively easy to produce. This ties to the last characteristic. The key term here is relatively. If a culture of one of the organisms can be obtained and the know-how to grow or culture it, (provide a suitable environment, provide nutrients, allow it to reproduce, etc.) the quantity can be increased using basic procedures with easily obtainable equipment.
- Have delayed effects. All living biological agents have a definite time period between the time a victim is subjected to the agent and when the symptoms begin to appear. This is referred to as the incubation period, the time when the agent is reproducing in the body and defeating its natural defense systems. This incubation period can be as short as a few hours to days and in some cases weeks. Even toxins, which do not grow and reproduce, may take hours to produce symptoms.

Clues to an Attack

Symptoms that would develop after a BW attack would be delayed and nonspecific, making the initial diagnosis difficult. Healthcare providers should seek a number of clues when trying to identify the cause of an unusual infectious outbreak. A BW attack should be considered if any of the following are present:

- Large epidemic with unprecedented number of ill or dying.
- Initial susceptibility first observed in HIV(+) individuals. (canary in a coal mine).
- Particularly high volumes of patients complaining primarily of respiratory symptoms that are severe and are associated with an unprecedented mortality rate.
- The cause of the infection is unusual or impossible for the particular region (such as the Ebola virus which is rarely seen outside of Africa). The agent may require clinical and laboratory diagnosis.
- Multiple, yet simultaneous outbreaks.
- The epidemic is caused by a multi-drug-resistant pathogen, previously unknown.
- Sick or dead animals of multiple types are encountered.
- The delivery vehicle for the agent is identified.
- Prior intelligence reports or claims by aggressors of a BW attack.

Categories of Biological Agents

Bacteria and Viruses

Both bacteria and viruses are living organisms and as such, require an environment in which to live and reproduce.

- They can enter the body through inhalation or ingestion, through a break in the skin, or through other body openings or orifices. In a deliberate use, inhalation through the lungs is usually the targeted route of entry.
- As mentioned earlier, once the organisms invade the body, they begin to grow and reproduce. They can also produce toxins which may poison the body. The human body has built-in defense mechanisms, but if they are overwhelmed or not effective, then the specific symptoms associated with the particular organism or disease begin to appear. Fever, vomiting, and diarrhea are

frequently early symptoms. Depending on the particular disease, effects will continue to develop and can, in many cases, completely disrupt normal body functions and cause death.
- Some bacteria and viruses can cause epidemics by being transmitted from one infected individual to another. This is true of only a few of the agents such as pneumonic plague (bacteria), smallpox, and viral hemorrhagic fevers (viruses).

Toxins

Toxins are poisonous substances produced as a by-product of pathogens, plants, and even some animals. Snake venom is a good example of a toxin. Toxins are not living organisms, but they are in fact chemical compounds, often proteins or protein-like materials. They can enter the body the same way pathogens can. Toxins are not contagious.

There are numerous naturally occurring toxins. How they affect humans will vary. For purposes of this text, they are grouped into three categories:
- **Neurotoxins:** These attack the nervous system. They are fairly fast-acting and can act in a manner opposite to that of the nerve agents by preventing nerve to muscle stimulation. Symptoms such as mental confusion, loss of balance, vision problems, tremors, or seizures are not uncommon.
- **Cytotoxins:** These are cell poisons. They are slower acting and can have a variety of symptoms: vomiting, diarrhea, rashes, blisters, jaundice, bleeding, or general tissue deterioration.
- **Other toxins:** There are numerous other modes of action of toxins, which are beyond the discussion at hand.

Biological Agents

Anthrax (Bacteria)

Anthrax is a bacteria. It occurs naturally in cattle, sheep, and other hoofed animals. It is normally transmitted to man through cuts or abrasions in the arms and hands. Anthrax can form spores which make the organism more resilient. In spore form, it can be transmitted to man through the respiratory tract, where it is a much greater threat (mortality can reach 80-90 percent). Early symptoms (in the first one to two days) are nonspecific and include fever, chills, malaise, and possibly chest pain. Late signs and symptoms (three to five days) are cyanosis (bluish skin), respiratory distress, rapid heart rate, and low blood pressure. Sometimes in cutaneous anthrax, itching of an exposed skin surface occurs first, followed by a lesion and swelling. Symptoms normally occur within 24-72 hours. An infective dosage by aerosol is roughly 8,000-10,000 spores per person, but may be as low as 1,300 spores/person, with an incubation period of 1 to 7 days. Treatment involves the use of antibiotics and treating the specific symptoms.

The organism that produces the disease anthrax is the pathogenic bacteria Bacillus anthracis. It is a rod-shaped, gram-positive, aerobic, sporulating microorganism with the spores constituting the usual infective form. It is found worldwide. The spores are very stable and can remain viable for years in soil and water, under certain conditions. Spores will resist sunlight for several days. Anthrax is primarily a disease of herbivorous animals such as cattle, sheep, goats, and horses; but, other animals might also become infected. Humans who have contact with infected animals normally contract the disease through scratches or abrasions of the skin on hands or forearms. Due to the widespread immunization of animals, outbreaks that affect humans are rare.

To produce disease, the microorganism is optimally employed in its spore form. The most common infection in nature is as a result of a skin infection or lesion. The inhalation form is the most dangerous, with an 80-90 percent mortality rate. The organism gets into the body and is engulfed in macrophages, but

144

survives due to its encapsulation. The macrophages transport the organism to the lymph nodes in the center of the chest (mediastinum). The organisms multiply, produce toxins, and invade the blood system and then other tissues. Death occurs due to the effects of anthrax toxins, invasion of other organ systems, and sepsis (generalized infection).

Cutaneous anthrax can be treated effectively with some antibiotics. Similar treatment with antibiotics such as ciprofloxacin, doxycycline, or penicillin for pulmonary and intestinal infections may be useful in the very early stages but is of lesser value after the disease is well established. Intensive care may be necessary for advanced infections.

Brucellosis (Bacteria)
The Brucellae are a group of gram-negative cocco-bacillary organisms, of which four species are pathogenic in humans. Abattoir and laboratory worker infections suggest that Brucellae spp. are highly infectious via the aerosol route. It is estimated that inhalation of only 10 to 100 bacteria is sufficient to cause disease in humans. The relatively long and variable incubation period (5-60 days) and the fact that many infections are asymptomatic under natural conditions has made it a less desirable agent for weaponization, although large aerosol doses may shorten the incubation period and increase the clinical attack rate. Brucellosis infection has a low mortality rate (5 percent of untreated cases) with most deaths caused by endocarditis or meningitis. It is an incapacitating and disabling disease in its natural form.

Signs and Symptoms: Incubation period from 5-60 days; average of 1-2 months. Highly variable. Acute and subacute brucellosis are nonspecific. Irregular fever, headache, profound weakness and fatigue, chills, sweating, arthralgias, myalgia. Depression and mental status changes. Osteoarticular findings (i.e., sacroiliitis, vertebral osteomyleitis). Fatalities are uncommon.

Treatment includes doxycycline and rifampin for a minimum of six weeks. Ofloxacin with rifampin is also effective. Therapy with rifampin, a tetracycline, and an amino glycoside is indicated for infections with complications such as endocarditis or meningoencephalitis. No approved human vaccine is available. Avoid consumption of unpasteurized milk and cheese.

Decontamination includes standard precautions for healthcare workers. Person-to-person transmission via tissue transplantation and sexual contact has been reported but is insignificant. Environmental decontamination can be accomplished with a 0.5 percent hypochlorite solution.

Cholera (Bacteria)
Vibrio cholerae is a short, curved, motile, gram-negative, nonsporulating rod. There are two serogroups, O1 and O139, that have been associated with cholera in humans. The O1 serotype exists as two biotypes, classical and El Tor. The organisms are facultative anaerobes, growing best at a pH of 7.0, but able to tolerate an alkaline environment. They do not invade the intestinal mucosa, but rather "adhere" to it. Cholera is the prototype toxigenic diarrhea, which is secretory in nature. All strains elaborate the same enterotoxin, a protein molecule with a molecular weight of 84,000 daltons. The entire clinical syndrome is caused by the action of the toxin on the intestinal epithelial cell. Fluid loss in cholera originates in the small intestine with the colon being relatively insensitive to the toxin. The large volume of fluid produced in the upper intestine overwhelms the capacity of the lower intestine to absorb. Transmission is made through direct or indirect fecal contamination of water or foods and by heavily soiled hands or utensils. All populations are susceptible, while natural resistance to infection is variable. Recovery from an attack is followed by a temporary immunity which may furnish some protection for years. The organism is easily killed by drying. It is not viable in pure water, but will survive up to 24 hours in sewage, and as long as 6 weeks in certain

types of relatively impure water containing organic matter. It can withstand freezing for 3 to 4 days. It is readily killed by dry heat at 117°C, by steam and boiling, by short exposure to ordinary disinfectants, and by chlorination of water.

Signs and Symptoms: Incubation period 4 hours to 5 days; average 2-3 days. Asymptomatic to severe with sudden onset. Vomiting, headache, intestinal cramping with little or no fever followed rapidly by painless, voluminous diarrhea. Fluid losses may exceed 5 to 10 liters per day. Without treatment, death may result from severe dehydration, hypovolemia, and shock.

Treatment includes fluid and electrolyte replacement. Antibiotics (tetracycline, ciprofloxacin or erythromycin) may shorten the duration of diarrhea and, more importantly, reduce shedding of the organism.

A licensed, killed vaccine is available but provides only about 50 percent protection that lasts for no more than 6 months. Vaccination schedule is at 0 and 4 weeks, with booster doses every 6 months.

Decontamination includes standard precautions for healthcare workers. Personal contact rarely causes infection; however, enteric precautions and careful hand-washing should be employed. Bactericidal solutions (hypochlorite) would provide adequate decontamination.

Plague (Bacteria)
Plague (black death) is caused by the organism Yersinia pestis, a gram-negative bacillus. It is a very communicable biological warfare agent. There are three primary types of plague that affect humans. They are bubonic, septicemic, and pneumonic.

Plague or black death is another bacteria normally transmitted to humans from rats through the bite of infected fleas. It can also be aerosolized and be transmitted to humans through the respiratory tract causing pneumonic plague. Untreated pneumonic plague has a mortality rate of 90-100 percent. The incubation period is 2 to 6 days for bubonic plague and 3 to 4 days for pneumonic plague. Bubonic plague has a mortality rate of 25 to 50 percent. Early symptoms are high fever, chills, headache, spitting up of blood, and shortness of breath. Bubonic plague is not directly communicable from person to person. Vaccines are available; however, the current plague vaccine protects against bubonic, but not pneumonic plague. Prompt treatment is essential and is usually effective. The choice of antibiotic will vary with the type of infection and severity of the disease. Treatment involves using antibiotics treating specific symptoms.

Bubonic plague, the most common type in nature, is transmitted from rats to humans by the bite of an infected flea. The disease is perpetuated by the rat-flea-rat transmission cycle. The flea bites are usually on the lower extremities.

The bacilli spread rapidly through the lymphatic system, causing enlarged lymph nodes (buboes) in the groin. The bacilli may escape the nodes, invade the bloodstream, and produce a generalized, often fatal infection (septicemic plague). The spleen, lungs, and meninges may also be affected. Pneumonic plague, which may result from the septicemic form or from inhalation of the organism, spreads rapidly until the entire lung area is involved in a hemorrhagic pneumonic process.

Tularemia (Bacteria)
Francisella tularensis, the causative agent of tularemia, is a small, aerobic nonmotile, gram-negative cocco-bacillus. Tularemia (also known as rabbit fever and deer fly fever) is a zoonotic disease which humans typically acquire after contact of their skin or mucous membranes with tissues or body fluids of

146

infected animals, or from bites of infected deerflies, mosquitoes, or ticks. Less commonly, inhalation of contaminated dusts or ingestion of contaminated foods or water may produce clinical disease. Respiratory exposure by aerosol would cause typhoidal or pneumonic tularemia. F. tularensis can remain viable for weeks in water, soil, carcasses, and hides, and for years in frozen rabbit meat. It is resistant for months to temperatures of freezing and below. It is rather easily killed by heat and disinfectants. Inhaling as few as 10 to 50 organisms will cause disease.

Within 2 to 10 days of exposure, victims will begin to develop fever, chills, swollen lymph nodes, headache, generalized muscle pain, nonproductive cough, and sometimes pneumonia. Almost everyone exposed will become infected, but, if treated, only about 5 percent will die.

Secondary transmission does not occur; however, universal precautions should still be practiced. Treatment includes supportive care and administration of antibiotics. An investigational vaccine is available.

Q-Fever (Rickettsia)
Q-Fever is a disease caused by rickettsia, an organism which has some characteristics of bacteria and some of viruses. Coxiella burnetii is a rickettsia (bacteria-like organism) that causes Q-fever, also known as Query fever and North Queensland fever.

This organism can be found in the milk of infected cows, sheep, and goats, and in dust-laden air from dairy cattle barns and goat pens that harbor infected animals. In humans, the disease appears to be transmitted by inhalation of dust contaminated with material (feces or tissues) from infected animals. Raw milk from cows and goats, dried milk, raw wool, hides, infected meat, goat hair, and tick feces, as well as cultures of infected tissues, have all been involved in establishing infections.

Q-fever is an influenza-like disease that is moderately incapacitating and is characterized by the sudden onset of acute fever, headache, chills, weakness, and profuse perspiration. A pneumonitis occurs in many cases with cough, scanty expectoration, and chest pains. Acute pericarditis, acute hepatitis, and generalized infections have been reported. The incubation period is 2 to 3 weeks with a mortality rate of less than 1 percent of the infected individuals.

Vaccines have been effective; however, vaccines should not be used in individuals with a previous history suggestive of Q-fever unless preceded by a hypersensitivity skin test with a small dose of vaccine to avoid severe reactions. Tetracycline antibiotics are used to treat and are generally effective. Supportive treatment is required. Recovery from an attack confers immunity for at least 1 year. The disease is relatively noncontagious between humans. Recovery occurs in most cases without treatment after 2 days to 2 weeks.

Smallpox (Viral)
Smallpox is caused by the variola virus. It occurs in at least two strains, one of which causes variola major and the other causes a milder disease, variola minor. Although there is a good vaccine available, this virus poses a threat because of the aerosol infectivity of the virus.

Variola may have been used by the British against native Americans during the French and Indian War, (giving them contaminated blankets from beds of smallpox victims). There was an epidemic within the Indian community in this part of the country during that time period.

A very effective vaccination is available, but other treatment is limited. There is no effective chemotherapy, and treatment of clinical cases remains supportive.

Smallpox is a virus. There is an effective vaccine; however, without this protection the aerosolized virus presents a respiratory threat. The incubation period is 10-12 days after which a victim will begin to feel ill with fever, rigors, vomiting, headache, and backaches. Two to three days later lesions begin to appear. Some light-skinned victims will exhibit a rash. Following these early symptoms, the rash will become more evident after two to three days, turning to lesions. The mortality rate can reach 30 percent. Treatment involves supportive therapy.

Venezuelan Equine Encephalitis (VEE)
VEE is another virus. It occurs in nature in mules, donkeys, and horses. Transmission is normally through mosquito bites but transmission as an aerosol has been proven, so inhalation through the respiratory tract is possible. The incubation period is usually 2-6 days and can be as short as 1 day. Human symptoms are influenza-like, with an abrupt onset of inflammation of the meninges of the brain, severe headache, chills, fever, dizziness, drowsiness, tremors or convulsions, nausea, vomiting, occasional paralysis, and a lack of muscular coordination. The disease is usually acute and of short duration (3-5 days). VEE has a mortality rate of about 1 percent and recovery occurs without intervention. Treatment is supportive.

Venezuelan equine encephalomyelitis (VEE) is caused by the virus Venezuelan equine encephalitis. VEE is usually found in Central and South America, Mexico, and the dry, hot, irrigated farming areas of the western, midwestern, southwestern, and eastern United States.

Horses serve as the major source of the virus with mosquitoes acting as a vector transmitting it to humans. Normally, equine outbreaks of the disease precede human outbreaks of the disease. The mosquitoes probably can transmit the virus throughout their life. Transmission of the virus by inhalation of aerosols in laboratories is common. Transmission person-to-person may occur but has not been demonstrated.

Treatment is supportive only; no specific therapy exists. Antibiotics are not effective, but an investigative vaccine has been used effectively to protect factory workers and others at high risk. This vaccine also proved effective in protecting horses. The control of infection in horses will help prevent/reduce additional human cases.

Viral Hemorrhagic Fevers (Viral)
The viral hemorrhagic fevers are a diverse group of human illnesses that are due to RNA viruses from several different viral families: the Filoviridae, which consists of Ebola and Marburg viruses; the Arenaviridae, including Lassa fever, Argentine and Bolivian hemorrhagic fever viruses; the Bunyaviridae, including various members from the Hantavirus genus, Congo-Crimean hemorrhagic fever virus from the Nairovirus genus, and Rift Valley fever from the Phlebovirus genus; and Flaviviridae, such as Yellow fever virus, Dengue hemorrhagic fever virus, and others. The viruses may be spread in a variety of ways, and for some there is a possibility that humans could be infected through a respiratory portal of entry. Although evidence for weaponization does not exist for many of these viruses, their potential for aerosol dissemination or weaponization, or likelihood for confusion with similar agents which might be weaponized.

Ebola virus disease was first recognized in the western equatorial province of Sudan and the nearby region of Zaire in 1976; a second outbreak occurred in Sudan in 1979, and in 1995 a large outbreak (316 cases) developed in Kikwit, Zaire from a single index case. Subsequent epidemics have occurred in Gabon and the Ivory Coast. A related virus was isolated from a group of infected cynomolgus monkeys imported into the United States from the Philippines in 1989.

As of yet, this Ebola Reston strain has not been determined as a cause of human disease. The African strains have caused severe disease and death, and it is not known why this disease only appears infrequently or why

148

the most recent strain appears to be less pathogenic in humans. Marburg disease has been identified on four occasions as causing disease in humans: three times in Africa, and once in Germany, where the virus got its name. The first recognized outbreak of Marburg disease involved 31 infected persons in Germany and Yugoslavia who were exposed to African green monkeys, with seven fatalities. It is unclear how easily these filoviruses can be spread from human to human, but spread definitely occurs by direct contact with infected blood, secretions, organs, or semen. The reservoir in nature for these viruses is unknown.

Argentine hemorrhagic fever (AHF), caused by the Junin virus, was first described in 1955 in corn harvesters. It is spread in nature through contact with infected rodent excreta. From 300 to 600 cases per year occur in areas of the Argentine pampas. Bolivian hemorrhagic fever, caused by the related Machupo virus, was described subsequent to AHF in northeastern Bolivia. These viruses have caused laboratory infections, and airborne transmission via dusts contaminated with rodent excreta may occur. A related African arenavirus, Lassa virus, causes disease which is widely distributed over West Africa.

Congo-Crimean hemorrhagic fever (CCHF) is a tick-borne disease which occurs in the Crimea and in parts of Africa, Europe, and Asia. It can also be spread by contact with infected animals or nosocomially in healthcare settings. Rift Valley fever occurs only in Africa, and can occasionally cause explosive disease outbreaks. Hantavirus disease was described prior to World War II in Manchuria along the Amur River, later among United Nations troops during the Korean conflict, and since that time in Korea, Japan, and China. Hemorrhagic disease due to hantaviruses also occurs in Europe (usually in a milder form) and a nonhemorrhagic Hantavirus Pulmonary Syndrome occurs in the Americas and probably worldwide.

Yellow fever and dengue fever are two mosquito-borne fevers which can cause a hemorrhagic fever syndrome and have great historic importance in the history of military campaigns and military medicine.

All of these viruses (except for dengue virus) are infectious by aerosol or fomites. Since most patients are viremic, there is a potential for nosocomial transmission to patients, medical staff, and particularly laboratory personnel. Hantavirus infections are an exception, as at the time of presentation, viremia is waning and circulating antibody is present.

Signs and Symptoms: VHFs are febrile illnesses which can be complicated by easy bleeding, petechiae, hypotension and even shock, flushing of the face and chest, and edema. Constitutional symptoms such as malaise, myalgia, headache, vomiting, and diarrhea may occur in any of the hemorrhagic fevers.

Treatment includes intensive supportive care. Antiviral therapy with ribavirin may be useful in several of these infections. Convalescent plasma may be effective in Argentine hemorrhagic fever.

The only licensed VHF vaccine is yellow fever vaccine. Prophylactic ribavirin may be effective for Lassa fever, Rift Valley fever, CCHF, and possibly HFRS.

Decontamination includes contact precautions for healthcare workers. Decontamination is accomplished with hypochlorite or phenolic disinfectants. Isolation measures and barrier nursing procedures are indicated.

Botulinum (Neurotoxin)
Botulinum is another of the toxins and is one of the most toxic substances know to humans. It normally affects victims after the ingestion of improperly canned food. The toxin can be aerosolized and presents an inhalation threat. Symptoms are opposite of nerve agent intoxication. Initial symptoms may include weakness, malaise, dizziness, and nausea. Other symptoms include difficulty swallowing and speaking, blurred or double vision, sensitivity to light, and muscular weakness progressing from the head downward.

Unlike nerve agents, botulinum toxin does not produce copious body secretions. In severe cases, death results from respiratory paralysis. Symptoms usually begin 24 to 72 hours after ingestion of contaminated food or inhalation of the toxin. A delay in symptoms may range from 6 to 8 days, depending on the amount of toxin and its absorption from the digestive tract or from the lungs.

Botulinum toxin is produced by the bacteria Clostridium botulinum. The principal reservoir of these bacteria is soil, but because they cannot grow in the presence of oxygen, natural exposures to the toxin occur via improperly preserved canned foods. The bacteria grow and produce toxin while the food sits on the shelf. There are seven known types of toxin (A through G).

In natural cases, this toxin normally enters the body through the digestive system. Poisoning comes entirely from the toxin already formed in the ingested material. Digestive tract secretions do not destroy it. The toxin could also possibly enter the body through inhalation in a BW attack. Botulinum toxin is among the most potent biological toxins known. Mortality rate is 60 percent or higher in untreated cases. Botulinum toxin acts by inhibiting acetylcholine release.

Medical care consists of supportive measures, including mechanical ventilation. An antitoxin is available; its administration should take place immediately upon suspecting botulism poisoning. Treatment with antitoxin after severe symptoms set in is usually ineffective. The antitoxin will not usually reverse existing paralysis.

Staphylococcus Enterotoxin Type B (SEB),(Cytotoxin)

SEB is a toxin. It is normally ingested, causing food poisoning. Symptoms can appear within a few minutes of exposure to large aerosolized doses. Inhaled SEB can cause vomiting, and diarrhea if some toxin is also swallowed; however, the most prominent symptoms are fever, cough, chills, and prostration which will usually last 1-2 weeks, (as opposed to SEB food poisoning which lasts 8-12, or at most 24 hours). The incubation period is also about 6 hours for inhaled SEB. Recovery takes 2-3 weeks. Treatment is supportive and an antitoxin is available.

Staphylococcus aureous (a bacteria), produces Staphylococcal enterotoxin type B. This toxin is a rapid-acting toxin whose effects last longer than those of many chemical incapacitants.

SEB causes food poisoning that results from ingestion of the toxin rather than ingestion of the bacteria. Foods contaminated with SEB have a normal appearance, odor, and taste. Situations involving mass feedings and lack of refrigeration with improper food handling are responsible for many natural outbreaks; however, inhalation of aerosolized toxin is possible. Symptoms usually occur within six hours after ingestion.

There is no antitoxin currently available.

Ricin

Ricin is another toxin, with its origin as the castor bean plant. It is therefore readily available. Ricin normally enters the body through ingestion but can be aerosolized. It can also be induced through injection. The toxin attaches to cell surfaces of a variety of tissues, particularly the stomach lining if ingested, or the moist, upper respiratory tissues if inhaled. Ricin inhibits protein synthesis. The incubation period is 24 to 72 hours after which symptoms appear, including nausea, vomiting, bloody diarrhea, abdominal cramps, breathing difficulty, renal failure, and circulatory collapse, depending on the route of exposure. Victims can

150

linger for 10 to 12 days before death or recovery, depending upon the dose received. The untreated mortality rate is high, with death occurring after 36 to 72 hours. Ricin is 2 to 3 times more toxic than the nerve agent VX.

Treatment includes respiratory therapy and other supportive measures.

In 1979, a Bulgarian defector named Georgi Markov, who had been working for Radio Free Europe, was assassinated in London, England. Autopsy results revealed that he had been injected in the calf with a tiny pellet containing the cytotoxin ricin. The investigation revealed that as he had been walking home from work, two Bulgarian nationals had approached him and one poked Georgi with an umbrella designed to inject a micro-ball containing the ricin into this leg. Three days after the incident he died. It was later revealed that the technology to commit the crime was supplied to the Bulgarians by the former Soviet Union.

Ricin is a lethal cytotoxin that comes from the seeds of the castor bean plant, ricinus communis.

Treatment includes general supportive care including fluid support of circulation and respiratory support. There is no antitoxin currently available.

T-2 Mycotoxins

The trichothecene mycotoxins are low molecular weight (250 to 500 daltons) nonvolatile compounds produced by filamentous fungi (molds) of the genera Fusarium, Myrotecium, Trichoderma, Stachybotrys, and others. The structures of approximately 150 trichothecene derivatives have been described in the literature. These substances are relatively insoluble in water but are highly soluble in ethanol, methanol, and propylene glycol. The trichothecenes are extremely stable to heat and ultraviolet light inactivation. Heating to 1500°F for 30 minutes is required for inactivation, while brief exposure to NaOCl destroys toxic activity. The potential for use as a BW toxin was demonstrated to the Russian military shortly after World War II when flour contaminated with species of Fusarium was unknowingly baked into bread that was ingested by civilians. Some developed a protracted lethal illness called alimentary toxic aleukia (ATA) characterized by initial symptoms of abdominal pain, diarrhea, vomiting, prostration, and within days fever, chills, myalgia and bone marrow depression with granulocytopenia and secondary sepsis. Survival beyond this point allowed the development of painful pharyngeal/laryngeal ulceration and diffuse bleeding into the skin (petechiae and ecchymoses), melena, bloody diarrhea, hematuria, hematemesis, epistaxis and vaginal bleeding. Pancytopenia, and gastrointestinal ulceration and erosion were secondary to the ability of these toxins to profoundly arrest bone marrow and mucosa protein synthesis and cell cycle progression through DNA replication.

Signs and symptoms: Exposure causes skin pain, pruritus, redness, vesicles, necrosis, and sloughing of epidermis. Effects on the airway include nose and throat pain, nasal discharge, itching and sneezing, cough, dyspnea, wheezing, chest pain and hemoptysis. Toxin also produces effects after ingestion or eye contact. Severe poisoning results in prostration, weakness, ataxia, collapse, shock, and death.

There is no specific antidote. Superactivated charcoal should be given orally if the toxin is swallowed.

The only defense is to wear a protective mask and clothing during an attack. No specific immunotherapy or chemotherapy is available for use in the field.

Decontamination includes standard precautions for healthcare workers. Outer clothing should be removed and exposed skin should be decontaminated with soap and water. Eye exposure should be treated with copious saline irrigation. Once decontamination is complete, isolation is not required. Environmental decontamination requires the use of a hypochlorite solution under alkaline conditions such as 1 percent sodium hypochlorite and 0.1M NaOH with 1 hour contact time.

Nuclear Hazards

There was a time when many people feared a possible nuclear attack by the former Soviet Union. In response to federal civil defense recommendations, families built bomb shelters in their basements, and they stocked cellars with food and supplies in hope of surviving the nuclear fallout that was sure to follow. With the end of the cold war, the threat of thermonuclear war was lessened considerably. Now, a new type of threat is confronting society in which nuclear, biological, and chemical (NBC) weapons are being directed against civilian targets by terrorists for political and social gain.

It is important that First Responders (police, fire, emergency medical service [EMS], physicians, nurses, and disaster planners) understand radiation exposure and the consequences of conventional explosives to spread radioactive materials so that they may better respond to and treat victims of these events. During such a scenario, rescue should not be attempted until the incident scene is secured, routine monitoring is performed, and the responder is dressed in appropriate personal protective equipment (PPE).

To begin the discussion of radiological material and its potential use by terrorists, several terms must be defined and understood:

- **ATOM:** The smallest particle of an element that can exist either alone or in combination with another element; may be the source of vast potential energy.
- **NUCLEAR:** Of, relating to, or utilizing the positively charged central portion of an atom.
- **RADIATION:** Energy emitted as a result of the disintegration of the nucleus of an atom; this disintegration is also known as radioactive decay.
- **RADIOLOGICAL:** Of, or relating to, nuclear radiation.
- **RADIOACTIVE:** Capable of emitting nuclear radiation.

Radiation: In its simplest definition, radiation can be defined as either electromagnetic or particulate emissions of energy from the disintegration of the nucleus of an atom. This energy, when impacting on or passing through material, including people, can cause some form of reaction. This radiation is also referred to as ionizing radiation.

Radioactive material: Again, this is simply any material which is giving off some form of radiation.

Location of Radiological Material
Radiological material is used, transported, and stored in many locations around the United States. Among the locations where radiological material may be found are:

- Nuclear weapons storage facilities.
- Nuclear power plants.
- Government facilities (DOD, DOE).
- Hospitals and other medical facilities.
- Research and educational laboratories.
- Industrial manufacturing facilities.
- In transit.

In all cases, systems are required to be in place to ensure the safety of this material, such as special packaging requirements, special security, and special handling. These safeguards generally prove adequate; however, as radiological material is so widely used and transported, it is vulnerable to terrorist activity.

It is not inconceivable that a terrorist could obtain radioactive material from a medical facility or other activity and place it in a facility, more to cause an incident and scare a lot of people, rather than actually create casualties. This exact scenario occurred in Russia in November 1995. A 30-pound package containing explosives and Cesium, a radioactive material, was placed in a Moscow park by Chechan Separatists. In this instance, the device was located and rendered safe before it detonated. If it had detonated, it would have created a significant cleanup problem; Cs^{137} has a half-life of about 30 years.

Atomic Structure
There are three basic components of an atom.

- **Protons** reside in the nucleus of the atom, with the number of protons present determining the specific element (one proton present means that the atom is hydrogen, two protons present means the atom is helium, etc.). As the number of protons changes, the element changes. All protons have a positive (+) charge.
- **Electrons** orbit the nucleus of the atom and have almost no weight. All electrons have a negative (-) charge, equal in magnitude to the proton.
- **Neutrons** reside in the nucleus of the atom and have a weight similar to that of the proton and no electrical charge. While atoms of the same element must have the same number of protons, they may have different numbers of neutrons. Atoms of the same element, but with different numbers of neutrons, are called isotopes.

Ionizing Radiation
When ionizing radiation is absorbed by human bodies, it can cause changes to cells. Small amounts can be tolerated; larger amounts can be harmful. For purposes, this ionizing radiation can be classified as emissions of alpha particles, beta particles, and gamma rays.

Alpha particles are emitted from the nucleus of an atom and consist of 2 protons and 2 neutrons. They have a plus two (2^+) positive charge, limited range, and limited penetrating power. When an alpha particle is emitted from an atom, the releasing atom is changed. The atomic number decreases by two and the atomic weight decreases by approximately four. This new atom is normally radioactive. Alpha particles:

- Quickly lose energy and travel only one or two inches through air. They can be stopped by clothing or a piece of paper; and therefore, alpha emitters present only an inhalation or ingestion hazard.
- After intake, can be absorbed and retained by many organs, causing damage to the kidneys, liver, lungs, and bones in particular. Based on the chemical properties of the radioactive element involved, specific body organs may be targeted (radium targets bone structure, iodine targets the thyroid gland, etc.).
- Are characteristically emitted by elements such as plutonium, a nuclear weapon material and reactor fuel, and radium.

Beta particles are also emitted from the nucleus of an atom. They are similar to the electrons which orbit the nucleus and have a minus one (-1) negative charge, and depending on their energy, may have greater range and penetrating power than alpha particles. Atoms that emit beta particles also change, with their electrical charge increasing by +1, but their atomic weight remains approximately the same. In the most basic of theories, when a neutron breaks down, an electron is ejected and a proton is left in the nucleus. Beta particles:

- Lose energy more slowly than beta particles, and thus, travel farther in air (about ten feet).
- Can be stopped by material such as aluminum and other metals, plastic, and glass.
- Are more penetrating than alpha particles and, therefore, are considered a hazard to the eyes and bare skin (skin burns may result from high doses of beta radiation exposure).
- Beta emitters may be inhaled or ingested causing damage to internal body organs.

Gamma rays, as the name implies, are not particulate, but rather pure electromagnetic radiation, similar to x-rays but with a higher energy level. Gamma rays have long ranges and significant penetrating power. When an atom emits gamma radiation, there is no atomic change to the nucleus. Gamma radiation:

- Can easily travel several hundred feet through air.
- Can readily penetrate most materials (gamma is sometimes called penetrating radiation).
- Can be decreased or stopped by very dense materials such as lead, concrete, or steel.
- Are external radiation exposure hazards, traveling through the body and damaging tissues in their path.
- Are employed in commercial applications.

Neutrons:

- Can travel several hundred feet through air.
- Can be moderated by materials such as water, paraffin, or plastic.
- Are an external exposure hazard.
- Can be absorbed by stable atoms, causing them to become radioactive.
- Are employed in commercial applications.

Again, for purposes of this text, the concern is less with the mechanism of radiation action as with the hazard, the detection of it, and protection from it.

There are also nonionizing types of radiation. Examples of these are: fluorescent lights, lasers, and microwaves. In these examples, the radiation can cause tissue damage but does not cause molecular changes or ionization.

Examples of Radioactive Material
These are materials that emit ionizing radiation and are used in diagnosis (nuclear medicine), therapy (cancer treatment), industry (nondestructive testing), and for research purposes depending on the type of radiation emitted. A number of radioactive materials, including radioactive waste, are commercially shipped in specialized containers. Radioactive materials are chemically and physically similar to their nonradioactive counterparts. Radioactive materials behave in the body in a similar manner as their nonradioactive counterparts (for example, radioactive iodine behaves the same as stable, nonradioactive iodine).

Terrorists and Nuclear Material
Terrorist use of radioactive materials or a nuclear device constitutes a plausible threat. Such an incident could occur in one of five ways:

Simple Radiological Device: This is the deliberate act of spreading radioactive materials without the use of an explosive device. An example would be the placement of a high activity radioactive isotope in a public place exposing numerous individuals to various levels of radiation. Sealed sources could also be used to expose individuals near the source.

154

Two examples could be used in this context, although these were not terrorist events. They were the result of theft of sources. In the first case (Brazil), a hospital therapy source was stolen by two scrap dealers. The source, 1375 Ci of Cs^{137} was broken up and dispersed. The incident was not detected for 15 days. It resulted in 249 people being contaminated, four people dying, and 112,800 people requiring monitoring. The medical response and clean-up phases took several months to complete. In this case there was both an exposure and a contamination problem.

The second incident occurred in Mexico in 1983. A Co^{60} therapy device was stolen and broken apart by a young man in Juarez. A small vial containing some 6,000 small, pin-head sized Co^{60} sealed sources was opened, spilling some of the contents into a pickup truck bed. The device was sold for scrap and ended up in recycled steel. In January 1984, a transport truck carrying a load of contaminated steel took a wrong turn into Los Alamos National Laboratory and set off gamma alarms, thus the accident was discovered. Ten persons were overexposed in this accident, most of whom worked in or visited the scrap yard. Nobody was contaminated in the accident.

Radiological Dispersal: A radiological dispersal device does not cause a nuclear reaction. Such a device is formed by combining an explosive agent (TNT or a plastic explosive) with radioactive materials that may have been stolen, for example, from a hospital or local industry. A similar type of event could also occur from a failed nuclear weapon detonation. Under these circumstances, only the conventional component of the bomb explodes, rather than a nuclear reaction, causing a widespread release of plutonium. In either case, the initial explosion kills or injures those closest to the bomb, while the radioactive substances remain to expose and contaminate survivors and emergency responders.

Reactor: Most people are aware of the reactor accidents of Three-Mile Island and Chernobyl. The accident at Chernobyl was caused as the result of approximately eight safety systems being bypassed. The experiment being carried out at the time resulted in the melt-down of the core and also a severe explosion from the hydrogen bubble formed, resulting in the roof of the reactor being blown off and serious widespread contamination of the vast areas of land. This accident caused the death of 28 individuals from acute radiation injury.

In the Western World, probability of terrorism involving a reactor is low. This is due to the high security surrounding a reactor together with the safety systems incorporated into the reactor. There is extensive shielding around a reactor, therefore, a significant amount of explosives would be required to breach this containment. This is a low probability event.

Improvised Nuclear Device (IND): This is any device designed to cause a nuclear detonation. This type of device, if successfully detonated, would cause widespread damage on the scale of Hiroshima and Nagasaki with the release of gamma rays, neutrons, and radioactive fallout. Construction of such a device to produce a nuclear detonation would be difficult as it is not easy to get the weapon to detonate correctly. Realistically, at best, a terrorist might be able to achieve a partial yield producing reduced effects of that caused by a nuclear weapon. In some cases only the conventional high explosives in the IND will detonate, resulting in environmental contamination with plutonium or uranium. In this event, the IND is effectively a radiological dispersal device.

The Federal Bureau of Investigation (FBI) feels that it is unlikely that terrorists will have the engineering sophistication and access to high-grade nuclear materials that are required to build such a device, but any detonation of an improvised or stolen device would generate high levels of radiation.

Nuclear Weapon: The probability of stealing a nuclear weapon in the western world is very remote because of the high security surrounding these devices. However, a Russian general has stated publicly that 50 to 100 one-kiloton suitcase nuclear weapons are unaccounted for in the former Soviet Union.

Consider the consequences of a one kiloton yield; the following would occur within one minute around the point of ground zero:
- Blast range would reach a distance of approximately 400 yards.
- Thermal radiation would reach the same distance as the blast.
- Nuclear radiation (i.e., gamma and neutron) would reach approximately half a mile.
- The radioactive fallout could produce very high exposure rates, up to half a mile.
- The added factor of the electromagnetic pulse, which only applies to high aerial bursts (several kilometers), would result in damage to electronic equipment.

As the size of the weapon increases, the effects encompass a greater distance. Individuals close enough to a nuclear explosion will be killed from the blast wave, thermal pulse, or the fires ignited from the explosion. Most survivors in the vicinity of the explosion will quickly become symptomatic from the radiation exposure; many of them will also suffer from significant deceleration injuries and burns.

Exposure and Contamination
Exposure to radiation does not indicate that radioactive contamination has necessarily occurred.

The difference between exposure and contamination may be demonstrated by the analogy of a skunk's odor. If the skunk sprays and anyone smells the odor, he has been exposed. If the skunk sprays someone, contamination has occurred.

Routinely Occurring Radiation Exposure
Radiation exposure occurs routinely from the following:
- External terrestrial objects such as rocks containing radium and thorium.
- External cosmic sources such as the sun.
- Naturally occurring radio nuclides into the body (K^{40}, C^{14}, etc.).
- Radio nuclides that are inhaled, such as radon.
- Medical diagnostic procedures, such as X-rays and nuclear medicine scans.
- Consumer products such as smoke detectors.

Basic Radiation Units of Measurement
To quantify amounts of radiation exposure in terms of biological effect, the term rem (or millirem) is used. It has a specific definition, but the concern here is with the level of exposure rather than a definition.

rad = radiation absorbed dose (deposition of 100 ergs of radiation energy per gram of absorbed material)

$$RBE = relative\ biological\ effectiveness$$
$$rem = (rad)(RBE)$$
$$rem = roentgen\ equivalent\ in\ man$$

Common Radiation Exposures
This table reflects naturally occurring radiation doses (and doses received during normal activities) to provide a point of reference and for comparison. The threshold for any real consequences begins around 200 rem. The LD_{50} is around 450 rem.

The average annual radiation exposure has been calculated as:

Naturally occurring	295 mrem
Medical	52 mrem
Consumer products	10 mrem
Other	3 mrem
Total	**360 mrem**

Health Risks During an Incident

The three radiation concerns at an incident involve whole body exposure, intake of radioactive material (through the respiratory and digestive tracts), and contamination by radioactive material. Incidents involving either an explosion or fire will elevate the potential for intake or contamination due to the spreading of the radioactive material in the form of small fragments (dust) or smoke.

Risk depends upon several factors:

- The dose (total amount of radiation received); the larger the dose received, the greater the health risk becomes.
- The dose rate (the length of time over which the dose is received); dose rate exposures are categorized as follows:
  - **Acute:** A large dose occurring over a short period of time. Acute exposures normally pose a high health risk with symptoms occurring within hours or days. Symptoms of acute radiation exposure are burns of the skin, vomiting, and indigestion.
  - **Chronic:** Small doses occurring over a long period of time. Chronic exposures normally pose a smaller health risk with symptoms (tumors, etc.) delayed for years.

As previously discussed, alpha and beta emitters generally pose only internal exposure hazards. Gamma radiation, however, poses an external hazard for a distance of hundreds of feet.

Protection

The radiation exposure received will depend on the type and strength of the radiation source. This exposure can be mitigated by the effective use of multiple resources:

Time

The radiation dose is reduced in proportion to reduction of exposure time. For example, if exposed to a radioactive source emitting a dose rate of 100 mrem per hour, an exposure time of 15 minutes will produce a total radiation dose of 25 mrem.

Distance

Distance is also critical for reducing radiation exposure dose. While alpha particles only travel a little over an inch in air, and beta particles will travel only a few yards in air, gamma rays will travel extensive distances. As a result, gamma rays pose the greatest threat of exposure, but responders will receive a smaller dose of radiation the farther away they are from the source. In the case of gamma rays, the intensity decreases in proportion to the square of the distance. The US Department of Energy (DOE) recommends personnel not required for response be kept 2,000 feet from the radioactive source.

Shielding

Radiation can also be mitigated, or partially mitigated, by various materials. Alpha radiation is stopped by a sheet of paper, beta radiation is stopped by aluminum foil or clothing, and gamma rays are only reduced by dense materials such as lead or earth.

- Alpha travels approximately 1-1.5 inches in air and cannot penetrate unbroken skin or paper.
- Beta travels approximately 10 feet in air and can penetrate a few millimeters of tissue. It can be stopped by light layers of clothing, aluminum foil, or an average book (approx. 1-1.5 inches thick).
- Gamma travels indefinitely in air and can penetrate the human body. Intensity is reduced by heavy, dense materials such as steel, concrete, earth, or lead.

Rescue, Evaluation, and Treatment

Prior to initiating plans for rescue, the following should be considered when responding to any incident potentially involving radioactive materials:

- If a radioactive material is known or suspected to have been released, it should be assumed that all property and personnel are contaminated. Approach to the site should be made with caution, surveying for evidence of hazardous materials. Position personnel and vehicles at a distance of 150 feet upwind from the site (2,000 feet or more in the case of a nuclear explosion).
- The identification of the radioactive material and the extent of both the exposure/contamination will require specialized detection devices and outside assistance, such as Hazardous Material Response Teams (HMRTs), state radiological health officials, Radiological Safety Officers (RSOs), Radiological Assistance Program (RAP), etc. This should not be considered a primary responsibility of EMS personnel. However, it is desirable that all EMS personnel be equipped with personal dosimeters which measure their level of exposure. The extent of their exposure can be determined at a later date.
- EMS personnel should not enter the area without personal protection, including a respirator or high-efficiency particulate air (HEPA) filter mask, eye protection, and gloves.

Check for Presence of Radioactive Contamination

Checking for radioactive contamination should be done prior to any rescue and decontamination efforts. Identification of local resources prior to the event will enable proper resource utilization at the time of the release. Many hospitals will have an RSO who can assist in the determination of scene contamination. State and county emergency management officials may assist in the identification of local experts. These experts should be identified in the planning process.

Regardless of who is tasked with surveying for radioactive contamination, it must be remembered that different measuring devices respond to different types of radiation. Most available survey meters can measure beta and gamma radiation; some have a shield which can screen out beta and measure gamma only.

Several detection devices might be needed to protect against inadvertent spread of contamination after a nuclear terrorism incident. Emergency treatment areas, triage or reception areas, and decontamination dirty dump areas can be monitored to help assess the level of hazard and efficacy of decontamination. Monitoring will not be limited to patients; First Responders will also require screening if they have worked in a potentially contaminated area or handled patients or equipment from one.

Establish a Hot Line and Decontamination Area

A hot line should be established that will separate the clean and contaminated sides of the release area for all responding personnel. If the identity of the radioactive material is unknown, the limits of the contamination must be found (using survey meters) so that a hot line and clean area can be established. A decontamination area should also be set up, preferably upwind and upgrade (uphill) from the release area near the treatment stations. While the hotline is being established, attention to accident victims should begin.

Triage

Medical sorting, or triage, is the key to effectively managing large numbers of sick and wounded. Successful triage is built on sorting victims in an orderly, timely, and efficient manner that maximizes existing resources. It includes the immediate classification of patients according to type, seriousness of the injury, and the likelihood of survival. Triage also includes the establishment of priorities for treatment and evacuation to ensure that the medical resources available benefit the largest number of people.

The principles of triage in a radiological event are similar to a hazardous materials incident or accident scene. Victims are classified with regard to the need for treatment and are categorized as requiring minimal treatment, immediate care, delayed care, or as expectant. Since the degree of radiation injury may not be initially apparent, triage criteria will need to be based on conventional injuries and complaints. The triage method used will vary according to local jurisdictions and their standard operating procedures (SOPs).

Victims who have received very high doses of radiation from a gamma or neutron source might exhibit signs and symptoms that would indicate their level of exposure. Neurologic signs such as confusion or delirium indicate a lethal dosage of radiation. Other signs of lethal radiation injury include high fever, profuse vomiting, and bloody diarrhea within 2 hours of exposure (nearly 100 percent mortality).

Limit Further Radiation Exposure

The most important part of victim rescue is removing them from the exposure area. Survival depends not only on the dose received, but also how long the individual is exposed to the source. During victim rescue, a significant way to reduce the responders' level of radiation exposure is to limit the amount of time spent in the hazardous environment. However, there may be times when you must move a patient quickly before a complete assessment can be accomplished. This may be especially true in a terrorist event when the scene is hazardous. Other considerations include patient repositioning or gaining access to other injured individuals. Quickly assessing and removing the victim from the area may be the only safe approach. In this case, use rapid immobilization and techniques such as cradle carry, shoulder drag, foot drag, blanket drag, one-rescuer assist, etc. Only life-saving rescue actions should be undertaken in a high radiation area, as determined by radiological experts.

Illness and Injury Treatment

Other associated illnesses and injuries should be treated according to Basic Life Support (BLS) and Basic Trauma Life Support (BTLS). Treatment (including lifesaving procedures) should not be delayed for decontamination, although treatment might be delayed to ensure the safety of the first responders. Expose wounds and cover them with a sterile dressing.

Decontamination

If evidence of contamination is detected or suspected and the patient's condition permits, the victim can be decontaminated at the scene. Pre-hospital personnel should be dressed in appropriate PPE (dictated by the incident commander or radiation safety officer [RSO]) before decontaminating the patient. The victim's clothing and personal items should be removed and placed in a labeled plastic bag. Ideally, a soap and water shower should be provided, washing from head to toe, and all of the runoff gathered into a collection pool or container. Cotton-tip swabs can be used to remove contamination from nostrils and external ear canals; however, this should not be done in the field in most cases because careful taking of nasal swabs and their measurement by a trained RSO or health physicist is used to determine how much contamination the victim may have inhaled. After showering, the victim should be re-surveyed and checked for continued presence of radioactive contamination. If present, the decontamination procedure should be repeated. This decontamination procedure is also appropriate for those victims who may be contaminated with both radioactive substances and hazardous materials (including chemical agents).

If the patient is unstable, merely removing his/her clothing will eliminate 80 percent of the contamination. After removing the clothing, wrap the patient in a clean sheet to help contain any remaining contamination. This simple procedure will allow safe and expeditious transport to an emergency department (ED) for further assessment, stabilization, and definitive decontamination.

Patient Transportation

Ideally, a clean ambulance that has not been in the contamination area should transport the accident victim. The patient should be packaged for transport by wrapping them with a blanket or sheet to minimize the spread of contamination and possible contamination of EMS personnel. EMS personnel caring for the patient should follow routine universal precautions. Hospitals should be notified of the patient transport as discussed above. The EMS vehicle and crew should not return to regular service until the ambulance, personnel, and equipment have undergone monitoring and necessary decontamination by the RSO.

Unlike many hazardous materials that possess certain properties which can alert the responder to over-exposures (odor, taste, irritation), radiation has no such warning properties. Preventing the radioactive material from entering the body or protecting against external radiation is the best protection.

Incendiary Devices and Reactions

Incendiary devices are intended to start fires. They range from military weapons like napalm and fougasse to the tools used by arsonists. They may be relatively sophisticated or very crude. This section discusses the types of incendiary devices and incendiary reactions a responder may encounter in an incident involving criminal or terrorist activity. It is important to note that information on incendiary devices and booby traps is freely available on the Internet and terrorist manuals seized both from foreign and domestic groups contain specific instructions for constructing such devices. Incendiary booby traps have been found not only in war zones such as Afghanistan, Palestine, and Bosnia, but also at militia compounds and illegal drug laboratories in the United States.

Chemical Incendiaries

White Phosphorus

Elemental phosphorus does not exist free in nature but can be manufactured from phosphate rock. Elemental phosphorus can exist in several forms referred to by the color of the material (white, yellow, and red). White phosphorus (P_4) is a waxy solid that ignites spontaneously in air, yielding dense clouds of toxic white smoke containing phosphorus compounds. This has been used on the battlefield both as an incendiary to attack enemy troops and positions and also for smokescreens and signals. White phosphorus munitions range from air-dropped bombs and artillery shells to hand grenades. In Vietnam, white phosphorus munitions were called Willie Peter or Willie Pete. White phosphorus grenades burn at about 2000°C and throw burning phosphorus particles considerable distances. Phosphorus particles imbedded in flesh will reignite causing painful burns.

160

White phosphorus can be stored for short periods under water but reacts slowly with water to make toxic phosphine gas (PH_3). White phosphorus ignites spontaneously in air above 80°F and the resulting fire cannot be suppressed with normal fire hoses. The smoke from burning white phosphorus is intensely irritating and is converted to phosphoric acid in the lungs and on contact with mucous membranes. Although white phosphorus is very toxic, the toxicity of the element and the phosphorus oxides in the smoke are not the reason for use and are incidental to the use as incendiaries and smokescreens.

When phosphorus is burned in air, the product is the highly hygroscopic white solid P_4O_{10} (commonly called phosphorus pentoxide, P_2O_5); this is the P(V) oxide. In a limited supply of air the P(III) oxide, P_4O_6 (called phosphorus trioxide) contaminated with unreacted phosphorus is obtained. The oxides both react with water to form acids:

$$P_4O_6 + 6H_2O \rightarrow 4H_3PO_3 \text{ phosphorous acid}$$
$$P_4O_{10} + 2H_2O \rightarrow 4HPO_3 \text{ metaphosphoric acid}$$
$$P_4O_{10} + 6H_2O \rightarrow 4H_3PO_4 \text{ orthophosphoric acid}$$

Thermite Incendiaries-Thermate
The thermite reaction is an oxidation reduction reaction where aluminum powder and iron oxide react to give aluminum oxide and molten iron metal.

$$Fe_2O_3 + 2 \text{ Al} \rightarrow Al_2O_3 + 2 \text{ Fe}$$

This reaction generates temperatures of approximately 4000°F and the molten iron is capable of burning a hole through steel plate. This reaction was used in the late 19th and early 20th centuries to produce molten iron for welding uses such as joining together railroad rails.

Normally this reaction requires some oxidizer or fuse to start. Laboratory demonstrations typically use magnesium ribbon as a fuse to start the reaction. Arsonists have used this reaction with different time-delay initiators or chemical reactions to start the process. The ingredients for the thermite reaction can be found in most high school and college laboratories and can easily be purchased in bulk from chemical supply houses. Information on the construction of thermite devices is freely available on the Internet.

For military applications, a binder and/or additional oxidizers are added to create thermate. A classic example is the thermate grenade used by the US military which consists of a mixture of aluminum powder, iron oxide, and potassium nitrate. This is ignited with the standard grenade fuse and burns at greater than 4000°F, producing molten iron that fuses together metal parts, burns through steel, and deforms metal structural features. This is not generally used as an anti-personnel weapon but is used to render equipment, vehicles, and artillery inoperable.

An important point to note is that thermite and thermate reactions and incendiaries cannot be suppressed with normal fire fighting techniques. Water sprayed on the molten metal can lead to the generation of hydrogen gas and a violent gas explosion.

NAPALM: The name given to a group of gelled gasoline and fuel-oil mixtures that are used for a number of incendiary purposes ranging from anti-personnel bombs to the fuel in flame-throwers. The addition of gelling agents to the hydrocarbon fuel allows changes to the physical properties of the mixture such that the burning mixture sticks to objects and people and becomes more destructive than the unmodified fuel.

The original napalm was a mixture of gasoline, palmitic acid soap, and napthenic acid soap. (**Na**phthenic + **Palm**itic = napalm). The different recipes for making napalm and instructions for making amateur napalm bombs and flame-throwers are available on the Internet and in numerous pamphlets and in anarchist, terrorist, or soldier-of-fortune publications. An improvised napalm made from gasoline and detergent has been used in a number of terrorist attacks around the world.

US military incendiaries use a variation of napalm containing gasoline, benzene, and polystyrene.

FOUGASSE OR "FOU GAS": A particularly deadly area weapon or booby trap is the use of fougasse. This is basically a device for throwing flaming fuel oil or gasoline as a sheet of flame over a large area as an anti-personnel weapon. In its simplest form, this is a drum of fuel oil or gasoline with an explosive charge wired to the bottom and pointed in a specific direction. When the explosion is triggered, it throws burning fuel over a large area igniting anything flammable. This was used extensively as an anti-personnel perimeter defense in Vietnam but could just as easily be done anywhere fuel oil or flammable liquids are stored.

FUEL-AIR BOMBS (Military and Nonmilitary): Fuel-air bombs have been used by the military of a number of countries. The US has used them in Vietnam, Kosovo, Iraq, and Afghanistan. The typical fuel-air explosive consists of a container for fuel and two explosives. The first explosive opens the fuel canister and vaporizes the fuel that the second explosive then ignites in the air. This is equivalent to an unconfined vapor cloud explosion or dust explosion which is encountered in nonmilitary catastrophes. The resulting explosion of burning gases causes a searing fireball followed by a massive blast wave. Pressures at the center of the explosion can reach 427 psi (about twice what conventional explosives typically generate) and temperatures at the center of the blast are between 2500° and 3000°C. Outside of the gas cloud the blast wave travels at over 9,800 feet/second generating a vacuum behind the wave front that pulls loose objects into the advancing explosion front. The resulting explosion is devastating and both American and Russian assessments consider these bombs to be equivalent to small tactical nuclear weapons in their devastating power without the drawback of residual radiation. Those who are not killed outright by the blast typically suffer severe burns and blunt force trauma from the shock wave.

A similar nonmilitary application of the same principle has been used by Palestinian guerillas and in other recent civil war conflicts as well as in the US. A simple fuel-air explosive can be made from a propane cylinder and two explosives. Even a single relatively low-power explosive device can rupture and ignite a propane cylinder from a household barbecue, causing a powerful fireball with a massive blast area. These types of bombs and booby traps have been found in such settings as the Columbine High School massacre, in white supremacist standoffs, and in illegal drug laboratories.

INCENDIARY CHEMICAL REACTIONS: These are used by arsonists. There are a number of chemical reactions that have been used by arsonists because they are pyrophoric (i.e., they spontaneously ignite), but usually there is some time delay between mixing the chemicals and the beginning of the fire. Arsonists typically use these reactions to start a fire and surround the reaction with flammable materials that will be ignited by the flame generated by the reaction.

SWIMMING POOL CHLORINE AND BRAKE FLUID: Swimming pool chlorine or HTH is a dry calcium hydroxide-calcium hypochlorite mixture. It is a strong oxidizer that liberates chlorine when mixed with water.

$$Ca(OCl)_2 \text{ in water} \rightarrow Ca^{2+} + Cl_2 + O_2$$

There are two general kinds of brake fluid available in the US. Several groups of brake fluid are based on ethylene glycol/polyethylene glycol/glycol ether chemistry and another is a silicone-based fluid. Both types

162

of brake fluid will react with calcium hypochlorite, causing rapid oxidation leading to flame.

$$Ca(OCl)_2 + brake\ fluid \rightarrow FIRE!!$$

Since the mixture contains its own oxidizer, the standard fire fighting technique of blocking oxygen to smother the fire does not work. These fires are difficult to extinguish until the reaction is complete. After the reaction is complete, these fires are basically the secondary fires started in flammable or combustible materials surrounding the reaction and these fires can be extinguished by "normal" fire fighting techniques.

In a typical arson case using this chemistry, the arsonist places the calcium hypochlorite tablets or powder in the bottom of a container and places paper or cloth towels on top of the chemical. Brake fluid is then poured on top of the cloth or paper. The time delay for this reaction to ignite depends on the length of time it takes for the brake fluid to soak down to the hypochlorite, which in turn depends on the number of towels used.

POTASSIUM PERMANGANATE AND GLYCERIN: Potassium permanganate is another powerful oxidizer that reacts with combustible materials generating heat and flame. The classic reaction which has been used by some arsonists is to pour glycerin into a hollow formed in the permanganate. This reaction may be slow to start and anhydrous glycerin or glycerin with a very low water content may take up to 10 minutes to ignite. (This is an unusual case where adding a few drops of water to the reaction will actually cause the reaction and resulting fire to be quicker!)

$$14KMnO_4 + 4C_3H_5(OH)_3 \rightarrow 7K_2CO_3 + 7Mn_2O_3 + 5CO_2 + 16H_2O + FIRE$$

This reaction is used as the igniter to start the thermite reaction discussed earlier in this chapter.

This reaction has also been used to start fires in places such as clothing stores where there is a lot of combustible material. An envelope is prepared by putting potassium permanganate in the corner of the envelope and adding a glycerin-based hair cream or hand cream into the opposite end of the envelope. The envelope is then placed upright in the pocket of clothing on a rack where the creamy glycerin-based gel slowly flows down to mix with the permanganate. Depending on the materials chosen, this leads to a fire some minutes later.

POTASSIUM CHLORATE, SUGAR, AND SULFURIC ACID: The exact chemistry of the reaction between potassium chlorate ($KClO_3$), sugar, and sulfuric acid is not precisely known. It is known that the reaction of chlorate and acid generates chloric acid ($HClO_3$) which is an explosive gas and a powerful oxidizer that reacts with many organics to generate flames.

$$KClO_3 + H_2SO_4 \rightarrow HClO_3$$
$$HClO_3 + Organics \rightarrow FIRE!!$$

This reaction has been used in a number of arson cases and can also be used as a booby trap by mixing gasoline and sulfuric acid in a bottle and then propping the bottle where it will be knocked into a pile of the potassium chlorate and sugar mixture. The resulting fire accelerated by the gasoline can be violent.

In another arson situation the acid is placed in a test-tube or bottle sealed with a cork stopper and the bottle mouth and cork are wrapped with duct tape or masking tape. The bottle is then laid down in the mixture of potassium chlorate and sugar. The resulting fire occurs when the acid eats its way through the tape and drops into the mixture. Only one drop is needed to catalyze the reaction. In the absence of acid, the potassium chlorate-sugar mixture is stable for several weeks.

FIRE LIQUID-WHITE PHOSPHORUS IN CARBON DISULFIDE OR BENZENE: White phosphorus and yellow phosphorus are pyrophoric and react violently with oxygen in the air. Phosphorus is also quite soluble in carbon disulfide and other organic solvents like benzene. These solutions are stable for days if air is excluded. In an arson event the solution of phosphorus is poured onto a combustible material such as cloth rags. When the solvent evaporates, it leaves behind a coating of finely divided elemental phosphorus which bursts into flames igniting the combustible material. The choice of solvent (carbon disulfide versus benzene versus toluene or xylene) determines how fast this evaporation occurs and provides the arsonist with time to leave the scene before the fire starts.

SODIUM PEROXIDE AND ALUMINUM POWDER: This is an arson technique which allows a fire to be started days or weeks after the arson is set up. Sodium peroxide powder and aluminum powder may be mixed and are stable for periods of weeks in the absence of water. The presence of water causes a violent pyrophoric reaction which throws burning aluminum in every direction, igniting any oxidizable or organic material present.

$$Na_2O_2 + 2Al + 3H_2O \rightarrow 2NaOH + Al_2O_3 + 2H_2 \text{ (balanced)}$$

This arson technique typically is done by placing the sodium peroxide-aluminum mixture on top of flammable or combustible material (such as wooden crates in a warehouse) where rain will likely leak through the roof onto the mixture. Depending on the weather, the arsonist could be in a different state or country when the fire occurred.

METALLIC POTASSIUM OR METALLIC SODIUM: Both metallic potassium and metallic sodium react violently with water to generate flammable hydrogen gas and heat. The heat of reaction is usually enough to cause the hydrogen to ignite.

$$K + H_2O \rightarrow KOH + \tfrac{1}{2}H_2 + \text{Heat and Flame}$$
$$Na + H_2O \rightarrow NaOH + \tfrac{1}{2}H_2 + \text{Heat and Flame}$$

Arson fires have been started by cutting up small pieces of the metal and placing them some place where they will get wet. This is a less "reliable" arson technique since these metals tend to oxidize slowly in the air and become nonreactive if not exposed to water in a relatively short time (days).

Chemical Hazards

Among lethal chemical warfare (CW) agents, the nerve agents have had an entirely dominant role since World War II. Nerve agents acquired their name because they affect the transmission of nerve impulses in the nervous system. All nerve agents belong chemically to the group of organo-phosphorus compounds. They are stable and easily dispersed, highly toxic, and have rapid effects both when absorbed through the skin and via respiration. Nerve agents can be manufactured by means of fairly simple chemical techniques. The raw materials are inexpensive and generally readily available.

It was not until the early 1930s that German chemists observed that organo-phosphorus compounds could be poisonous. In 1934, Dr. Gerhard Schrader, a chemist at IG Farben, was given the task of developing a pesticide. Two years later a phosphorus compound with extremely high toxicity was produced for the first time. According to contemporary regulations, discoveries with military implications had to be reported to

164

the military authorities, which was also done with Schrader's discovery. This phosphorus compound, given the name tabun, was the first of the substances later referred to as nerve agents.

A factory for production of the new CW agent was built and a total of 12,000 tons of tabun was produced during the years 1942-1945. At the end of the war, the Allies seized large quantities of this nerve agent. Up to the end of the war, Schrader and his co-workers synthesized about 2,000 new organo-phosphorus compounds, including sarin (1938). The third of the classic nerve agents, soman, was first produced in 1944. These three nerve agents are known as G-agents in the American nomenclature. The manufacture of sarin never started properly, and up to 1945 only about 1,000 pounds of this nerve agent was produced in a pilot plant.

Immediately after the war, research was mainly concentrated on studies of the mechanisms of the nerve agents in order to discover more effective forms of protection against these new CW agents. The results of these efforts led, however, not only to better forms of protection but also to new types of agents closely related to the earlier ones.

By the mid-1950's a group of more stable nerve agents had been developed, known as the V-agents in the American nomenclature. They are approximately ten-fold more poisonous than sarin and are thus among the most toxic substances ever synthesized.

The first publication of these substances appeared in 1955. The authors, R. Ghosh and J. F. Newman, described one of the substances, known as amiton, as being particularly effective against mites. At this time, intensive research was being devoted to the organo-phosphorus insecticides both in Europe and in the United States. At least three chemical firms appear to have independently discovered the remarkable toxicity of these phosphorus compounds during the years 1952-53. Surprisingly enough, some of these substances were available on the market as pesticides. Nonetheless, they were soon withdrawn owing to their considerable toxicity to mammals also.

In the United States, the choice fell in 1958 on a substance known by its code name VX as suitable as a CW agent of persistent type. Full-scale production of VX started in April 1961 but its structure was not published until 1972.

Terrorist Use of Chemicals
The use of chemical warfare agents by terrorists against US civilians represents a national threat. While the US government prepares teams and countermeasures to deal with this threat, local communities must develop their own regional plans, protocols, and resources to care for the victims of a chemical terrorist attack. Communities must develop protective systems that will enable first responders to effectively perform decontamination in the field, to treat patients, and to protect against cross-contamination.

On June 27, 1994, the Aum Shinrikyo, a well-funded Japanese religious cult, initiated the use of chemical warfare agent terrorism in Japan. The nerve agent GB, or sarin, was manufactured in a secret facility in Japan and was first released in Matsumoto, Japan with about 280 casualties and 7 deaths. Nine months later, on March 20, 1995, sarin was released in five separate subway cars in downtown Tokyo. There were 12 deaths, hundreds injured (a few dozen seriously), and 5,500 who sought medical care. Over 80 percent of those found their own transportation to the medical facilities. One hundred thirty-two of the first responders were injured, a few of the hospital staff suffered cross-contamination from the chemical, and a few of the responders required admission to hospitals. Knowledge about the effects of chemical agents, how to protect oneself, and how to decontaminate and treat victims is particularly important.

Chemical warfare agents are hazardous chemicals that have been designed for use by the military to irritate, incapacitate, injure, or kill. Some have local effects on the eyes, skin, or airways (crowd-control agents, chlorine), some have only systemic effects (hydrogen cyanide), and some have both (nerve agents and vesicants).

Each of the chemical agents to be discussed is a chemical compound, and, therefore, has characteristics and behaves in ways that are understandable and predictable. The more that is known about these agents and their characteristics, the better equipped responders will be to mitigate their effects.

Physical Properties
If the agent and the temperature conditions that exist are known, then the physical state of the agent can be known. For example, mustard agent freezes at approximately 57°F; therefore, its use in a colder climate should not be anticipated (or if used, a significant vapor hazard would not be expected). Likewise, many agents have very low boiling points, so they would be expected to be in a gaseous state, presenting an inhalation threat, but not lingering in the area for any significant length of time.

Vapor density can also have an effect on persistency. Agents which are heavier than air will tend to settle in low spots where they will linger (persist) longer than if in an open area.

For our purposes, substances with high vapor pressures will evaporate more rapidly than those with low vapor pressures.

Volatility and persistency are directly related to vapor pressure and used to express how rapidly an agent will evaporate, and thus dissipate.

The more volatile an agent, the more rapidly it will evaporate. Most agents are initially disseminated as liquids. In many cases, the liquid itself is a threat by absorption through the skin. After dissemination, most agents begin to evaporate, creating a vapor hazard.

For comparison with chemical agents:

$$\text{Vapor Pressure of } H_2O \text{ at } 25°C = 23.7mm\ Hg$$
$$\text{Volatility of } H_2O \text{ at } 25°C = 22,933\ mg/m^3$$

The term "persistency" is a relative term, as there is no precise definition. Generally, agents which will evaporate within a few minutes are considered nonpersistent. Those that will evaporate in a period of hours are considered semi-persistent. Those that remain for longer periods of time (days) are considered persistent.

Volatility is the weight of vapor present in a unit volume of air, under equilibrium conditions, at a specified temperature. It is a measure of how much material (agent) evaporates under given conditions. The volatility depends on vapor pressure. It varies directly with temperature. We express volatility as milligrams of vapor per cubic meter (mg/m^3).

More than the vapor pressure or volatility is required to judge the effectiveness of a chemical agent, however. The degree of toxicity of the agent and its physiological action are also required. A highly toxic chemical agent of relatively low volatility, such as the nerve agent tabun (GA), may be far more lethal than a less toxic chemical agent of much higher volatility, such as the choking agent phosgene (CG).

Chemical Properties
Hydrolysis is the term used to indicate the reaction of a substance with water and the associated decomposition that occurs. Hydrolysis is important for understanding how some agents affect us biologically and is also important with respect to decontamination. The rate of hydrolysis indicates how fast the decomposition process occurs.

Hydrolysis Products: Following a reaction between the agent and water, other compounds will be produced. These products are the hydrolysis products.

Reaction with Metals: Many chemical agents will react with metals causing corrosion or damage.

Physiological Properties

Rate of Detoxification: The rate of detoxification refers to the speed with which the body is able to counteract the effects of a poisonous substance. Many chemical agents are essentially cumulative in their effects and will cause recurring effects throughout the remainder of an individual's life because the human body detoxifies them very slowly or not at all.

Detoxification relates to the body processes of absorption, distribution, metabolism, and elimination. Not all agents are detoxified or metabolized.

Rate of Action: The rate of action of a chemical agent is the rate at which the body reacts to, or is affected by, that agent.

Toxicity: Toxicity is related to the dose required per unit of weight to cause effects on the body. Toxicity is usually expressed in terms of incapacitating dosage or lethal dosage.

Routes of Entry

Routes (or portals) of Entry: Describes how an agent gets into the body.
Most agents are disseminated as aerosols or gases and enter the body through the respiratory tract; however, some liquid agents enter via skin contact. In some instances, if the vapor concentration is high enough or the vapor exposure long enough, vapors can penetrate the skin and cause the same effects as skin contact with liquid agent.

The eyes are of particular concern, because they are especially sensitive to a number of agents. Some agents may enter the body by ingestion of contaminated food or liquid. In two instances, assassins have injected chemical agents into their victims.

Nomenclature, Military Designation and CAS Numbers
Each chemical agent is a chemical compound made of specific elements. All have scientific names and formulas which describe their chemical composition, but of interest are the common names they have been given and the shorthand designations. These are important for three reasons:
- Many of the military detectors refer to these shorthand designations.
- Many HAZMAT technicians and other technical personnel, especially military response teams, will be using these symbols.
- They are much easier to remember.

Both the common name and symbol of specific individual agents are given. Additionally, the agents have all been assigned CAS numbers (Chemical Abstract Service). Additional HAZMAT reference data can be acquired by using the CAS numbers.

Weather

Weather conditions have a significant effect on the behavior of chemical agents. Temperature, wind speed and direction, humidity, and air stability all influence how long an agent will remain in an area. To a degree, the weather conditions also influence how vulnerable individuals are, because they affect persistency. The longer an agent remains in an area, the longer an unprotected individual is exposed to its effects. Some specific conditions are as follows:

- A lapse or unstable air stability condition provides the least effective area coverage, as the agent cloud rises above people.
- The inversion air stability condition is optimal, as it keeps the agent near the ground.
- The most effective wind speed to provide the largest area coverage is 6-10 miles per hour.

Toxicity

Each of the agents to be discussed were designated as militarily significant because of their toxicity. Through extrapolation from animal tests, toxicities for each of the agents have been determined. While toxicity is a relative figure and will vary, it will provide an idea of how much agent it takes to kill or incapacitate.

Toxicity is normally expressed as a concentration of agent in parts per million (ppm), or milligrams (mg) of agent per cubic meter (m^3). This toxicity is also expressed based on what effect is being described: LC_{50} means the lethal concentration that would kill 50 percent of the exposed population; IC_{50} means the incapacitating concentration that would incapacitate 50 percent of the exposed population.

When toxicity is expressed considering time, then the expression would be LCt_{50} or ICt_{50} and expressed as mg-min/m^3,or parts per million (ppm) based on a specific time of exposure (e.g., 1 minute, 30 minutes, etc.).

ICt_{50} and LCt_{50} for people are based on a 154 lb (70 kg) man, typically breathing at a rate of 15 liters per minute.

Classes of Chemical Agents

The military has classified chemical agents according to how they affect individuals, initially as either toxic or incapacitating, and then further by their specific actions on the individual.

Note that there are five categories of toxic agents:

- Choking
- Blood
- Blister
- Nerve
- Crowd-control

Under each category are the individual symbols for the agents to be discussed. There are many more agents, but these are considered the most likely ones a terrorist might employ.

Although there may be specific incapacitating agents in various national inventories, they are not covered in this text because their use by a terrorist is improbable.

Choking Agents

Choking agents were first used during World War I with notable effectiveness. There are two choking agents that will be mentioned: phosgene (CG) and chlorine (CL). Both of these agents have various industrial uses and are shipped as liquids daily throughout the US. Upon release, they evaporate rapidly–becoming nonpersistent gases, and therefore, inhalation threats.

Both have recognizable odors: phosgene smells like newly mown hay and chlorine smells like a swimming pool. The rate of action in high concentrations is rapid; but in lower concentrations, other than the irritating smell, the symptoms might be delayed for several hours.

Symptoms include coughing, choking or gagging, and tightness in the chest. As the agent is inhaled, it irritates the respiratory tract, starting with the trachea and continuing down into the lungs.

These agents hydrolyze with mucous secretions, forming hydrochloric acid which then burns tissue of the respiratory tract. This irritation causes the mucous membranes in the trachea and the lining of the lungs to secrete additional fluid. Eventually this fluid buildup is such that it interferes with the oxygen flow. The lungs literally fill with fluid (dry land drowning).

Diphosgene (DP or trichloromethylchloroformate) and triphosgene (TP or trichloromethylcarbonate) are phosgene-like oily liquids or in the case of very pure TP is a powder. They decompose easily to give phosgene and other toxic components. Treat them as you would phosgene.

Blood Agents

Blood agents are another type of agent used in World War I. Two will be discussed: hydrogen cyanide (AC) and cyanogen chloride (CK).

Like the choking agents, CG and CL, these agents have a variety of commercial uses and are, therefore, readily available. Both are very volatile and, therefore, nonpersistent. As they are gases, their route of entry is the respiratory tract.

Hydrogen cyanide has a vapor density of 0.93 (lighter than air) and will rise. It also has a low flash point (64°F) so it may well ignite if released using an explosive device.

The agents are absorbed by the blood stream and carried throughout the body. Under normal conditions, the blood releases the oxygen it carries from the lungs to the individual body cells. Blood agents bond to the enzyme cytochrome oxidase and prevent this oxygen transfer. An abundance of oxygen in the venous system is why the skin appears red.

The body has the ability to detoxify hydrogen cyanide more rapidly than the other agents, so exposure to low concentrations is not as deadly or cumulative. Both agents hydrolyze fairly rapidly; however, cyanogen chloride hydrolyzes more slowly than hydrogen cyanide.

Blister Agents

Like the choking agents, blister agents were also used in World War I, because once all of the combatants had protective masks, choking agents were not as effective. Another agent was required. Blister agents filled the void because they had two primary routes of entry: inhalation and absorption through the skin.

There are three blister agent types: the mustard family (H, HD, HN, and HT), lewisite (L) and phosgene oxime (CX).

The mustards and lewisite are liquids, while phosgene oxime is a solid (prismatic crystalline powder) with a melting point of 40°C. They all present a vapor hazard, and mustard and lewisite also present liquid hazards. Mustard freezes (becomes a solid) at 57°F, so it would not be present as a liquid in the colder times of year.

There are a number of different mustard compounds. They are mustard (H), distilled mustard (HD), nitrogen mustard (HN), sesquimustard (Q), and dimustard ether-T (HT). All have basically the same effects and toxicity. HT is sometimes used to lower the freezing point of H or HD. Mustard has the odor of garlic, while lewisite smells like geraniums.

The rate of action for skin contact is fast with all the blister agents. Mustard is a very insidious agent as it causes no pain nor is there any other indication of its presence for a period of 4-24 hours. It is also carcinogenic (as is lewisite). With lewisite and phosgene oxime there is immediate pain at the site of contact. The vapor effects of all three of these agents take longer to cause casualties, both on the eyes and through inhalation.

Symptoms vary according to concentration. Vapor or liquid in the eyes will cause some tearing, burning, and a gritty feeling. Inhalation effects can cause coughing and perhaps a raspy or hoarse voice.

Liquid or vapor skin contact will cause blistering. The area contaminated will start turning red, followed by blister formation. The blisters are deep, similar to second-degree burns, and occur anywhere that contact is made. Moist areas of the body are more susceptible, even when covered with clothing. As a result, these agents must be removed from the skin immediately.

Blister Agent Poisoning

The physiological action of blister agents produces extreme irritation, whether for the eye, respiratory tract, or skin. Reports from Iran and Iraq during their war in the 1980s are of horrible, painful deaths due to lung damage. Skin blisters break, leaving large open wounds; however, additional blisters are not created from the fluid of broken blisters. There is some hydrolysis, but very little detoxification.

Blister agents require both respiratory protection and protective clothing. The mask will protect not only the respiratory tract, but also the eyes and face, and protective clothing covers the remainder of the body. These agents are absorbed, by most clothing, which will then off-gas.

First aid involves removing all liquid agent from the skin immediately. Decontamination requires pinching or blotting agent off the skin rather than rubbing or wiping. After agent removal, flush with water or dilute bleach.

The lethal inhalation toxicity for mustard is 231 ppm (one minute exposure). Blister formation on the skin from liquid, however, will occur at a much lower concentration; in fact, the LD_{50} for skin contact is only 7 grams per person.

Nerve Agents

Nerve agents were discovered in the mid-1930s when German scientists were looking for better pesticides. Because there were many rat-infested ships docking in German ports, the scientists needed to find a better way to fumigate the ships. The story goes that the scientists pumped this new pesticide into the holds of a ship and then went down inside to see if it had been effective in killing the rats. The test was a success because not only did all the rats die, but so did the individuals conducting the test.

Nerve agents are the most toxic of all the weaponized military agents. These agents can cause sudden loss of consciousness, seizures, apnea, and death. GB, or sarin, is one of the more commonly stockpiled nerve agents, and it may be inhaled as a vapor or cause toxic effects by contact with the skin in the liquid form. VX is mainly a liquid skin hazard at normal ambient temperatures. These chemicals are easily absorbed through the skin, eyes, or lungs.

Nerve agents are stored and transported in the liquid state. The initial diagnosis of nerve agent exposure is made by presenting clinical signs and symptoms, with confirmation by laboratory tests or onsite detection. The G-agents such as sarin (GB), soman (GD), and tabun (GA) are liquids at normal temperatures, although sarin evaporates at about the same rate as water. In liquid form, the G-agents can be absorbed through the skin and eyes; vapor is absorbed by inhalation and through the eyes, but not through the skin unless the concentration of vapor is extremely high. The G-agents liquids are more effective in penetrating skin when the chemical is trapped between the skin and clothes. GB rapidly evaporates and is considered to be a nonpersistent agent; that is, it does not remain on terrain or objects very long, whereas VX is persistent due to its low volatility. Though liquid at normal temperatures, VX has the consistency of motor oil and has a very low volatility, seldom presenting a vapor hazard. VX is much more toxic (100 to 150 times) than sarin when on the skin because sarin evaporates from the skin surface.

Most people are familiar with insecticides, many of which are organo-phosphorus compounds similar to nerve agents. As a result, nerve agents have been referred to as "insecticides for people." Many pesticides are organo-phosphorus compounds; however, others such as sevin are carbamates. Some of the experimental carbamates made at Edgewood Arsenal in the 1960s were as toxic as VX.

The most important nerve agents included in modern CW arsenals are:

- **Tabun:** o-ethyl dimethylamidophosphorylcyanide, with the American denomination GA. This nerve agent is the easiest to manufacture. Consequently, it is more likely that developing countries start their CW arsenal with this nerve agent, whereas industrialized countries consider tabun to be out-of-date and of limited use.
- **Sarin:** isopropyl methylphosphonofluoridate, with the American denomination GB, a volatile substance mainly taken up through inhalation.
- **Soman:** pinacolyl methylphosphonofluoridate, with the American denomination GD, a moderately volatile substance which can be taken up by inhalation or skin contact.
- **Cyclohexyl methylphosphonofluoridate:** with the American denomination GF, a substance with low volatility which is taken up through skin contact and inhalation of the substance either as a gas or aerosol.
- **o-ethyl-S-diisopropylaminomethyl methylphosphonothiolate:** better known under the American denomination VX, a persistent substance which can remain on material, equipment, and terrain for long periods. Uptake is mainly through the skin but also through inhalation of the substance as a gas or aerosol.

When pure, the G-agents are both colorless and odorless, however there may be a slight fruity odor, if impure. VX is also odorless but may have a slight yellow color, and a sulfur smell, if impure. As the name implies, these agents affect the nervous system.

Nerve agents attack or interfere with the normal chemistry at the nerve muscle junction. Muscles work by contracting and relaxing. To stimulate contraction, the nerve endings activate a chemical called acetylcholine, which acts as an electrical conductor to bridge the gap between the nerve ending and the muscle or gland. Following the contraction, the muscle secretes an enzyme called acetylcholinesterase which neutralizes the acetylcholine, breaking the electrical contact, and allowing the muscle to relax. Nerve agents inhibit acetylcholinesterase production, and, therefore, the neutralization of acetylcholine. Thus the muscle receives constant stimulation, causing it to twitch, and tire quickly. As this occurs, fluids build up in the trachea and bronchioconstriction occurs making it more difficult to breath. Death usually results from cardiopulmonary failure.

The symptoms of nerve agent poisoning are fairly recognizable: dimness of vision (pinpointing of pupils), runny nose, drooling, difficulty breathing/tightness of the chest, nausea, vomiting and diarrhea, muscle jerking or twitching, involuntary urination/defecation, coma, and death. Depending on where the agent contacts the body, pinpointing of the pupils is not always seen. Depending on the concentration and exposure time, effects can all occur in a very few minutes.

Use the mnemonic SLUDGE:

> **S**alivation
> **L**acrimation (Tearing)
> **U**rination
> **D**efecation
> **G**astrointestinal (increase in secretions in tract) effects
> **E**mesis (vomiting)

Binary Chemical Nerve Gas
Binary chemical weapons mix two, separate, relatively nontoxic chemicals in flight to create a toxic chemical agent.

GB BINARY: Methylphosphonyl difluoride (DF) is initially located in one canister, while a mixture (OPA) of isopropyl alcohol and isopropyl amine is located in a separate canister. When the weapon is fired (or otherwise delivered), a disk between the canisters ruptures, and the two components react in flight to produce GB.

GD BINARY: Methylphosphonyl difluoride (DF) is initially located in one canister, while a mixture of pinacolyl alcohol and an amine is located in a separate canister. When the weapon is fired (or otherwise delivered), a disk between the canisters ruptures, and the two components react in flight to produce GD.

VX BINARY: O-Ethyl O-2-diisopropylaminoethyl methylphosphonite (QL) is initially located in one canister, while elemental sulfur is located in a separate canister. When the weapon is fired (or otherwise delivered), a disk between the canisters ruptures, and the two components react in flight to produce VX.

Comparative Toxicities
A comparison of the approximate lethalities of the agents discussed is presented below. They are based relative to chlorine in terms of respiration. Using chlorine as a baseline:
- Cyanogen chloride (CK) is twice as toxic.
- Phosgene (CG) is 6 times more toxic.
- Hydrogen cyanide (AC) is 7 times more toxic.

172

- Mustard (H) is 13 times more toxic.
- Sarin (GB) is 200 times more toxic.
- VX is 600 times more toxic.

For skin toxicity, 10 milligrams of VX equals 1 to 2 grams of mustard or sarin. Less than a pinhead of mustard is required to achieve a small blister.

Toxic Agent LD$_{50}$s on Skin

AGENT	AMOUNT
GA	14 mg/kg
GB	24 mg/kg
GD	5 mg/kg
GF	30 mg/kg
VX	10 mg/kg

Comparison of oral LD$_{50}$s between WMD types of material. Notice where the toxic chemicals appear in this list.

Toxic Agent Oral LD$_{50}$s

AGENT	LD$_{50}$ (mg/kg)	SOURCE
Botulinum toxin	0.000001	Bacterium
Ricin	0.003	Plant (Castor Bean)
VX	0.14	Chemical Agent
T-2 Toxin	1.2	Fungal Myotoxin
Soman (GD)	5	Chemical Agent
Sarin (GB)	24	Chemical Agent
Lewisite	50	Blister Agent
Sulfur mustard	100	Blister Agent
Hydrogen cyanide	100	Blood Agent
Chlorine	400	Choking Agent

Crowd-Control Agents

Irritating agents, lachrymators (chemicals which stimulate lachrymal glands to produce tears), crowd-control agents, and tear gas are synonyms for a group of aerosol-dispersed chemicals (solid particles) that produce eye, nose, mouth, skin, and respiratory tract irritation. This class of chemical agents causes involuntary eye closing due to irritation. For police, this is an effective weapon as it can disable an assailant. It is widely used in the civilian arena for self-protection. The deleterious effect is transient (about 30 minutes after exposure).

Tear Gas

Tear gases are usually not lethal unless inhaled in large quantities, and they affect people by inhalation and topical contact to mucus membranes and skin. General effects are tearing and sneezing; these agents can cause lung tissue damage and may lead to pulmonary edema (excess liquid in lung tissue). These complications may develop hours to a day after exposure.

Tear gases have been known since the middle of the 19th century. Chloropicrin (PS) was first synthesized from picric acid (2,4,6-trinitrophenol) and calcium hypochlorite (chloride of lime) in 1848. It was manufactured by this method during World War I and used both as an irritant and as a lethal chemical during that conflict. Although its toxicity makes chloropicrin a poor crowd-control agent, it continues to be used as a soil sterilant, a grain disinfectant, and an intermediate in synthesis, e.g., of methyl violet.

Although not widely appreciated, the use of tear gases predates the use of lethal chemical warfare agents. Several belligerents in World War I had been using munitions filled with irritants from almost the beginning of hostilities. Ethyl bromoacetate was used in August 1914, chloroacetone in November 1914, and mixtures of xylyl bromide, xylylene bromide, and benzyl bromide in January 1915. Bromobenzylcyanide (CA) was used by both the French and Americans towards the end of World War I. All these compounds are extreme irritants capable of severely limiting the effectiveness of unprotected troops.

During World War I, the tear gas a-chloroacetophenone (CN) was investigated in the United States, but production plants remained unfinished in November 1918. Police in many countries adopted CN, which works primarily as an eye irritant, as a crowd-control agent between World War I and World War II. During World War II, all belligerents manufactured CN in large quantities.

During the 1950s, one limitation of CN became apparent; determined demonstrators could avoid much of the effect of CN by closing their eyes. o-Chlorobenzylidine malononitrile (CS) was adopted as a CN replacement when it was found to have wider ranging effects. CS tear gas takes effect almost immediately, causing severe burning and involuntary closing of the eyes, copious tearing, extreme burning in the nose, a tendency to breathe through the mouth, extreme burning in the throat, and coughing. In some cases there can be nausea and vomiting. CS also causes a burning sensation on exposed parts of the body. A desirable feature of CS as a crowd-control agent is that recovery quickly follows when the affected person is no longer exposed to CS; fresh air is a rapid antidote.

CS and CN are both solid materials that are used in crowd control as pyrotechnics; a burning pyrotechnic candle disperses a solid aerosol of the agent. Alternatively, as a liquid solution of CN or CS can be dispersed aerosol spray in products such as Mace™. In this application, a one percent (CN) to two percent (CS) solution in an inert solvent is sprayed through an aerosol nozzle.

Older mixtures of materials that may be used or remanufactured by terrorist organizations include CNC, CNS, and CNB.

CNS is a formulation of chloroacetophenone (CN). CNS was formulated not so much as a tear agent but as a vomiting agent. CNS was an American chemical warfare materiel developed after WWI; it has a mixture of 23 percent chloroacetophenone (CN), 38.4 percent chloropicrin (PS), and 38.4 percent chloroform.

CNB was adopted in 1920 and remained in use until it was replaced by chloroacetophenone and chloropicrin in chloroform. The advantages claimed for CNB was that its lower chloroacetophenone content made it more satisfactory than chloroacetophenone in chloroform (CNC) for training purposes.

174

Newer agents are OC (Oleoresin capsicum) which is a mixture of synthetic and natural pepper oils. It causes a burning sensation wherever it hits bare skin, mucus membranes, or eyes. Reaction varies on concentration from lacrimation to incapacitation. Wash in cold water and mild detergent to decontaminate pepper spray.

Even though crowd-control agents generally do not have lasting effects, their significance as a terrorist weapon should not be underestimated. This point was demonstrated in early 1997 when a crowd-control agent, possibly pepper spray, was disseminated inside Baltimore-Washington International (BWI) airport. The event caused a portion of the airport to close, and several travelers were transported to local hospitals for treatment. If the perpetrators were attempting to disrupt airport operations, they certainly accomplished their objective, even though the agent involved was not a lethal one.

Vomiting Agents
Diphenylchloroarsine (DA), 10-chloro-5,10-dihydrophenarsazine (DM, Adamsite), and diphenylcyanoarsine (DC) are closely related chemical compounds developed near the conclusion of World War I. All three compounds are solids when pure and must be used as aerosols. These agents are used in either thermal grenades or smoke generators. The effects of all three are similar: severe irritation of the eyes, nose, and throat. If the agent is inhaled for 1-2 minutes, tightness of the chest and headache are experienced. The headache develops into general nausea, which can result in vomiting in approximately three minutes. Under concentrations expected to occur under combat conditions, fatalities are not expected; however, these compounds can be fatal at higher concentrations.

DA, the first in the series, was used by German troops in 1917. DA was considered a significant development because it penetrated the activated carbon gas mask filters deployed in World War I. Its irritant behavior was considered more important than its lethality. DA was used in combination with phosgene and diphosgene; DA caused victims to remove their masks to sneeze, cough, or vomit, rendering them vulnerable to the toxic effects of the other agents. DA alone saw some use as a crowd-control agent up to the 1930s.

DC was used by the Germans in 1918. It was intended to combine the vomiting potential of DA with the lethality of cyanide. However, DC did not prove particularly lethal in tests.

DM was discovered by German scientists in 1913 (German Patent Application 281049, July 1913 to F. Bayer and Co.), but it was never used by Germany. It was independently discovered by Major Robert Adams working at the University of Illinois and also by a British team, both at the beginning of 1918. DM was produced, but not used, by the Americans at the end of the war. Franke states that "according to very incomplete reports [it] was used by the Italian Army." It was produced by many nations for use as a crowd-control agent until it was superseded by alpha-chloroacetophenone (CN) and similar tear agents. It was also found to be effective as a pesticide against marine borers, which kept it in production for years. By 1920, gas mask filters had been improved to protect against aerosol particles, which may account for the termination of this line of development.

By mutual agreement, DA and DC are not to be used by any of the NATO members. Use of DA, DC, and DM against civilians was banned by the Western nations by the 1930s because of their nausea causing effects and the toxicity of their arsine-based by-products. There is documentation of limited Soviet production of DA in 1936. DC was a standard agent (Red No. 1) in the arsenal of the Japanese Imperial Forces between 1931 and 1945. Adamsite was prepared by all the belligerent states during World War II. Smoke generators filled with a mixture of adamsite and alpha-chloroacetophenone were also developed. By 1967, protection had advanced to the point that the value of DA, DC, and DM in combat was considered questionable.

Adamsite is an irritating and vomiting agent that acts very similar to CN and CS, but the onset of its effects is delayed for minutes compared with seconds for CN and CS. In addition, adamsite does not cause skin irritation.

Clark I which is DA (diphenylchloroarsine) and Clark II which is DC (diphenylcyanoarsine) have similar structures and similar properties to that of adamsite. They behave in similar manners and are used for the same function.

Industrial and Other Chemicals

Psychogenic Materials

Psychogenic materials like LSD and mescalin can be used in terrorist attacks on communities. They would lead to mass confusion and disruption of all normal functions. Application through several routes is possible.

LSD has the chemical name 9,10-didehydro-N,N-diethyl-6-methyl-8b-ergoline-8-carboxamide, and has the molecular formula $C_{20}H_{25}N_3O$ and formula weight 323.44. Its CAS registry number is 50-37-3. The melting point of LSD is 80-85°C.

In 1938, Albert Hofmann and A. Stoll of the Sandoz Research Laboratories first synthesized LSD along with several other derivatives of lysergic acid. However, it was not until April 1943 that the hallucinogenic properties of this substance were accidentally discovered by Hofmann and subsequently confirmed by self-experimentation. During the 1950s, LSD was the subject of considerable interest as a potential chemical warfare agent. In both the US and Britain, test subjects voluntarily ingested LSD in an effort to determine whether LSD could serve as a nonlethal incapacitant. Other tests were done involuntarily; Project MKULTRA tested LSD (along with a large number of other behavior-modifying and psychoactive drugs) on unwitting subjects. At least two fatalities were tied directly to these testing programs; it is probable that more deaths are indirectly related.

The action of LSD on the nervous system results from it being a potent serotonin antagonist. The binding of LSD makes it a useful research tool. In addition, it should be noted that LSD is listed as a Schedule I Controlled Substance (DEA Controlled Substances Code 7315). The potential for abuse of LSD is another reason for the extensive body of research on this substance.

The military has weaponized a similar type of material. BZ (3-quinuclidinyl benzilate, also known as QNB) is an incapacitating agent. Approximately 30 minutes after exposure to a BZ aerosol, symptoms such as disorientation with visual and auditory hallucinations begin to appear. The symptoms peak in four to eight hours and may take up to four days to pass.

Industrial Chemicals

Many industrial compounds and natural products can be used to create terror or disruption. Literally hundreds of these materials exist. Many are transported routinely up and down the highway on a daily basis. They can be found in high school and college laboratories across the country. They can be ordered in large quantities in some cases using a credit card across the Internet. Many are available from science stores in local malls. Clandestine laboratories have many of them and use some of them as booby traps.

The Chemistry of Explosives and Propellants

A distinction must be made between explosives and explosions. There are a number of definitions of what constitutes an explosion. They typically describe a sudden and violent release of energy with damage potential both from the shock wave and also from potential shrapnel sent flying by the release of energy or the rupture of the vessel containing the explosion. Under this type of definition, the rupture of a steam powered boiler due to excess steam pressure or a runaway chemical reaction that exceeds the rupture pressure of the reactor would be considered explosions. Explosives, on the other hand, are compounds and mixtures that are designed for the specific purpose of creating an explosion.

There are materials which are intentionally used for explosives or propellants, and those which are shock-sensitive but are not used for explosives.

Professionals in the field of explosives technology also distinguish between dense and diffuse explosions. A dense explosion is one that occurs in a small area typically due to the decomposition of an explosive. A diffuse explosion is one that occurs over a large area due to the detonation or deflagration of a cloud of dust or flammable vapor. A dust explosion such as is seen in grain elevators or an unconfined vapor cloud explosion where a flammable mixture explodes in the air are both examples of diffuse explosions. Dust explosions and unconfined vapor cloud explosions may be extremely violent and can involve material such as fuel oil or flour which would not explode under other conditions.

Uses of Explosives

In addition to the obvious military uses of explosives for battle, explosives are used in construction, mining, oil exploration and oil and gas recovery, and as propellant for rockets. Military explosives are divided into high-explosives and low-explosives depending on their rate of decomposition and use.

Decomposition Rate - Detonation Versus Deflagration

DEFLAGRATION : A rapid reaction and burning of material with the presence of gas generation, heat, and light. Deflagration may be spectacular in its effects and may lead to an explosion of the containing vessel. Depending on the substance, it may be possible to watch the progress of the deflagration in real-time.

DETONATION: A more rapid reaction process where the rate of reaction is so fast that a "shock wave" is built up in the mass of the exploding material. A detonation is a supersonic wave structure consisting of a shock wave, a reaction zone, and a trailing mixture of burning gas. As the shock wave travels through the medium, it compresses and heats up the medium triggering rapid chemical reactions which cause a significant buildup of heat increasing the rate of reaction. A chemical reaction may start as a deflagration and become a detonation as the combustion process continues.

A measure of the explosivity of a material is its brisance or tendency to undergo a sharp energetic reaction. Compounds and mixtures with a high brissance are typically considered to be high-explosives. Compounds like TNT (trinitrotoluene) or nitroglycerine have a high brisance and are high-explosives, whereas low-explosives like gunpowder have a low brisance value. The term brisant is also used to apply to very explosive materials.

GUNPOWDER: A mixture of potassium nitrate (saltpeter), charcoal, and sulfur which is still available today for muzzle loading rifles and pistols and as a propellant for solid fuel rockets, although it is not used much as an explosive. First invented by the Chinese and used for military purposes from the 8th century onwards, it was the major explosive and propellant for military use until the latter half of the 19th century when other more powerful explosives were developed. In 1802, E. I. du Pont founded a gunpowder mill on the banks of the Brandywine River in Wilmington, Delaware to begin what is now one of the oldest chemical companies in the United States, E. I. du Pont de Nemours and Company.

Gunpowder has numerous drawbacks for use in military or civilian applications:

- It is difficult to mill and mix the ingredients consistently to achieve a homogeneous product. Any variations in consistency lead to unpredictable variations in strength and reaction rate that can lead to serious problems with armaments and with the use of gunpowder as a commercial explosive.
- Burning gunpowder produces large amounts of thick heavy smoke which tended to obscure battlefield visibility after a short time.
- Gunpowder is extremely moisture sensitive and it is nearly impossible to set off wet powder.

AMMONIUM NITRATE (NH_4NO_3): Used primarily as a fertilizer and is sold and shipped in large quantities. It is stored in large quantities in any area where agriculture is a significant part of the economy. Ammonium nitrate by itself undergoes significant deflagration incidents if an ignition source starts the reaction. No additional fuel source is necessary and no oxygen is required since ammonium nitrate contains both oxidizer and fuel in its composition. Ammonium nitrate deflagrations may transition to explosions due to the large volume of hot gas generated.

AMMONIUM NITRATE-FUEL OIL MIXTURES (AMFO): Used commercially for blasting, particularly in the mining, oil, and natural gas industries. Ammonium nitrate-fuel oil mixtures will detonate with an initiating explosion such as blasting caps or detonating cord. AMFO is officially classified as a blasting agent by the US government. The devastating effect of an AMFO explosion in the hands of a terrorist is obvious from the damage done in the April 1995 Oklahoma City bombing.

Ammonium nitrate-fuel oil mixtures may be prepared in advance and be shipped in tubes or may be prepared on-site. Multi-compartment trucks with ammonium nitrate slurry in one compartment and fuel oil in a separate compartment are shipped to mining, petroleum, and construction sites on a frequent basis.

In 1970, DuPont began selling water gel explosives consisting of ammonium nitrate, methylamine nitrate, fuel oil, aluminum powder, and water for blasting purposes. Water gel explosives have the advantage of being insensitive to shock and friction and normally require a detonator to explode. Ammonium nitrate and potassium nitrate are also used as oxidizers in various mixtures in dynamites and in polymer-based explosives (PBX).

GUANIDINE NITRATE: Used extensively in military munitions particularly by the Germans during WWI. Its use was discontinued after World War I because it tended to corrode shells and munitions over time, leading to numerous accidental explosions. Guanidine nitrate was produced by nitrating "guano" or excrement which was mined from bat caves and seabird rookeries worldwide and sent to Germany for processing.

GUNCOTTON or **NITROCELLULOSE:** Produced by treating cotton with nitric and sulfuric acids. There are a number of different grades and uses depending on the degree of nitration:

- Guncotton or smokeless powder (cellulose hexanitrate) is used as the propellant in many munitions (such as small arms bullets). It has numerous advantages over gun powder in consistency of composition and performance and especially because it burns with little smoke.

- Nitrocellulose (cellulose tetranitrate and lesser nitrated cellulose) can be dissolved in organic solvents and then cast as a film. This was one of the early plastics and was used for applications like ping-pong balls, playing cards, motion picture film, and lacquer for expensive furniture. Unfortunately, partially nitrated cellulose degrades over a period of years explaining why most of the early motion pictures made with nitrocellulose film have totally degraded and can no longer be viewed.

The more heavily nitrated cellulose (guncotton) can be caused to detonate while the lesser nitrated nitrocellulose will not detonate. However, nitrocellulose burns rapidly and can generate enough hot gas to burst its container in an explosion even if the material does not actually detonate. Nitrocellulose was used along with nitroglycerin and petrolatum to produce a smokeless powder known as cordite.

NITROGLYCERINE: Is an oily liquid produced by nitrating glycerin with nitric and sulfuric acid. It has a sweetish taste and is a powerful vasodilator used for treating angina and for relieving symptoms of heart attack. Nitroglycerin is highly shock sensitive which limits its use. In 1866, Alfred Nobel determined that mixing nitroglycerin with diatomaceous earth stabilized the material and dynamite continues to be used today for construction and mining purposes. Nitroglycerin is also used in some smokeless powders. Although extremely shock sensitive without the presence of diatomaceous earth, silica, clay, or carbon, modern nitroglycerin-based explosives require an initiating charge such as a blasting cap to detonate. There are numerous nitroglycerin-based dynamites and nitroglycerin is also used in mixtures for bullet and military munition primary charges.

TNT (TRINITROTOLUENE): Is widely used for munitions and is a component in numerous composite explosives including amatol, pentolite, tetrytol, tritonol, picratol, ednatol, and composition B (a mixture of RDX and TNT). In a refined form, TNT is among the most stable of high explosives which can be stored for extended periods. It is shock and friction insensitive and does not form explosive metal compounds. It reacts with strong bases to form unstable shock-sensitive by-products.

PICRIC ACID (TRINITROPHENOL)**:** Picric acid is a military high explosive used to set off less sensitive explosives such as TNT. Picric acid is very unstable especially when dry and is extremely shock and friction sensitive. Picric acid forms unstable metal salts which may explode on contact, due to friction or with only minor heating. The Germans and Japanese used metal picrates in the detonators for their World War II torpedoes because of the certainty that the detonators would explode on contact. Ammonium picrate is more stable than most picrate compounds and is used in armor-piercing shells to allow the shell to pierce the tank shell before detonating. Picric acid is fairly toxic and an irritant to eyes, skin, and respiratory tract. Picric acid penetrates the skin and may cause serious kidney or liver damage.

Picric acid continues to have some laboratory uses as a reagent but it is always stored with at least 10 percent water to avoid the issue of explosability.

TETRYL (2,4,6-TRINITROPHENYLMETHYLNITRAMINE): Was used extensively as the booster charge in munitions in World Wars I and II. It has since been discontinued in favor of other explosives and is no longer produced in the US. Remaining stocks of tetryl and tetryl-based munitions are being destroyed by the US government.

RDX (CYCLOTRIMETHYLENETRINITRAMINE): Is also called cyclonite or hexagen and is usually used in a mixture with other explosives, oils or waxes. It is rarely used alone. RDX may be mixed with waxes, desensitizers, or oils. RDX is considered the most powerful and brisant of the military high explosives. It forms the basis for the most common military explosives:

- **Composition A** mixtures are a mixture of RDX and a plasticizing wax and are used as a bursting charge in naval rockets and in land mines.
- **Composition B** mixtures are mixtures of RDX and TNT. Some mixtures also contain desensitizers. Composition B mixtures are used for bursting charges in army projectiles and in rockets and land mines.
- **Composition C** mixtures contain RDX, some other explosive, plasticizers, and waxes. They are moldable demolition charges which can be shaped by hand to make shape charges. Composition C-4 is frequently called "plastique" or plastic explosive.
- **Cyclotol** is the name given to 3 mixtures of RDX and TNT and is used in shaped charges, special bursting projectiles, and grenades.
- **HBX-1, HBX-2, and HBX-3** are mixtures of RDX, TNT, aluminum powder, wax, and calcium carbide. These are castable mixtures used in missile warheads and in underwater demolition.
- **H-6** is a mixture of RDX, TNT, aluminum powder, waxes, and calcium chloride. It is the standard charge for general purpose bombs used by the US military.

PETN (PENTAERYTHRITOL TETRANITRATE): A favorite explosive of terrorists because it can be molded into shapes and can escape detection by x-ray machines. PETN is normally mixed with other explosives, with plasticizers such as latex, or with waxes to make it moldable. The plastic explosive SEMTEX is a mixture of PETN and RDX. Semtex molded inside a portable radio was responsible for the destruction of Pan Am flight 103 over Lockerbie, Scotland in 1988.

HMX (CYCLOTETRAMETHYLENETETRANITRAMINE): An explosive generated as a by-product of RDX synthesis. It is used in explosive mixtures with TNT, etc. Brisance studies show HMX and RDX are virtually identical in their explosive properties.

TETRACENE (also called TETRAZENE): Is used as a primer and in mixtures with other primary high explosives to cause detonation of low explosive materials. Tetrazene is highly shock sensitive and sensitive to heat.

MERCURY FULMINATE: Is a highly sensitive primary explosive. It is so sensitive that accidents during manufacture are numerous. Mercury fulminate is unstable when it comes into contact with aluminum, magnesium, zinc, copper, brass, or bronze.

LEAD STYPHNATE: Is a primary explosive used in mixtures with other primary explosives in detonators. Lead styphnate has the advantage of being relatively heat insensitive compared to other primary explosives.

LEAD AZIDE ($Pb(N_3)_2$): Has a high ignition temperature and is the most widely used primary explosive. Lead azide is commonly stored in aluminum capsules and is stable for storage for long periods if dry. Lead azide will react with copper, zinc, and cadmium to form less stable salts. Water does not reduce the shock sensitivity of lead azide. Lead azide is widely used as a primary detonator for high explosive devices with initiation of explosion by heat or fire.

SODIUM AZIDE (NaN_3): Is used as the initiator for automotive air bag inflation. Sodium azide is stable if dry but reacts with other metals when wet, leading to less stable compounds including hydrazoic acid HN_3, which is highly unstable and toxic. Sodium azide is also used as a reagent for some chemical analyses and for some protein studies. A number of explosions have occurred as the result of sodium azide in laboratory wastes reacting with metal drain pipes to make unstable compounds in the drain.

DDNP (DIAZODINITROPHENOL): Is used as the initiating explosive in propellant primer devices. DDNP is very shock sensitive dry but immersion in water desensitizes it from shock. DDNP is less friction sensitive than mercury fulminate and more powerful than mercury fulminate or lead azide.

POLYMER-BASED EXPLOSIVES (PBX): There are several major classes of explosives generally grouped under the class name of polymer-based explosives. These include:

- Strong oxidizers and explosive materials mixed with inert polymers such as nylon or Teflon®, polyesters or polyolefins, or butyl rubber. These mixtures have significant advantages for some applications because they are water resistant, very shock-insensitive, and can be molded or extruded into uniform shapes. Propellents for solid-fuel rockets are prepared by mixing the oxidizer with the stable polymer during manufacture. The polymer thus serves as both a means to stabilize the explosive and also serves as fuel.
- Polymers incorporating nitrated monomers can be prepared by polymerizing the nitrated compounds along with unnitrated monomers. This has a significant advantage in allowing the explosive properties of the polymer to be designed to a high degree of precision.
- Polymers containing explosive additives such as ethylene glycol dinitrate (EGDN). These additives are typically mixed in with the polymer to increase the explosability of the polymer and are part of a mixture of explosives added to the polymer.

SHOCK SENSITIVE MATERIALS NOT USED FOR EXPLOSIVE PURPOSES: There are a number of classes of compounds that are shock or heat sensitive which are not used for explosive or propellant purposes. Typically these materials are considered to be too sensitive or unstable to use for this purpose or are too toxic.

NITROGEN-HALOGEN COMPOUNDS: Nitrogen compounds, including ammonia and proteins, can react with halogens to form nitrogen-halogen compounds like NH_2Cl (chloramine), $NHCl_2$ (dichloramine), and NCl_3 (Trichloramine). All of these compounds are highly toxic (the chloramine formed by the reaction of bleach and ammonia is more toxic than hydrogen cyanide and causes a number of deaths each year among unsuspecting folks cleaning house). The trihalides are explosives which are extremely shock sensitive.

ETHER PEROXIDES: Ethers are used extensively as reaction solvents in industry because they are very nonreactive and have good dissolving power for many organic compounds. One unfortunate reaction is that ethers will pick up oxygen from the air to form ether peroxides (RO-OR). Ether peroxides become a problem when there is a high enough concentration in solution so that they begin to crystallize. Crystals of ether peroxide are powerful explosives and are extremely unstable. The act of opening a bottle of ether containing crystallized peroxides may cause the bottle to detonate. Incidents have been reported where the act of placing a beaker on the same lab bench has caused ether peroxides to detonate, and there are also reports of the vibration from passing trucks causing explosions. For this reason, ethers are typically shipped under a nitrogen blanket to exclude oxygen and they are required to be tested for peroxides on a regular schedule after a bottle is opened.

PERCHLORATE ACID AND PERCHLORATE SALTS ($HClO_4$): Perchloric acid is a strong mineral acid which is also a powerful oxidizer which can react violently with organic materials. The salts of perchloric acid such as ammonium perchlorate and potassium perchlorate are used in making pyrotechnics and in some explosives. Perchlorate salts will explode violently upon heating and can react with organic materials to cause violent fires. Perchloric acid continues to be used in some industrial processes and in laboratory applications. Fires and explosions have been reported from the reaction of perchloric acid fumes with the contents of ventilation ducts and fume hood exhausts.

ACETYLENE DERIVATIVES-ACETYLIDES: Acetylene used for cutting torches is normally shipped with the acetylene dissolved in a carrier solvent such as acetone. This is to keep the concentration low because acetylene can begin self-initiated polymerization and polymerize violently. Acetylene also forms salts with active metals such as copper, tin, and silver which are extremely shock sensitive.

Dissemination Devices

While knowledge of the capabilities and characteristics of chemical, biological, and radiological agents is useful in the remediation effort after an incident, the ability to recognize both the potential for an event and the tools of an NBC terrorist may enable the emergency responder to anticipate and prevent or mitigate the effects of the attack.

Dissemination devices can be categorized based on how they disseminate the agent or material.

DIRECT DEPOSIT DEVICES: Mechanical and employed to execute an attack on a specific target with minimal collateral damage. These devices are normally constructed to inject the agent directly into the target and can be built into items as common as canes, pens, or an umbrella. These weapons pose no downwind collateral hazard. The effects of these devices are the most easily controlled.

BREAKING DEVICES: Those mechanical weapons which encapsulate the agent and release it when broken. They are optimally constructed from common items such as light bulbs, balloons, or thermos bottles and by inserting the agent and sealing the device. The loading process is dangerous, and as risky to the terrorist as to the target. The devices are employed simply by throwing them at the intended victims. Breaking devices cause point dissemination and create some downwind hazard to unprotected individuals. The effects of these devices are moderately controllable.

BURSTING/EXPLODING MECHANICAL DEVICES: Those which employ an explosive to break the agent container and disseminate the agent. These devices are usually configured with the explosive at one end of a tube, with the explosion forcing the agent out the other end, or with the explosive surrounded by the agent. Bursting devices always have an agent reservoir, a chamber for the explosive, and usually employ either a timer or a command detonation switch. These devices pose a wider area hazard than either the surgical strike or breaking devices; they may produce a larger downwind hazard area due to the increased amount of agent involved and the explosive nature of the dissemination, if the blast and resulting heat do not consume the agent. The effects of these devices are predictable but may deviate from the expected.

MECHANICAL SPRAYING DEVICES: Contain an agent reservoir, but rather than an explosive charge, they employ pressure to disseminate the agent. The pressure may be either supplied independently of, or applied directly to, the agent reservoir. They can be employed either as point dissemination weapons, as with an aerosol can, or as line source generating weapons, as might be accomplished with a device incorporated into an automobile exhaust system. Of the mechanical employment devices, the effects of these weapons are the least controllable and pose the largest area hazard. One example of the extent to which a spray attack can reach is the employment of a biological agent simulant off the coast of San Francisco from September 20-26, 1950. During this time, two vessels released clouds of a harmless bacteria on six occasions. The result was contamination of 117 square miles of the San Francisco area.

VECTORS: Usually disseminate only living biological agents. A vector is a carrier of the bacteria and may be an insect or a contaminated item such as clothing, food, or water. As vectors are not weather dependent, this type dissemination is the least predictable and controllable. The vectors, if airborne, can range up to 40 miles within a day's time.

BINARY DEVICES: Most chemical ammunition can be described as unitary, which implies that it contains one active ready-to-use CW agent. Binary technology implies that the final stage in the synthesis of the nerve agent is moved from the factory into the warhead, which thus functions as a chemical reactor. Two initial substances which are stored in separate containers are mixed and allowed to react and form the nerve agent when the ammunition (bomb, projectile, grenade, etc.) is on its way towards the target.

Until the actual moment of use, the ammunition contains only relatively nontoxic initial substances. It is, therefore, considered to be safer to manufacture, store, transport and, finally, destroy. However, some critics question whether this practically untested type of new ammunition is reliable. The technique for mixing substances in bombs and rockets is complicated and requires space. The reaction has to be controlled (e.g., the temperature) and the process should preferably take place without solvents.

Binary components for the three most common nerve agents (American code names are given in parentheses) are the following:

- **Sarin** (GB-2): Methylphosphoryldifluoride (DF) + isopropanol. The isopropanol is included in a mixture (OPA) with isopropylamine which binds the hydrogen fluoride generated.
- **Soman** (GD-2): Methylphosphoryldifluoride (DF) + pinacolylalcohol. The pinacolylalcohol is included in a mixture with an amine, typically isopropylamine, which binds the hydrogen fluoride generated.
- **VX-2**: o-ethyl o-2-diisopropylaminoethyl methylphosphonite (QL) + sulphur.

Potential Terrorist Targets

In order to increase the potency of an NBC agent, the best place for a terrorist to release it is within an enclosed space (indoors). Outside, the winds will rapidly dissipate vapors until they are too thinly concentrated to have a noticeable effect on passers by. Sunlight will also kill most biological agents within two hours.

Wherever the agent is released, large crowds ensure more casualties, more panic, and more media attention. High-profile events assure instant media coverage, fame, and recognition for the group that caused the incident. These payoffs of a successful strike at an event such as the Olympics counterbalance the difficulty of breaching the increased security.

Critical facilities and infrastructure in the government may also be the target of terrorism, such as the Federal Building in Oklahoma City or the Lincoln Tunnel in New York. The same industries that produce or use poisonous chemicals usually store large quantities nearby, making them a potential target for the attack. Security is often low and the sites are usually easily accessible from main thoroughfares. A recent example in Texas involved two men who attempted to bomb a storage tank filled with poison gas. Their motive was not terrorism, but rather a diversionary tactic for their planned holdup of an armored car. Had they been successful, the incident would have been as deadly as any terrorist NBC attack. At particular risk are the vehicles used to transport potential NBC agents; placarded trains and trucks move regularly through populated areas in most cities.

Particular buildings, such as city halls, federal office buildings (e.g., IRS, FBI offices), and military installations are considered likely targets. In brief, almost any facility that is of interest to the terrorist's cause can become the target of an NBC attack.

Responder Actions

If you are able to recognize a dissemination device before it functions:

- Stay upwind of the site, if possible.
- Notify the proper personnel, according to local SOP.
- Do not touch, cover, or move the device. If the device is inside a facility, do not remove it. Taking the device outside could create a greater hazard.

After an attack:

- Isolate the area. Closing doors and windows in the immediate area of the device could contain the release.
- If feasible, move upwind.
- Notify the proper personnel, according to local SOP.

Steps for mitigation of NBC incident:

- Incident size-up and assessment
- Scene control/establishment of perimeter(s)
- Product identification/information gathering
- Establishment of a decontamination area
- Pre-entry examination and determination/donning of appropriate protective clothing and equipment
- Entry planning/preparation of equipment
- Entry into a contaminated area and rescue of victims (as needed)
- Containment of spill/release
- Neutralization of spill/release
- Decontamination of victims/patients/rescuers
- Triage of ill/injured
- ALS Care
- Hospital/expert consultation
- BLS care/specific antidotes
- Transport of patients to appropriate hospital
- Post-entry evaluation examination of rescuers/equipment
- Complete stabilization of the release/collection of evidence
- Delegation of final clean up to responsible party
- Record keeping/after-action reporting
- Complete analysis of actions/recommendations to action plan

For easy reference, chemical data sheets for the most common materials within the five categories of toxic agents are included in the final sections of this chapter.

Chocking Agent
Chemical Data Sheets

Choking agents like chlorine are severely irritating to eyes, throat, and lungs. They may kill by causing chemical burns to the respiratory system leading to chemical emphysema and death due to destruction of lung tissue leading to lungs filled with fluid. They may also cause permanent blindness and damage to exposed skin.

186

Material	**Phosgene**
Chemical Name	Carbonyl chloride
Structure	(structure of phosgene: O double-bonded to C, with Cl and Cl)
History and Use	Phosgene was first developed in 1810. Phosgene was first used in the dye industry in the late 19th century to process colorfast materials. The Germans introduced CG in 1915 for use in World War I. By some estimates, more than 80 percent of all chemical agent fatalities in World War I were due to phosgene. In the late 1920s, many countries manufactured phosgene as a chemical warfare agent; it still remains in the chemical arsenals. Phosgene is also an important industrial compound used in the preparation and manufacture of many organic chemicals. Phosgene (CG) is a chemical agent with a normally short duration of effectiveness. Phosgene is used as a chemical intermediate, notably in the production of the following: compact discs, lightweight eyeglasses, and shatterproof glass which is made from polycarbonate resins in which phosgene is a monomer. Other uses are in foams, paints, fibers, adhesives, and spandex which are made from polyurethanes, in which the diisocyanate monomers are made using phosgene isocyanate. It is also used in the manufacture of intermediates for pharmaceuticals and agricultural chemicals.
Military Designation	**CG**
CAS	75-44-5
Formula	$COCl_2$
Appearance and Odor	Colorless gas with a new mown hay odor at low concentrations, suffocating at higher concentrations; a fuming liquid below 47°F. White cloud visible in higher concentrations (HCl).

Chemical and Physical Properties	Molecular Weight: 98.91
	Boiling point: 8°C (46°F)
	Freezing/melting point: -178°C (-128°F)
	Vapor pressure:
	    At +20°C (68°F): 1,173 mm Hg (22.7 psi)
	    At 0°C (32°F): 555 mm Hg (10.7 psi)
	    At -10°C (14°F): 365 mm Hg (7.1 psi)
	Vapor density: 3.4
	Volatility:
	    528,000 mg/m³ @ -40°C (-40°F)
	    2,200,000 mg/m³ @ -10°C (14°F)
	    4,300,000 mg/m³ @ 7.6°C (46°F)
	    6,340,000 mg/m³ @ 25°C (77°F)
	Solubility in water: slightly soluble in water, 0.9 percent
	pH: acidic

	Odor Threshold: 0.5 to 1.0 ppm
	Specific Gravity:
	      1.419 @ 0°C (32°F)
	      1.381 @ 20°C (68°F)
	      11.6 lb/gal

Incompatibilities	Reacts explosively with thionyl chloride or potassium; reacts violently with ammonia or amines, and strong acids; reacts with alcohol to form chloroformates and hydrogen chloride; thermal decomposition may occur in the presents of iron salts and result in explosion.
Persistency	Short; however, vapor may persist for some time in low places under calm or light winds and stable atmospheric conditions (inversion).
Flammability	Noncombustible.
Physiological Properties	Phosgene is a corrosive, highly toxic gas used as a delayed-casualty agent resulting in fluid buildup in the lungs ("dry land drowning"). It affects the upper respiratory tract, skin, and eyes and causes severe respiratory damage as well as burns to the skin and eyes. Acute inhalation may cause respiratory and circulatory failure with symptoms of chills, dizziness, thirst, burning of eyes, cough, viscous sputum, dyspnea, feeling of suffocation, tracheal rhonchi, burning in throat, vomiting, pain in chest and cyanosis. Rapid progression to pulmonary edema and pneumonia, and death from respiratory and circulatory failure may occur. Pulmonary edema can suddenly occur up to 48 hours after exposure. Phosgene is a severe mucous membrane irritant. Chronic inhalation may cause irreversible pulmonary changes resulting in emphysema and fibrosis. Acute skin contact lesions similar to those of frostbite and burns; it is a severe skin irritant. Chronic skin contact may result in dermatitis. Acute eye contact may result in conjunctivitis, lacrimation, lesions similar to those of frostbite, and burns; chronic eye contact may result in conjunctivitis. Slight gassing produces dryness or burning sensation in the throat, numbness, pain in the chest, bronchitis, and shortness of breath. The least concentration that can cause immediate throat irritation is 3 ppm; 4 ppm causes immediate irritation of the eyes; 4.8 ppm causes cough. Brief exposure to 50 ppm may be rapidly fatal.
Toxicity	ICt_{50} (inhalation): 1,600 mg-min/m^3 LC_{L0} (inhalation, 5 min): 1,010 mg-min/m^3 LC_{L0} (inhalation, 30 min): 10,800 mg-min/m^3 LCt_{50} (inhalation): 3,200 mg/m^3 TC_{Lo} (inhalation, 30 min): 3,030 mg-min/m^3 LC_{50}: 791 ppm ICt_{50}: 395 ppm
Exposure Data	PEL: 0.1 ppm TLV-C: 0.2 ppm
Emergency Response Action Levels	IDLH: 2 ppm

Rate of Detoxification	Not detoxified, cumulative effect
First Aid	Inhalation: remove victim to fresh air; keep individual calm and avoid any unnecessary exertion or movement; maintain airway and blood pressure; trained persons should administer oxygen if breathing is difficult; give artificial respiration if victim is not breathing; seek medical attention immediately. Eye Contact: flush eyes immediately with running water or normal saline for at least 15 minutes; hold eyelids apart during irrigation; do not delay rinsing to avoid permanent eye injury; seek medical attention immediately. Skin Contact: unlikely that emergency treatment will be required; gently wrap affected part in blankets if warm water is not available or practical to use; allow circulation to return naturally; if adverse effects occur, seek medical attention immediately. Ingestion: treat symptomatically and supportively; if vomiting occurs, keep head lower than hips to prevent aspiration; seek medical attention immediately.
Decontamination	Flush with water containing sodium bicarbonate or soda ash.
Hydrolysis Rate	Rapid: rain destroys effectiveness. Reaction products: Hydrogen chloride, carbon monoxide, acidic when wet. Phosgene hydrolyzes rapidly; hydrolysis of a 1 percent solution of phosgene in water is complete within 20 seconds at 0°C.
Environmental Fate	The fate of phosgene released on land is unknown. While it adsorbs strongly to relatively dry soil, it is likely to volatilize and hydrolyze when released on soils with a high moisture content. If released in water, phosgene would be rapidly lost by volatilization and slowly hydrolyze. It is very persistent in the atmosphere and would be transported long distances and diffuse to the stratosphere where it would be lost by photolysis.
Protective Equipment	Respiratory protection is required. Chemical resistant clothing is required. Level A, B, or C may be used depending on monitoring results.

Material	**Chlorine**
Chemical Name	Chlorine
Structure	$Cl-Cl$
History and Use	Chlorine (Cl) is a chemical agent with a normally short duration of effectiveness. It was used during World War I, causing 10-15 percent of the chemical agent casualties, and is widely used today as an industrial chemical. It is a major chemical feeds stock, produced predominantly by the electrolysis of brine in the chlor-alkali industry. Chlorine is used in bleaching, water disinfection, and in the manufacture of chlorinated hydrocarbons, synthetic rubbers, and plastics. A special note should be that chlorine's reactivity-chlorine is extremely reactive and will cause some materials to burst into flame or explode on contact.
Military Designation	**CL**
CAS	7782-50-5
Formula	Cl_2
Appearance and Odor	Greenish-yellow gas, liquid, or rhombic crystals. Bleach-like odor at very low concentrations. Suffocating irritating pungent odor.

Chemical and Physical Properties	Molecular Weight: 70.90
	Boiling point: -34°C (-29°F)
	Freezing/melting point: -101°C (-150°F)
	Vapor pressure:
	    At +20°C (68°F): 4,800 mm Hg (93 psi)
	    At +40°C (105°F): 7,815 mm Hg (151 psi)
	    At +46°C (115°F): 9,034 mm Hg (174 psi)
	Vapor density: 2.49
	Volatility: 19,369,000 mg/m^3
	Solubility in water: slightly soluble in water 6.52 g/L total (4.40 g/L Cl_2
	                 in equilibrium with 1.57 g/L HOCl and 1.06 g/L Cl)
	pH: acidic
	Odor Threshold: 0.3 to 3 ppm
	Specific Gravity:
	    1.5649 @ -35°C (31°F)
	    13 lb/gal

Incompatibilities	Chlorine is a very reactive material. It is a strong oxidizer and will cause spontaneous combustion of several organic materials. Chlorine when wet is extremely corrosive to metals.
Persistency	Very short; vapor may persist in low places under calm or light winds.
Flammability	Noncombustible, but is an extremely good oxidizer and will increase combustion rates.
Physiological Properties	Skin contact may cause skin irritation with discomfort or rash. Eye contact

| | may cause eye irritation with discomfort, tearing, or blurring of vision. Eye damage may be permanent and may include blindness. Liquid chlorine poses cryogenic hazards; skin or eye contact with liquid may cause frostbite burns. Inhalation may cause irritation of upper respiratory passages; nonspecific discomfort such as nausea, headache, or weakness; or corrosion of teeth.

Higher exposures may cause skin burns or ulceration; eye corrosion with corneal or conjunctival ulceration; temporary lung irritation with cough, discomfort, difficulty breathing, or shortness of breath; followed in hours by severe shortness of breath, requiring prompt medical attention; asthma-like reactions with shortness of breath, wheezing, or cough, possibly occurring on subsequent re-exposure to concentrations below established exposure limits; or temporary alteration of the heart's electrical activity with irregular pulse, palpitations, or inadequate circulation. Death may occur from gross overexposure.

Chlorine is extremely irritating to the mucous membranes of the eyes and the respiratory tract at 3 ppm. Combines with moisture to form HCl. Both of these substances, if present in quantity, cause inflammation of the tissues with which they come in contact. A concentration of 3.5 ppm produces a detectable odor; 15 ppm causes immediate irritation of the throat. Concentrations of 50 ppm are dangerous for even short exposures; 1000 ppm may be fatal, even when exposure is brief. |
|---|---|
| Toxicity | LC_{50}:137 ppm/1H
LCt_{50}: 6551 ppm for a 1-minute exposure (19,000 mg-min/m^3)
ICt_{50}: 620 ppm for a 1-minute exposure (1,800 mg-min/m^3) |
| Exposure Data | TLV-TWA: 0.5 ppm
TLV-Ceiling: 1 ppm
OSHA PEL-Ceiling: 1 ppm |
| Emergency Response Action Levels | IDLH Value:10 ppm |
| Rate of Detoxification | Rapid. |
| First Aid | Decontaminate victim first.

Vapor: irritating to eyes, nose, and throat. Immediate reaction to high concentrations; delayed reaction to lower concentrations. Will burn eyes. Move to fresh air. If breathing has stopped, give artificial respiration (but NOT mouth-to-mouth). If breathing is difficult, give oxygen. IF IN EYES, hold eyelids open and flush with plenty of water.

Liquid: will burn skin and eyes. Will cause frostbite. Flush affected areas with plenty of water. IF IN EYES, hold eyelids open and flush with plenty of water. DO NOT RUB AFFECTED AREAS. |
| Decontamination | Flush with water containing sodium bicarbonate or soda ash. |

Street Smart^{TM} Chemistry

Hydrolysis Rate	Slow. Reacts to generate hydrochloric and hydrochlorous acids.
Environmental Fate	The stability of free chlorine in natural water is very low because it is a strong oxidizing agent and rapidly oxidizes inorganic compounds. It also oxidizes organic compounds, but more slowly than inorganic compounds. Chlorine reacts with organic precursors that are found in many source waters to produce a potential carcinogen, such as chloroform or chloramine.
Protective Equipment	Respiratory protection is required. Chemical resistant clothing is required. Level A, B, or C may be used depending on monitoring results.

Blood Agent
Chemical Data Sheets

Blood agents like hydrocyanic acid act on a cellular level reacting with and deactivating the enzymes necessary to transport oxygen and generate biochemical energy.

Material	**Hydrogen Cyanide**
Chemical Name	Hydrocyanic Acid
Structure	$HC \equiv N$
History and Use	Hydrogen cyanide is a useful industrial material. It is used for the manufacture of polymers, dyes, sweeteners, metal polishes, metal plating, gold refining, pharmaceuticals, specialty chemicals, and photography processes. Hydrogen cyanide is used commercially as a rodenticide and insecticide for fumigating enclosed spaces.
Military Designation	**AC**
CAS	74-90-8
Formula	HCN
Appearance and Odor	Very volatile liquid or colorless gas smelling of bitter almonds.

Chemical and Physical Properties	Molecular weight: 27
	Boiling point: 26°C (78°F)
	Freezing/melting point: -13°C (8.2°F)
	Vapor pressure:
	    At -17.8°C (0°F): 100 mm Hg (2 psi)
	    At 9.8°C (50°F): 400 mm Hg (7.7 psi)
	    At 25°C (77°F): 740 mm Hg (14 psi)
	Vapor density: 0.93
	Volatility:
	    37,000 mg/m^3 @ -40°C (-40°F)
	    1,080,000 mg/m^3 @ 25°C (77°F)
	Solubility in water: miscible
	pH: acidic
	Odor Threshold: 0.8 to 4.5 ppm
	Specific Gravity:
	    0.699 g/l @ 22°C (72°F)
	    5.74 lb/gal
	Polymerization:
	    Can occur violently in the presence of heat, alkaline materials, or moisture. Once initiated, polymerization becomes uncontrollable since the reaction is autocatalytic, producing heat and alkalinity; confined polymerization can cause a violent explosion. HCN is stabilized with small amounts of acid to prevent polymerization; it should not be stored for extended periods unless routine checks for stabilizer are performed.

Incompatibilities	Unstable with heat, alkaline materials, and water. Do not store wet HCN; may react violently with strong mineral acids; experience shows mixtures with about 20 percent or more sulfuric acid will explode; effects with other acids are not quantified, but strong acids like hydrochloric or nitric would probably react similarly.

Persistency	Short; the agent is highly volatile, and in the gaseous state it dissipates quickly in the air.
Flammability	Extremely flammable material. Flash point: -18°C (0°F) LEL: 5.6 percent UEL: 40 percent
Physiological Properties	A deadly human and experimental poison by all routes. Hydrocyanic acid and the cyanides are true protoplasmic poisons, combining in the tissues with the enzymes associated with cellular oxidation. They thereby render the oxygen unavailable to the tissues and cause death through asphyxia. The suspension of tissue oxidation lasts only while the cyanide is present; upon its removal, normal function is usually restored. HCN does not combine easily with hemoglobin, but it does combine readily with met hemoglobin to form cyan met hemoglobin. This property is utilized in the treatment of cyanide poisoning when an attempt is made to induce met hemoglobin formation. The presence of cherry-red venous blood in cases of cyanide poisoning is due to the inability of the tissues to remove the oxygen from the blood. Lips take on a pinkish color (purple coloring in dark-complexioned individuals), breathing becomes more difficult as the body becomes unable to absorb oxygen from the blood, vomiting is possible, unconsciousness, flushed hot and dry skin, violent convulsions, cessation of regular breathing, occasional gasps, and dilation of the pupils. Death occurs within 15 minutes if kept in contact with a lethal concentration. Exposure to concentrations of 100–200 ppm for periods of 30–60 minutes can cause death. At 300 ppm, HCN is rapidly fatal. In cases of acute cyanide poisoning death is extremely rapid, although sometimes breathing may continue for a few minutes. In less acute cases, there is cyanosis, headache, dizziness, unsteadiness of gait, a feeling of suffocation, and nausea. Where the patient recovers, there is rarely any disability.
Toxicity	LC_{50}: Rat inhalation 142 ppm/30 min LCt_{50} (inhalation, 0.5 min): 2,000 mg-min/m^3 LCt_{50} (inhalation, 30 min): 20,600 mg-min/m^3 LD_{50} (skin):100 mg/kg (liquid) NOAEL (inhalation): 670 mg-min/m^3 RfD (ingestion): 0.750 mg/l (liquid)
Exposure Data	TLV-Ceiling: 4.7 ppm OSHA PEL-TWA: 10 ppm
Emergency Response Action Levels	IDLH Value: 50 ppm
Rate of Detoxification	Very fast (0.017mg/kg/min).
First Aid	Inhalation: remove patient to fresh air, and lay patient down; administer

	oxygen and amyl nitrite; keep patient quiet and warm; even with inhalation poisoning, thoroughly check clothing and skin to assure no cyanide is present; seek medical attention immediately. Eye Contact: flush eyes immediately with plenty of water; remove contaminated clothing; keep patient quiet and warm; seek medical attention immediately. Skin Contact: wash skin promptly to remove the cyanide while removing all contaminated clothing, including shoes; DO NOT DELAY; skin absorption can occur from cyanide dust, solutions, or HCN vapor; absorption is slower than inhalation, usually measured in minutes compared to seconds; HCN is absorbed much faster than metal cyanides from solutions such as sodium, potassium, or copper cyanide solutions; even after washing the skin, watch the patient for at least 1 to 2 hours because absorbed cyanide can continue to work into the bloodstream; wash clothing before reuse and destroy contaminated shoes. Ingestion: give patient one pint of 1 percent sodium thiosulphate solution (or plain water) immediately by mouth and induce vomiting; repeat until vomit fluid is clear; never give anything by mouth to an unconscious person; give oxygen; seek medical attention immediately.
Decontamination	Aeration of area. Use solutions of sodium hypochlorite. Keep the pH above 11 with the addition of soda ash.
Hydrolysis Rate	Rate: Rapid in 5 percent solution of NaOH, slow in acids Hydrolysis products: Ammonia, formic acid, amorphous brown solids
Environmental Fate	Terrestrial Fate: By analogy to the fate of cyanides in water, it is predicted that the fate in soil would be pH dependent. At soil surfaces with pH <9.2, it is expected that volatilization of hydrogen cyanide would be an important loss mechanism for cyanides. In subsurface soil, cyanide present at low concentrations would probably biodegrade. In soil with pH <9.2, hydrogen cyanide is expected to be highly mobile, and in cases where cyanide levels are toxic to microorganisms (i.e., landfills, spills), this compound may leach into groundwater. Atmospheric Fate: Most cyanide in the atmosphere is expected to exist almost entirely as hydrogen cyanide gas. The reaction of hydrogen cyanide with photochemically generated hydroxyl radicals proceeds fairly slowly. The half-life for the reaction of hydrogen cyanide vapor with hydroxyl radicals in the atmosphere has been approximately 334 days. Hydrogen cyanide is expected to be resistant to direct photolysis. The relatively slow rate of degradation of hydrogen cyanide suggests that this compound has the potential to be transported over long distances before being removed by physical or chemical processes. Since hydrogen cyanide is miscible in water, it appears that wet deposition may be an important fate process.

Protective Equipment	Respiratory protection is more important than skin protection. Level A, B, or C may be useful.

Material	**Cyanogen chloride**
Chemical Name	Cyanogen chloride
Structure	$Cl-C\equiv N$
History and Use	Cyanogen chloride is heavier than air and has been assessed as having a capability to break down charcoal protective mask filters after repeated exposures to high concentrations. It is used in the manufacture of specialty chemicals
Military Designation	**CK**
CAS	506-77-4
Formula	CNCl
Appearance and Odor	Cyanogen chloride is a colorless gas with a sharp, pepperish odor similar to that of most tear gases; choking, lachrymatory, and irritating odor. The odor of CK often goes unnoticed because it is so irritating to the mucous membranes. CK is a liquid at temperatures below 55°F.

Chemical and Physical Properties	Molecular weight: 61.5
	Boiling point: 14°C (55°F)
	Freezing/melting point: -6°C (-21°F)
	Vapor pressure: At +25°C (77°F): 1,230 mm Hg (24 psi)
	Vapor density: 2.1
	Volatility:
	    2,600,000 mg/m^3 @ 12.8°C (55°F)
	    6,132,000 mg/m^3 @ 25°C (77°F)
	Solubility in water: slightly soluble - 6-7 percent
	pH: acidic
	Odor threshold: pungent at 1 ppm
	Specific gravity:
	    1.186g/l @ 20°C (68°F)
	    9.9 lb/gal
	Polymerization: may polymerize violently.

Incompatibilities	Unstable; polymerizes without stabilizer; stable for less than 30 days in canister munitions; will polymerize to form the solid cyanuric chloride which is corrosive and may explode. Decomposes to 2,4,6-trichloro-s-triazine which can polymerize violently.
Persistency	Short; vapor may persist in jungle and forest for some time under suitable weather conditions.
Flammability	Nonflammable, but will decompose to yield hydrochloric acid, chlorine, and hydrogen cyanide.
Physiological Properties	Cyanogen chloride irritates the eyes and respiratory tract, even in low concentrations. Acute exposure produces intense irritation of the lungs characterized by coughing and breathing problems, which may quickly lead

to a pulmonary edema. Inside the body, cyanogen chloride converts to hydrogen cyanide, which inactivates the enzyme cytochrome oxidase, preventing the utilization of oxygen by the cells. The general action of CK, interference with the use of oxygen in the body, is similar to that of AC. However, CK differs from AC in that it has strong irritating and choking effects and slows breathing.

Poison by ingestion, subcutaneous, and possibly other routes. Toxic by inhalation. Human systemic effects by inhalation: lachrymation, conjunctiva irritation, and chronic pulmonary edema or congestion. A primary irritant. A severe human eye irritant. Lips take on a pinkish coloring (purple coloring in dark-complexioned individuals), breathing becomes more difficult as the body becomes unable to absorb oxygen from the blood, the patient chokes, and breathing rate slows. These effects are accompanied by a strongly irritating tearing effect on the eyes. Death occurs within 15 minutes if kept in contact with a lethal concentration.

Toxicity	LC_{50}: 4,400 mg/m^3/1M LCt_{50} respiratory: 11,000 mg-min/m^3 ICt_{50} inhalation: 7,000 mg-min/m^3 NOAEL (inhalation): 1,525 mg-min/m^3 RfD (ingestion): 0.750 mg/l
Exposure Data	OSHA PEL: CL 0.3 ppm ACGIH TLV: CL 0.3 ppm
Emergency Response Action Levels	None established.
Rate of Detoxification	Very fast (0.02-0.1 mg/kg/min).
First Aid	Inhalation: if the patient is conscious, direct first aid and medical treatment toward the relief of any pulmonary symptoms; put patient immediately at bed rest with head slightly elevated; seek medical attention immediately; administer oxygen if there is any dyspnea or evidence of pulmonary edema; in case of long exposures, combined therapy, with oxygen plus amyl nitrite inhalations and artificial respiration is recommended. Eye Contact: flush affected areas with copious amounts of water immediately; hold eyes open while flushing. Skin Contact: wash skin promptly to remove the cyanogen chloride; remove all contaminated clothing, including shoes; do not delay. Effects of contact or inhalation may be delayed. Ingestion: give victim water or milk; do not induce vomiting.
Decontamination	Use soap and water. Keep the pH high by addition of soda ash or sodium bicarbonate. Follow up with hypochlorite solution to detoxify the cyanide.

Hydrolysis Rate	Very slow, reacts to generate hydrochloric acid and hydrogen cyanide gas.
Environmental Fate	Similar to hydrogen cyanide, but no data available.
Protective Equipment	Respiratory protection and chemical protective clothing required. Level A or B. Use caution on Level C that the correct canister is used.

Blistering Agent
Chemical Data Sheets

Blistering agents (vesicants) attack the skin, eyes, and mucous membranes, causing severe damage and serious pain. Although blistering agents may be toxic by inhalation, their major impact is in attacking unprotected personnel and causing large numbers of painful nonlethal injuries requiring medical care.

202

Material	**Levinstein Mustard (H)** or **Distilled Mustard (HD)**
Chemical Name	bis (2-chloroethyl) sulfide
Structure	
History and Use	Mustard was described in the 1850s but it was not used during the Civil War as use of chemicals was considered "unsporting." Mustard was first synthesized by Meyer in 1886, although it had been produced in very poor yield by Guthrie some 25 years previously. Had Guthrie's preparation produced a higher yield, he likely would have been severely injured.

Mustard was first used by the Germans on the night of July 12–13, 1917 near Ypres in Flanders. The French introduced mustard into their arsenal in June 1918, the British in September 1918. In one of the supreme ironies of the history of chemical warfare, the British had tested mustard during the summer of 1916, but the developers had been unable to convince the military of its utility. Meanwhile, the Germans began developing mustard in September 1916 and first filled shells with mustard in the spring of 1917. The Germans waited to introduce mustard to the battlefield until they had accumulated a large supply, knowing that it would be difficult for the Allies to catch up; indeed, it took the French 11 months and the British 14 months before they were able to use the agent on the battlefield.

Subsequent documented uses of mustard include use in Morocco in 1925, in Ethiopia during 1935, in China between 1934 and 1944, and in the Iran-Iraq war by both sides. Large quantities were prepared by both the Allies and the Axis during World War II. Although no chemical warfare agents were used in Europe or in the Pacific, there was a release of mustard into Bari harbor in Italy in 1943. Mustard was stockpiled by the Soviet Union and the United States through the Cold War.

Note that mustard is frozen (solid) below 57°F. Unless it is mixed with something to lower the freezing point, it probably will not be used in cooler weather conditions. Sulfur mustard manufactured by the Levinstein process contains up to 30 percent impurities (mostly sulfur) and is known as H. Mustard made by a distillation procedure is almost pure and is known as HD (distilled mustard). |
Military Designation	**(H)** or **(HD)**
CAS	505-60-2
Formula	$(CICH_2CH_2)_2S$ (H contains approximately 30 percent sulfur impurities)
Appearance and Odor	Mustard agent liquid is colorless when pure, but it is normally a yellow to brown oily substance. Mustard agent vapor is colorless with a slight garlic- or mustard-like odor.
Chemical and Physical	Boiling point: 217.2°C (423°F)

Properties	Freezing/melting point: 14°C (57°F)
	Vapor pressure: At +25°C (77°F): 0.11 mm Hg (0.002 psi)
	Vapor density: 5.5
	Volatility:
	    610 to 920 mg/m^3 at 25°C (77°F)
	    75 mg/m^3 @ 0°C (solid) (32°F)
	    610 mg/m^3 @ 20°C (liquid) (68°F)
	    2,860 mg/m^3 @ 40°C (104°F)
	Solubility in water: 0.8 mg/l very sparingly
	pH: acidic
	Odor threshold: 2.30×10^{-3} ppm (2.3 ppb)
	Specific gravity:
	    1.2741 @ 20°C (68°F)
	    10.6 lb/gal
	Polymerization: No

Incompatibilities	Steam, strong acids, and oxidizing compounds.
Persistency	Despite the relative rapidity of the hydrolysis reaction, H has been found to persist in soil or even under water for decades. In such incidents of long-term persistence, the common thread is the presence of bulk H. While the hydrolysis of dissolved H is relatively fast, the dissolution of H does not occur rapidly. Can be active for at least three years in soil; stable for days to a week, under normal atmospheric temperature; slowly hydrolyzed by water; destroyed by strong oxidizing agents.
Flammability	Flash point:104°C (219°F); will burn to give off HCl and SO$_2$.
Physiological Properties	Confirmed human carcinogen with experimental carcinogenic, neoplastigenic, and tumorigenic data. A human poison by inhalation and subcutaneous routes. An experimental poison by inhalation, skin contact, subcutaneous, and intravenous routes. An experimental teratogen. A severe human skin and eye irritant. Human mutation data reported. A military blistering gas. Strongly affects the skin, eyes, lungs, and gastric system. Pulmonary lesions are often fatal. It penetrates the skin deeply and injures blood vessels. Minute amounts can cause inflammation. Secondary infections are common. Mustard acts first as a cell irritant and later as a cell poison. It destroys the cellular DNA across large areas of tissue, with the body responding by secreting large amounts of interstitial fluid and causing the formation of blisters. Local action may result in conjunctivitis; a reddening of the skin followed by the formation of blisters; and inflammation of the nose and throat, brachia, bronchi, and lung tissue. Healing is delayed because mustard interferes with blood vessel function and because the presence of large amounts of dead tissue serves as a good growth medium for bacteria. Very slow onset time. Symptoms occur only after 4–6 hours; can be delayed up to 24 hours.
Toxicity	Carcinogen.

	Burns at 10 μg LC_{50}: 1500 mg/m^3 LD_{50}: 100 mg/kg LCt_{50} inhalation: 231 ppm for a 1-minute exposure LCt_{50} skin (vapor): 10,000/mg-min/m^3 LCt_{50} skin (liquid): 7 g/person ICt_{50} inhalation: 21.5 ppm for a 1-minute exposure (150 mg-min/m^3) ICt_{50} skin (vapor): 2,000 mg-min/m^3 ICt_{50} eye: 12–150 mg-min/m^3 ICt_{50} eyes: 200 mg-min/m^3 ICt_{50} inhalation: 1,500 mg-min/m^3 ICt_{50} skin: 2,000 mg-min/m^3 @ 21.1 to 26.7°C (70° to 80°F) (humid environment) ICt_{50} skin:1,000 mg-min/m^3 @ 90°C (194°F) (dry environment) LCt_{50} inhalation: 1,500 mg-min/m^3 LC_{Lo} inhalation: 1,496 mg-min/m^3 (10 min) LD_{50} Oral: 0.7 mg/kg 1 percent lethality: 150 mg-min/m^3 No-deaths level: 100 mg-min/m^3 NOAEL: 1.4 mg-min/m^3(inhalation)
Exposure Data	PEL: 0.0005 ppm TWA: 0.003 mg/m^3
Emergency Response Action Levels	IDLH: 0.0001 mg/m^3 (0.0005 ppm)
Rate of Detoxification	Effects are cumulative.
First Aid	There is no treatment or antidote that can affect the basic cause of mustard agent injury. Instead, efforts must be made to treat the symptoms. By far the most important measure is to rapidly and thoroughly decontaminate the patient and thereby prevent further exposure. This decontamination will also decrease the risk of exposure to staff. Clothes are removed, the skin is decontaminated with a suitable decontaminant and washed with soap and water. If hair is suspected to be contaminated, it must be shaved off. Inhalation: remove victim from the source immediately; administer artificial respiration if breathing has stopped; administer oxygen if breathing is difficult; seek medical attention immediately. Eye Contact: speed in decontaminating the eyes is absolutely essential; remove person from the liquid source, flush the eyes immediately with water by tilting the head to the side, pulling the eyelids apart with the fingers, and pouring water slowly into the eyes; do not cover eyes with bandages; if necessary, protect eyes by means of dark or opaque goggles; seek medical attention immediately. Skin Contact: don respiratory protective masks and gloves; remove victim from agent source immediately; flush skin and clothes with 5-percent

205

	solution of sodium hypochlorite or liquid household bleach within 1 minute; cut and remove contaminated clothing; flush contaminated skin area again with 5-percent sodium hypochlorite solution; then wash contaminated skin area with soap and water; seek medical attention immediately. Ingestion: do not induce vomiting; give victim milk to drink; seek medical attention immediately.
Decontamination	Immediately flush contaminated skin or eyes with water and neutralize with a 2.5-percent solution of sodium thiosulfate. Dilute hypochlorite may also be used. A nonaqueous equipment decontamination solution "DS2" (2-percent NaOH, 70 percent diethylenetriamine, 28 percent ethylene glycol monomethyl ether) was developed in which the conjugate base of the glycol ether reacts rapidly with mustard via double elimination.
Hydrolysis Rate	Very slow. Hydrolysis products: Hydrochloric acid and thiodiglycol.
Environmental Fate	When released on soil at low concentrations, bis (2-chloroethyl) sulfide should be lost by hydrolysis and volatilization. Some leaching should also occur. However, no experimental data are available on the fate of very low concentrations of bis (2-chloroethyl) sulfide in soil. When bis (2-chloroethyl) sulfide is introduced into water at very low concentrations so that it is dissolved, it will rapidly hydrolyze, forming mustard chlorohydrin, and thiodiglycol. At 0, 25, and 40°C, the estimated half-lives of bis (2-chloroethyl) sulfide when dissolved in large amounts of water are 1.75 hr, 4 minutes, and 43 seconds, respectively. Volatilization will be slow by comparison. Hydrolysis in seawater will be a factor of 2.5 slower because of the common-ion effect exerted by the chloride ion. Despite its high rate of hydrolysis, undissolved bis (2-chloroethyl) sulfide may persist for longer periods of time because its rate of solution is slow. In the atmosphere, bis (2-chloroethyl) sulfide vapor will degrade primarily by reaction with photochemically produced hydroxyl radicals; the resulting half-life is 1.4 days. Releases in chemical warfare may be by aerial spraying or from bursting munitions that would shower droplets of the chemical agents over the terrain. The persistence of HD sprayed on several soils at a variety of weather conditions ranged from 31 to 51 hrs at 25°C and 50 to 92 days at 0°C. Persistence was lowest for heavy rain and highest in light rain. Persistence on snow has reported to range from 14–56 days. The bis (2-chloroethyl) sulfide does not appear to migrate into the snow, but rather stays on the surface. Disposal by land or sea burial might result in releases of large quantities of neat bis (2-chloroethyl) sulfide. Bulk quantities of bis (2-chloroethyl) sulfide buried on land may last for decades. When bulk quantities of bis (2-chloroethyl) sulfide are disposed of at sea, some bis (2-chloroethyl) sulfide will form a surface film that will disappear as a result of hydrolysis and volatilization within several days. Most of the bis (2-chloroethyl) sulfide will sink to the bottom of the water because bis (2-chloroethyl) sulfide is heavier than water. Bis (2-chloroethyl) sulfide will be degraded by hydrolysis; however, the hydrolysis will be limited by the rate of dissolution. The rate of dissolution will depend on the exposed surface, the amount of agitation, and the temperature. The temperature at the

	bottom of a body of water may be below 14.4°C and bis (2-chloroethyl) sulfide will then be a solid. Dissolution under these circumstances may take several months to years. Dissolved bis (2-chloroethyl) sulfide in the main body of seawater will be lost by hydrolysis with its half-life ranging from 15 min at 25°C to 175 min at 5°C.
Protective Equipment	Respiratory protection and chemical protective clothing required. Level A, B, and C may be used depending on air monitoring.

Material	**Nitrogen Mustard**
Chemical Name	ethylbis(2-chloroethyl)amine or 2,2'-dichloro triethylamine
Structure	
History and Use	HN-1 was the first compound of the HN series developed in the late 1920s and early 1930s. HN-1 was designed as a pharmaceutical (to remove warts) and became a military agent; HN-2 was designed as a military agent and became a pharmaceutical; HN-3 was designed as a military agent and is the only one of these agents that remains anywhere as a military agent. These agents are more immediately toxic than the sulfur mustards.
Military Designation	**HN1**
CAS	538-07-8
Formula	$C_6H_{13}Cl_2N$
Appearance and Odor	It is oily, colorless-to-pale yellow with a faint fishy or musty odor.

Chemical and Physical Properties	Molecular weight: 170
	Boiling point: 85°C (185°F) (decomposes)
	Freezing/melting point: -34°C (-29°F)
	Vapor pressure:
	    At 10°C (50°F): 0.077 mmHg (0.0015 psi)
	    At 25°C (77°F): 0.25 mmHg (0.005 psi)
	    At 40°C (104°F): 0.744 mmHg (0.014 psi)
	Vapor density: 5.9
	Volatility:
	    127 mg/m³ @ -10°C (14°F)
	    308 mg/m³ @ 0°C (32°F)
	    1520 mg/m³ @ 20°C (68°F)
	    2290 mg/m³ @25°C (77°F)
	    3100 mg/m³ @ 30°C (86°F)
	Solubility in water: Sparingly soluble in water
	pH: neutral to slightly acidic
	Odor threshold: none listed
	Specific gravity:
	    1.0861 at 23°C (73°F)
	    9.1 lb/gal
	Polymerization: Slowly

Incompatibilities	Strong oxidizers, strong base.
Persistency	Depends on the weather; somewhat shorter duration of effectiveness for HD, heavily splashed liquid of which persists 1 to 2 days under average weather conditions, and a week or more under very cold conditions.

Flammability	Not flammable, but will thermally decompose to generate nitrogen oxides and hydrochloric acid.
Physiological Properties	Irritates the eyes in quantities that do not significantly damage the skin or respiratory tract, insofar as single exposures are concerned. After mild vapor exposure, there may be no skin lesions. After severe vapor exposures or after exposure to the liquid, erythema may appear. Irritation and itching may occur. Later, blisters may appear in the erythematous areas. Effects on the respiratory tract include irritation of the nose and throat, hoarseness progressing to loss of voice, and a persistent cough. Fever, labored respiration, and moist rales develop. Bronchial pneumonia may appear after the first 24 hours. It has been observed that workers briefly exposed to nitrogen mustard in concentrations estimated to be between 10 and 100 ppm became severely ill with nausea, vomiting, and dilated pupils. Following ingestion or systemic absorption, material causes inhibition of cell mitosis, resulting in depression of the blood-forming mechanism and injury to other tissues. Severe diarrhea, which may be hemorrhagic, occurs. Lesions are most marked in the small intestine and consist of degenerative changes and necrosis in the mucous membranes. Ingestion of 2 to 6 milligrams causes nausea and vomiting.
Toxicity	LD_{50} dermal (mouse): 13 mg/kg ICt_{50} eye contact: 200 mg-min/m^3 ICt_{50} skin: 9,000 mg-min/m^3 LCt_{50} inhalation: 1,500 mg-min/m^3 LCt_{50} skin: 20,000 mg-min/m^3 (vapor) NOAEL inhalation: 2 mg-min/m^3
Exposure Data	TLV: 0.003 mg/m^3
Emergency Response Action Levels	None established.
Rate of Detoxification	HN-1 is not naturally detoxified by the body; therefore, repeated exposure produces a cumulative effect.
First Aid	Inhalation: remove from source immediately; give artificial respiration if breathing has stopped; administer oxygen if breathing is difficult; seek medical attention immediately. Eye Contact: flush eyes immediately with water for 10–15 minutes, pulling eyelids apart with fingers and pouring water into eyes; do not cover eyes with bandages; protect eyes with dark or opaque goggles after flushing eyes; seek medical attention immediately. Skin Contact: don respiratory mask and gloves; remove victim from source immediately and remove contaminated clothing; decontaminate the skin immediately by flushing with a 5 percent solution of liquid household bleach; wash off with soap and water after 3-4 minutes to remove decontamination agent and protect against erythema; seek medical attention immediately. To prevent systemic toxicity, decontamination should be done

	as late as 2 or 3 hours after exposure even if it increases the severity of the local reaction; further clean with soap and water. Ingestion: do not induce vomiting; give victims milk to drink; seek medical attention immediately.
Decontamination	Use vinegar to dissolve and remove material. To decompose, use strong base like sodium hydroxide. Use of hypochlorite solutions may produce some toxic chloramines.
Hydrolysis Rate	Toxic intermediate products are produced during hydrolysis. Approximate half-life in water at 25°C is 1.3 minutes. Decomposition comes through slow change into quaternary ammonium salts. Decomposition point is below 94°C.
Environmental Fate	NA
Protective Equipment	Respiratory protection and chemical protective clothing required. Level A, B, and C may be used depending on air monitoring.

210

Material	**Mechlorethamine, Nitrogen Mustard**
Chemical Name	2,2'-dichloro-n-methyldiethylamine or bis (2-chloroethyl) methylamine
Structure	
History and Use	HN-2, the second of a series of nitrogen mustard compounds developed in the late 1920s and early 1930s, was designed as a military agent and became a pharmaceutical substance called mustine. The chemical intermediate it produces is used as an antineoplastic drug. These agents are more immediately toxic than the sulfur mustards.
Military Designation	**HN2**
CAS	51-75-2
Formula	$(ClCH_2CH_2)_2NCH_3$
Appearance and Odor	HN-2 is a pale amber to yellow oily liquid; fruity odor in high concentrations; smells like soft soap with a fishy smell in low concentrations.

Chemical and Physical Properties	Molecular weight: 156
	Boiling point: 75°C (167°F) decomposes
	Freezing/melting point: -60°C (-76°F)
	Vapor pressure:
	    At 10°C (50°F): 0.13 mmHg (0.0025 psi)
	    At 25°C (77°F): 0.42 mmHg (0.008 psi)
	    At 40°C (104°F): 1.25 mmHg (0.024 psi)
	Vapor density: 5.4
	Volatility:
	    1,150 mg/m^3 @ 10°C (50°F)
	    3,580 mg/m^3 @ 25°C (77°F)
	    5,100 mg/m^3 @ 30°C (86°F)
	    10,000 mg/m^3 @ 40°C (104°F)
	Solubility in water: Slightly soluble in water 12 g/l
	pH: neutral to slightly acidic
	Odor threshold:
	Specific gravity:
	    1.15 at 20°C (68°F)
	    9.6 lb/gal
	Polymerization: Polymerized components will present an explosion hazard in open air.

Incompatibilities	Strong oxidizers, strong bases.
Persistency	Depends on munitions used and the weather; somewhat shorter duration of effectiveness for HD, heavily splashed liquid of which persists 1 to 2 days under average weather conditions and a week or more under very cold

	conditions.
Flammability	Flash point: 110°C (230°F)(open cup)
Physiological Properties	HN-2 is highly irritating to the eyes and throat; in high concentrations it can cause blindness. Absorbed into the bloodstream, it will seriously interfere with the functioning of hemoglobin and will eventually damage the endocrine system. HN-2 is a vesicant (blister agent) and alkylating agent producing cytotoxic action on the hematopoietic (blood-forming) tissues, which are especially sensitive. HN-2 is not naturally detoxified by the body; therefore, repeated exposure produces a cumulative effect.
Toxicity	Eye effects (rabbit, adult): 400 μg-severe irritation Eye effects (rabbit, adult): 20 μg/30M ICt_{50} eye contact: 100 mg-min/m^3 ICt_{50} percutaneous vapor: 9,500 mg-min/m^3 LCt_{50} inhalation: 3,000 mg-min/m^3 NOAEL inhalation: 2 mg-min/m^3
Exposure Data	Confirmed carcinogen.
Emergency Response Action Levels	None established.
Rate of Detoxification	None established.
First Aid	Inhalation: remove from source immediately; give artificial respiration if breathing has stopped; administer oxygen if breathing is difficult; seek medical attention immediately. Eye Contact: flush eyes immediately with water for 10–15 minutes, pulling eyelids apart with fingers and pouring water into eyes; do not cover eyes with bandages; protect eyes with dark or opaque goggles after flushing eyes; seek medical attention immediately. Skin Contact: don respiratory mask and gloves; remove victim from source immediately and remove contaminated clothing; decontaminate the skin immediately by flushing with a 5 percent solution of liquid household bleach; wash off with soap and water after 3–4 minutes to remove decontamination agent and protect against erythema; seek medical attention immediately. To prevent systemic toxicity, decontaminate as late as 2 or 3 hours after exposure even if it increases the severity of the local reaction; further clean with soap and water. Ingestion: do not induce vomiting; give victims milk to drink; seek medical attention immediately.
Decontamination	Use vinegar to dissolve and remove material. To decompose, use strong base like sodium hydroxide. Use of hypochlorite solutions may produce some toxic chloramines.
Hydrolysis Rate	Slow, except in presence of alkalis; products formed are complex polymeric

212

	quaternary ammonium salts; dimerizes fairly rapidly in water. Approximate half-life in water at 25°C is 4 minutes.
Environmental Fate	Mechlorethamine's production and use as an antineoplastic agent and its former production as a gas warfare agent may result in its release to the environment through various waste streams. If released to the atmosphere, mechlorethamine will mainly exist in the vapor phase in the ambient atmosphere based on an estimated vapor pressure of 65 mm Hg at 25°C. Vapor-phase mechlorethamine is degraded in the atmosphere by reaction with photochemically produced hydroxyl radicals with an estimated half-life of about 2 days. An estimated K_{oc} (water/octanol partition coefficient) of 74 suggests that mechlorethamine will have high mobility in soil. Volatilization from dry soil surfaces may be an important fate process based on its vapor pressure; however, mechlorethamine is not expected to volatilize from moist soil surfaces because of its low Henry's Law constant. Mechlorethamine is expected to rapidly hydrolyze in both moist soil and water. A hydrolysis half-life of 11 hours at 25°C was measured in water; methyldiethanolamine is the expected product from this reaction. Mechlorethamine is not expected to adsorb to suspended matter in the water column based on its K_{oc} value or to volatilize from water surfaces given an estimated Henry's Law constant of 8.5×10^{-8} atm-m^3/mole. Bioconcentration in aquatic organisms should not occur based on an estimated BCF (bioconcentration factor) value of 3.
Protective Equipment	Respiratory protection and chemical protective clothing required. Level A, B, and C may be used depending on air monitoring.

Material	**Trimustine**
Chemical Name	tris(2-chloroethyl)amine or 2,2',2"-trichlorotriethylamine
Structure	
History and Use	HN-3 was the last of the nitrogen mustard agents developed. It was designed as a military agent and is the only one of the nitrogen mustards that is still used for military purposes. It is the principal representative of the nitrogen mustards because its vesicant properties are almost equal to those of HD.
Military Designation	**HN3**
CAS	555-77-1
Formula	$N(CH_2CH_2Cl)_3$
Appearance and Odor	HN-3 is a colorless to pale yellow liquid with a butter almond odor; most stable in storage of three nitrogen mustards.

Chemical and Physical Properties	Molecular weight: 204.5
	Boiling point: 256°C (492°F) decomposes
	Freezing/melting point: 3.7°C (-25°F)
	Vapor pressure: At 25°C (77°F): 0.0109 mm Hg (0.0002 psi)
	Vapor density: 7.1
	Volatility:
	    13 mg/m³ @ 0°C (32°F)
	    121 mg/m³ @ 25°C (77°F)
	    180 mg/m³ @ 30°C (86°F)
	    390 mg/m³ @ 40°C (104°F)
	Solubility in water: Sparingly soluble in water 0.16 g/l
	pH: acidic
	Odor threshold:
	Specific gravity:
	    1.24 at 20°C (68°F)
	    10.3 lb/gal
	Polymerization: Slow but steady polymerization; polymerized components will present an explosion hazard in open air.

Incompatibilities	Strong oxidizers and strong base.
Persistency	Considerably longer than for HD. HN-3 use is emphasized for terrain denial. It can be approximately 2x or 3x the persistence of HD and adheres well to equipment and personnel, especially in cold weather.
Flammability	Material is not expected to be a fire hazard.
Physiological Properties	HN-3 is a cumulative poison that is highly irritating to the eyes and throat. Eye irritation, tearing, and photophobia develop immediately after exposure. The median incapacitating dose for eyes is 200 mg-min/m³. Blistering of

	the skin may occur after liquid exposure, severe or persistent exposure, or vapor condensation in sweat. Usually a rash will develop from liquid contamination within an hour, replaced by blistering between 6 and 12 hours after exposure. HN-3 interferes with hemoglobin functioning in the blood, hindering the production of new blood cells and destroying white blood cells.
Toxicity	ICt_{50} eye: 200 mg-min/m^3 ICt_{50} skin: 2,500 mg-min/m^3 LCt_{50} inhalation: 1,500 mg-min/m^3 LCt_{50} skin: 10,000 mg-min/m^3 NOAEL inhalation: 2 mg-min/m^3
Exposure Data	None established.
Emergency Response Action Levels	None established.
Rate of Detoxification	Respiratory protection and chemical protective clothing required. Level A, B, and C may be used depending on air monitoring.
First Aid	Inhalation: remove from source immediately; give artificial respiration if breathing has stopped; administer oxygen if breathing is difficult; seek medical attention immediately. Eye Contact: flush eyes immediately with water for 10-15 minutes, pulling eyelids apart with fingers and pouring water into eyes; do not cover eyes with bandages; protect eyes with dark or opaque goggles after flushing eyes; seek medical attention immediately. Skin Contact: don respiratory mask and gloves; remove victim from source immediately and remove contaminated clothing; decontaminate the skin immediately by flushing with a 5 percent solution of liquid household bleach; wash off with soap and water after 3-4 minutes to remove decontamination agent and protect against erythema; seek medical attention immediately. To prevent systemic toxicity, decontaminate as late as 2 or 3 hours after exposure even if it increases the severity of the local reaction; further clean with soap and water. Ingestion: do not induce vomiting; give victims milk to drink; seek medical attention immediately.
Decontamination	Use vinegar to dissolve and remove material. To decompose, use strong base like sodium hydroxide. Use of hypochlorite solutions may produce some toxic chloramines.
Hydrolysis Rate	Slow, except in presence of alkalis; products formed are complex polymeric quaternary ammonium salts; dimerizes fairly rapidly in water. Approximate half-life in water at 25°C is 4 minutes.

Street Smart^{TM} Chemistry

Environmental Fate	Tris(2-chloroethyl)amine belongs to the nitrogen mustard group of compounds. It is produced in small quantities as the hydrochloride and may enter the waste stream as such during the production process. If released to either soil or water, hydrolysis is expected to be a major fate process for tris(2-chloroethyl)amine, especially under weakly alkaline conditions. An estimated Henry's Law constant of 3×10^{-7} atm-m^3/mole indicates that this compound is essentially nonvolatile, and thus volatilization from water and moist soil will not be an important environmental fate process. An estimated K_{oc} value of 672 suggests that tris(2-chloroethyl)amine has a low to moderate mobility potential through soil. However, as hydrolysis may proceed quickly, mobility of this compound through the soil is not expected to be a major fate process. An estimated BCF value of 30 suggests that this compound will not bioconcentrate in aquatic organisms and hydrolysis should preclude bioconcentration from being a major fate process. If released to the atmosphere, tris(2-chloroethyl)amine is expected to degrade rapidly with a half-life of 5 hours. Insufficient data are available to predict the relative importance or rate of biodegradation in soil or water.
Protective Equipment	Respiratory protection and chemical protective clothing required. Level A, B, and C may be used depending on air monitoring.

Material	**Lewisite**
Chemical Name	dichloro (2-chlorovinyl) arsine
Structure	
History and Use	Lewisite was discovered near the end of World War I by a team of Americans headed by Capt. W. Lee Lewis working at Catholic University in Washington, DC. Lewisite was never used because of the armistice; a shipload of Lewisite-filled munitions was crossing the Atlantic at the cessation of hostilities. In an interesting footnote, the Germans had been searching for a nonpersistent vesicant in early 1918, but rejected Lewisite in favor of ethyldichloroarsine. Production took place in the United States, Great Britain, France, Italy, the Soviet Union, and Japan in the immediate post-war years. During World War II, the American, British, Soviet, German, and Japanese armies had considerable stocks of Lewisite available. Following World War II, Lewisite was considered obsolete by the major powers because of the discovery that 2,3-dimercaptopropanol ("British anti-Lewisite") was an inexpensive and effective antidote to Lewisite exposure. However, it may have been used recently by the Iraqis in addition to mustard agent. Industrially produced Lewisite has a strong penetrating geranium odor; the pure compound is odorless. Lewisite is actually a complex mixture of several compounds, all of which occur as cis- and trans-isomers. In chemical agent grade Lewisite, the L-1 isomer generally predominates. The three homologues form because Lewisite is produced by the catalyzed reaction of arsenic trichloride and acetylene. L-1 forms initially, but it will react with some of the acetylene to form L-2, which will in turn react to form L-3. Proper choice of the catalyst and reaction conditions are necessary for a reasonable yield of L-1. L-1 is the vesicant agent; it reacts with the active sites of certain enzymes. L-2 and L-3 are also toxic, but considerably less so than L-1.
Military Designation	**L**
CAS	541-25-3
Formula	$ClCHCHAsCl_2$
Appearance and Odor	Pure Lewisite is a colorless, oily liquid with very little odor. The plant sample (war gas) has a geranium-like odor and is an amber to dark brown liquid.

Chemical and Physical Properties	Molecular weight: 207
	 Boiling point: 190°C (374°F): decomposes
	      197°C (386°F): Trans isomer
	      170°C (338°F): Cis isomer
	 Freezing/melting point: -53°C (-64°F)
	      -1°C (30°F):Trans isomer

	-45°C (-49°F): Cis isomer
	Vapor pressure:
	    At 20°C (68°F): 0.22 mm Hg (0.004 psi)
	    At 25°C (77°F): 0.35 mm Hg (0.007 psi)
	Vapor density: 7.2
	Volatility:
	    1,060 mg/m^3 @ 0°C (32°F)
	    4,480 mg/m^3 @ 20°C (68°F)
	    8,620 mg/m^3 @ 30°C (86°F)
	Solubility in water: slightly soluble 0.5 g/L
	pH: not available
	Odor threshold: 1.40×10^{-2} mg/l (1.6 ppm)
	Specific gravity:
	    1.89
	    15.8 lb/gal
	Polymerization: Does not occur.

Incompatibilities	Strong base.
Persistency	Somewhat shorter than for HD; very short duration under humid conditions.
Flammability	Material itself does not burn or burns with difficulty.
Physiological Properties	Produces effects similar to mustard but additionally acts as a systemic poison causing pulmonary edema, diarrhea, restlessness, weakness, subnormal temperature, and low blood pressure. First and foremost, L is a blister agent, then a toxic lung irritant, and finally a systemic poison. In its liquid form, L will cause immediate eye irritation and permanent loss of vision if not decontaminated within one minute. L produces an immediate strong stinging sensation of the skin, with reddening beginning in 30 minutes. Blistering will appear after 30 hours. When inhaled in high concentrations, it may be fatal in as short a time as 10 minutes.
Toxicity	LCt_{50} eyes: <300 mg-min/m^3 LCt_{50} inhalation: 1,200 to 1,500 mg-min/m^3 LCt_{50} skin: >1,500 mg-min/m^3 LCt_{50} skin vapor: 100,000 mg-min/m^3 exposure LD_{Lo} (skin): 20 mg/kg 1 percent lethality: 150 mg-min/m^3 No-deaths Level: 100 mg-min/m^3 NOAEL oral: 0.5 to 1.0 mg/kg (estimated based on animal studies); as little as 2 ml on the skin can cause death
Exposure Data	TLV 0.003 mg/m^3
Emergency Response Action Levels	None established.
Rate of Detoxification	The body does not detoxify L.
First Aid	Inhalation: remove from the source immediately; give artificial respiration if breathing has stopped; administer oxygen if breathing is difficult; seek

218

	medical attention immediately. Eye Contact: speed in decontaminating the eyes is absolutely essential; remove person from the liquid source; flush the eyes immediately with water for 10-15 minutes by tilting the head to the side, pulling eyelids apart with fingers, and pouring water slowly into the eyes; do not cover eyes with bandages; if necessary, protect eyes by means of dark or opaque goggles; seek medical attention immediately. Skin Contact: remove victim from source immediately and remove contaminated clothing; immediately decontaminate affected areas by flushing with 10 percent sodium carbonate solution; wash off with soap and water after 3 to 4 minutes to protect against erythema; seek medical attention immediately. Ingestion: do not induce vomiting; give victim milk to drink; seek medical attention immediately.
Decontamination	Dimercaptopropanol, (British Anti-Lewisite) is best, but use of alkaline solutions of hypochlorite will work also.
Hydrolysis Rate	Rapid in the liquid or vapor state. It hydrolyzes in acidic medium to form HCl and nonvolatile (solid) chlorovinylarsenious oxide, which is a less potent vesicant than Lewisite. Hydrolysis in alkaline medium, as in decontamination with alcoholic caustic or carbonate solution, produces acetylene and trisodium arsenate (Na_3ASO_4). Therefore, decontaminated solution would contain toxic arsenic.
Environmental Fate	Lewisite has been produced as a chemical warfare agent and is considered the best arsenical war gas; its use as a war gas will release it directly to the atmosphere with subsequent dispersal to soil and water. If released to the atmosphere, it will degrade in the vapor phase by reaction with photochemically produced hydroxyl radicals (estimated half-life of about 1.2 days). Reaction with ozone will contribute to Lewisite's atmospheric degradation, but it will not be as rapid as reaction with hydroxyl radicals. If released to moist soil or water, Lewisite will hydrolyze readily to form Lewisite oxide. If released to soil surfaces, it will readily evaporate as long as it does not undergo conversion to the oxide. Lewisite's use as a war gas will expose humans through inhalation and dermal contact.
Protective Equipment	Respiratory protection and chemical protective clothing required. Level A, B, and C may be used depending on air monitoring.

219

Material	**Phosgene Oxime**
Chemical Name	dichloroformoxime
Structure	Cl \ >=N, Cl OH
History and Use	Phosgene oxime was the subject of German and Russian interest prior to and during World War II.
Military Designation	**CX**
CAS	None established.
Formula	Cl_2CNOH
Appearance and Odor	May appear as a colorless, low-melting point (crystalline) solid or as a liquid. It has a high vapor pressure, decomposes slowly at normal temperatures, and has a disagreeable, penetrating odor.

Chemical and Physical Properties	Molecular weight: 114
	Boiling point: 129°C (264°F)
	Freezing/melting point: 35 to 40°C (95 to 104°F)
	Vapor pressure:
	    At 25°C (77°F): 11.2 mm Hg (0.22 psi)
	    At 40°C (104°F): 13 mm Hg (0.25 psi)
	Vapor density: 3.9
	Volatility: 76,000 mg/m³ @ 40°C (104°F)
	Solubility in water: Forms hydrate that is very soluble in water (70 percent)
	pH: unknown
	Odor threshold: unknown
	Specific gravity: unknown
	Polymerization: unknown

Incompatibilities	Reacts violently in alkaline solution.
Persistency	Soil: approximately 2 hours. Surface (wood, metal, masonry, rubber, paint): relatively nonpersistent. Water: relatively nonpersistent.
Flammability	Not flammable; will combust to give HCN, nitrogen oxides, and HCl.
Physiological Properties	Produces instant and almost intolerable skin pain and local tissue destruction immediately on contact. CX vapors are violently irritating to the eyes. Very low concentrations can cause inflammation, lacrimation, and temporary blindness; higher concentrations can cause corneal corrosion and dimming of vision. Contact with the skin can cause skin lesions of the corrosive type. It is characterized by the appearance within 30 seconds of a central blanched area surrounded by an erythematous ring. Subcutaneous edema follows in about 15 minutes. After 24 hours, the central blanched area becomes necrotic and darkened, and an eschar is formed in a few days.

	Healing is accompanied by sloughing of the scab. Itching will sometimes occur during healing, delaying the process for up to two months. It is one of the most irritating chemicals known.
Toxicity	Beginning irritation (12 sec): 0.2 mg-min/m^3 Unbearable irritation (1 min): 3 mg-min/m^3 Ct_{50}: 200 mg-min/m^3 (eye) Ct_{50}: 2500 mg-min/m^3 (erythema) LCt_{50}: 3,200 mg-min/m^3 (estimated)
Exposure Data	None established.
Emergency Response Action Levels	None established.
Rate of Detoxification	Unknown.
First Aid	Inhalation: remove from the source immediately; give artificial respiration if breathing has stopped; seek medical attention immediately. Eye Contact: flush eyes immediately with copious amounts of water; seek medical attention immediately. Skin Contact: remove victim from the source immediately; decontaminate the skin immediately by flushing with copious amounts of water to remove any phosgene oxime which has not yet reacted with tissue; seek medical attention immediately. Ingestion: do not induce vomiting; seek medical attention immediately.
Decontamination	Wash with water. Neutralize with soda ash.
Hydrolysis Rate	Very slow in water at pH 7; 5 percent decomposition in 6 days at room temperature in acid solutions. Carbon dioxide, hydrochloric acid, and hydroxyl amine are hydrolysis products.
Environmental Fate	Unknown.
Protective Equipment	Respiratory protection and chemical protective clothing required. Level A, B, and C may be used depending on air monitoring.

Nerve Agent
Chemical Data Sheets

Nerve agents like tabun, sarin and VX act by blocking nerve impulses, causing convulsions and heart and respiratory failure. They are among the most toxic compounds produced. A lethal dose for a normal human is as small as the amount that would fit on a pin head.

Material	**Tabun**
Chemical Name	O-Ethyl N, N-dimethylphosphoramidocyanidate or dimethylphosphoramidocyanidic acid, ethyl ester
Structure	
History and Use	Tabun (GA) is generally believed to be the first of the nerve agents developed. The derivation of the agent symbol (GA) results from its country of origin, Germany, and its order of discovery. Tabun was originally discovered in 1936 by G. Schrader of I. G. Farben in Germany, and was first produced industrially in 1942 at Dyhernfurth-am-Oder in Silesia. A short history of the development of nerve gas describes the research and development of the nerve agents in Germany prior to and during World War II. Tabun was used by the Iraqis during the Iran-Iraq war. Tabun is a colorless liquid with a fruity odor. The industrial product has a brownish color and an odor reminiscent of bitter almonds due to the formation of hydrogen cyanide. Tabun produced by the Germans generally contains 5-20 percent chlorobenzene as solvent and stabilizer.
Military Designation	**GA**
CAS	77-81-6
Formula	$(CH_3)_2 N(C_2H_5O) CNPO$
Appearance and Odor	G-type nerve agents are clear, colorless, and tasteless liquids, chemically similar to organophosphate pesticides such as malathion or parathion. GA has a slightly fruity odor.

Chemical and Physical Properties	Molecular weight: 162
	Boiling point: 246°C (475°F)
	Freezing/melting point: -50°C (-58°F)
	Vapor pressure:
	    At 25°C (77°F): 0.07 mm Hg (0.001 psi)
	Vapor density: 5.6
	Volatility:
	    90 mg/m³ @ 0°C (32°F)
	    610 mg/m³ @ 25°C (77°F)
	    858 mg/m³ @ 30°C (86°F)
	Solubility in water: soluble 72 g/l
	pH: unknown
	Odor threshold: unknown
	Specific gravity:
	    1.07
	    8.9 lb/gal

	Polymerization: does not occur.
Incompatibilities	Unknown
Persistency	Heavy concentrations of liquid agent may persist for one to two days.
Flammability	78°C (172°F)
Physiological Properties	G-type nerve agents are considered to be nonpersistent chemical agents that may present a significant vapor hazard to the respiratory tract, eyes, or skin. GA-type nerve agents affect the body by blocking the action of the enzyme acetylcholinesterase. When this enzyme is blocked, large amounts of the chemical acetylcholine build up at critical places within the nervous system, causing hyperactivity of the muscles and body organs stimulated by these nerves. The signs and symptoms of exposure to GA-type nerve agents depend upon the route of exposure and the amount of exposure. Signs and symptoms are the same regardless of the route the poison enters the body (by inhalation, absorption, or ingestion): runny nose; tightness of chest; dimness of vision and myosis (pinpointing of the eye pupils); difficulty in breathing; drooling and excessive sweating; nausea; vomiting; cramps, and involuntary defecation and urination; twitching, jerking, and staggering; and headache, confusion, drowsiness, coma, and convulsion. These signs and symptoms are followed by cessation of breathing and death.
Toxicity	LCt_{50} respiratory: 135 mg-min/m^3 (15 l/minute) LCt_{50} skin, liquid: 1.5 gm/person LCt_{50} skin, vapor: 30,000 mg-min/m^3 ICt_{50} respiratory: 300 mg-min/m^3 LD_{50} skin: 14 to 15 mg/kg
Exposure Data	TLV: 0.0001 mg/m^3
Emergency Response Action Levels	None established.
Rate of Detoxification	Slow.
First Aid	Inhalation: hold breath and don respiratory protection mask; if severe signs of agent exposure appear, administer immediately, in rapid succession, all three nerve agent antidote kits Mark I injectors; use mouth-to-mouth resuscitation when approved mask-bag or oxygen delivery systems are not available; do not use mouth-to-mouth resuscitation when facial contamination exists; administer oxygen if breathing is difficult; seek medical attention immediately. Eye Contact: flush eyes immediately with water for 10–15 minutes, then don a respiratory protective mask. Although myosis may be an early sign of agent exposure, do not administer an injection when myosis is the only sign present; seek medical attention immediately. Skin Contact: don respiratory mask and remove victim's contaminated

	clothing; wash contaminated skin with copious amounts of soap and water immediately using 10 percent sodium carbonate solution, or 5 percent liquid household bleach; rinse well with water to remove decontamination; if local sweating and muscular symptoms occur, administer an intramuscular injection with the Mark I kit; seek medical attention immediately. Ingestion: do not induce vomiting; first symptoms are likely to be gastrointestinal; administer immediately 2 milligrams intramuscular injection of the Mark I kit autoinjectors; seek medical attention immediately.
Decontamination	Tabun and other G agents are rapidly hydrolyzed in basic solutions, e.g., Na_2CO_3, NaOH, or KOH; GA has a half-life of 1.5 minutes at pH 11 at 25°C. Several metal ions (Cu^{+2}, Pd^{+2}, Au^{+3}, Ag^+, Ni^{+2}, Co^{+2}, Zn^{+2}) catalyze the nonenzymatic hydrolysis of tabun. Use of 10 percent NaOH is recommended; if NaOH is not available, then the following decontaminants may be used instead and are listed in the order of preference: decontaminating agent (DS2), sodium carbonate, supertropical bleach slurry (STB), and sodium hypochlorite solution.
Hydrolysis Rate	Reacts slowly with water, but fairly rapidly with strong acids and alkalis. Hydrolysis may be catalyzed by phosphate. Hydrolysis products: hydrogen cyanide, phosphorus products, dimethylamine
Environmental Fate	Tabun's use as a chemical warfare agent will release the compound directly to the soil and air environments. If released to water or moist soil, tabun will hydrolyze rapidly. At 20°C, the times required for 99.9 percent decomposition in seawater and distilled water are 45 and 22 hours, respectively. Applications of tabun to soil surfaces will result in evaporation to the atmosphere. Field studies measuring the evaporation rate of tabun from soil found that 50 percent of applied tabun evaporated in 1.71 hours and that 90 percent evaporated in 4.66 hours. If released to the atmosphere, tabun will exist in the vapor phase, where it will be degraded rapidly by reaction with photochemically produced hydroxyl radicals (estimated half-life of 4.8 hours). Since tabun is miscible in water, physical removal from the atmosphere may occur through wet deposition. Exposure to tabun occurs through vapor contact, which is readily absorbable through not only the lungs and eyes but also the skin and intestinal tract.
Protective Equipment	Respiratory protection and chemical protective clothing required. Level A, B, and C may be used depending on air monitoring. Protective clothing will off-gas GA for approximately 30 minutes after contact with the vapor.

Material	**Sarin**
Chemical Name	isopropyl methylphosphonofluoride
Structure	 GB GF
History and Use	Sarin was discovered in Germany in 1938 by a team led by Dr. Gerhard Schrader. Large-scale combat use of sarin has not occurred, although its use is strongly suspected in an Iraqi attack on the village of Birjinni on August 25, 1988 (samples collected from the site four years later showed the expected breakdown products of sarin). It is not known with certainty whether or not sarin was used in the Iran-Iraq war. On March 20, 1995, the Aum Shinrikyo released sarin in the Tokyo subway, killing 12 and injuring 5,500 people in the first documented terrorist use of chemical weapons. A June 1994 incident that killed 7 and injured 200 in central Japan is now also believed to be the work of Aum Shinrikyo. Sarin was produced and stockpiled in large quantities by both the United States and the Soviet Union. Closely related to sarin is a compound referred to as GF, or cyclohexyl sarin. GF is also a colorless and odorless liquid.
Military Designation	**GB**
CAS	107-44-8
Formula	$(CH_3)(C_3H_7O)FPO$
Appearance and Odor	Sarin is a colorless and odorless liquid. Some describe the material as having a faint odor of Juicy Fruit® chewing gum (impure material).

Chemical and Physical Properties	Molecular weight: 140
	Boiling point: 158°C (316°F)
	Freezing/melting point: -56°C (-70°F)
	Vapor pressure:
	    At 25°C (77°F): 2.9 mm Hg (0.06 psi)
	Vapor density: 4.8
	Volatility:
	    4,100 mg/m³ @ 0°C (32°F)
	    22,000 mg/m³ @ 25°C (77°F)
	    29,800 mg/m³ @ 30°C (86°F)
	Solubility in water: miscible
	pH: unknown
	Odor threshold: unknown

	Specific gravity: 1.09 9.1 lb/gal Polymerization: does not occur.
Incompatibilities	Strong oxidizers and bases. Attacks tin, magnesium, cadmium-plated steel, and some aluminum. Slightly attacks copper, brass, and lead; practically no attack on 1020 steels, Inconel and K-monel.
Persistency	Evaporates as rapidly as water. May persist for one to two days.
Flammability	Nonflammable, but will combust to form HF and phosphorus oxides.
Physiological Properties	GB is a lethal anticholinesterase agent. Its toxic hazard is high for inhalation, ingestion, and eye and skin exposure. Due to its high volatility, it is mainly an inhalation threat. Its rate of detoxification in the body is low. Effects of chronic exposures are cumulative. Following a single exposure to GB, daily exposure to concentrations of any nerve agent insufficient to produce symptoms may result in the onset of symptoms after several days. After symptoms subside, increased susceptibility persists for one to several days. The degree of exposure required to produce recurrence of symptoms, and the severity of these symptoms, depends on duration of exposure and time intervals between exposures. Whether inhaled, absorbed through the skin, or ingested, the symptoms of GB poisoning are basically the same: runny nose; tightness of the chest; dimness of vision and pinpointing of the pupils; difficulty in breathing; drooling and excessive sweating; nausea; vomiting; cramps; involuntary urination and defecation; twitching, jerking, and staggering; headache, confusion, drowsiness, coma, and convulsion. These signs and symptoms are followed by a cessation of breathing and death. Symptoms appear more slowly from a percutaneous route of entry, with a lethal dose causing death within two hours. Respiratory doses can cause death within one to ten minutes. When absorbed through the skin, depending on the point of contact, pinpointed pupils may not be seen.
Toxicity	ICt_{50} skin: 35 mg-min/m^3 (15 l/min) ICt_{50} inhalation 0.5: 70 mg-min/m^3 (15 l/min) to 2 min LD_{50} skin: 24 mg/kg 1 percent lethality: 10 mg-min/m^3 No-death levels: 6 mg-min/m^3
Exposure Data	TLV: 0.0001 mg/m^3
Emergency Response Action Levels	None established.
Rate of Detoxification	Very slow; essentially cumulative.
First Aid	Inhalation: hold breath and don respiratory protection mask; if severe signs of agent exposure appear, administer immediately, in rapid succession, all three nerve agent antidote kits, Mark I injectors; use mouth-to-mouth

	resuscitation when approved mask-bag or oxygen delivery systems are not available; do not use mouth-to-mouth resuscitation when facial contamination exists; administer oxygen if breathing is difficult; seek medical attention immediately. Eye Contact: flush eyes immediately with water for 10-15 minutes, then don a respiratory protective mask. Although myosis may be an early sign of agent exposure, do not administer an injection when myosis is the only sign present; seek medical attention immediately. Skin Contact: don respiratory mask and remove victim's contaminated clothing; wash contaminated skin with copious amounts of soap and water immediately using 10 percent sodium carbonate solution or 5 percent liquid household bleach; rinse well with water to remove decontamination; administer an intramuscular injection with the Mark I Kit if local sweating and muscular symptoms occur; seek medical attention immediately. Ingestion: do not induce vomiting; first symptoms are likely to be gastrointestinal; administer immediately 2 milligrams intramuscular injection of the Mark I kit autoinjectors; seek medical attention immediately.
Decontamination	Sarin and other G-agents are rapidly hydrolyzed in basic solutions, e.g., Na_2CO_3, NaOH, or KOH; GB has a half-life of 0.5 minutes at pH 11 at 25°C. Catalysts for GB hydrolysis include hypochlorite anion (OCl-), several metal ions and their complexes (Cu^{+2}, UO_2^{+2}, ZrO^{+2}, MoO_2^{+2}, Th^{+4}), and iodosobenzoic acid derivatives. Current decontamination systems based on this chemistry include: solids, powders and solutions containing various types of bleach (NaOCl or $Ca[OCl]_2$) DS2 (2 percent NaOH, 70 percent diethylenetriamine, and 28 percent ethylene glycol monomethyl ether) towelettes moistened with NaOH dissolved in water, phenol, ethanol, and ammonia. Use of 10 percent NaOH is recommended; if NaOH is not available, then the following decontaminants may be used instead and are listed in the order of preference: decontaminating agent (DS2), sodium carbonate, supertropical bleach slurry (STB), and sodium hypochlorite solution.
Hydrolysis Rate	Hours to two days depending on acidity. Hydrolysis by-products: hydrofluoric acid under acidic conditions; fluoride salts under basic conditions.
Environmental Fate	Sarin's use as a chemical warfare agent will release the compound directly to the soil and air environments. If released to water, sarin will degrade through aqueous hydrolysis, which is pH dependent above pH 6.5. In distilled water at 25°C, the hydrolysis half-life ranges from 75 hours at pH 7 to 0.8 hour at pH 9. The hydrolysis rate increases in seawater due to the catalytic effect of ions; the seawater hydrolysis half-life at pH 7.6 and 25°C is about 1 hour. If released to soil, sarin will degrade through hydrolysis (in

	moist soils) and evaporate from soil surfaces. The soil hydrolysis rate will increase with increasing pH. Laboratory and field studies have demonstrated that sarin evaporates rapidly from nonabsorbing surfaces, even at extremely cold temperatures; at 10°C, the time required for 90 percent of 1 mm diameter droplets of sarin to evaporate from nonabsorbing surfaces is only 0.24 hour. Two soil persistence studies conducted by the US Army found that 90 percent or more of sarin added to soil will be lost in the first five days. If released to the atmosphere, sarin will exist in the vapor-phase where it will be degraded rapidly by reaction with photochemically produced hydroxyl radicals (estimated half-life of 10 hours). Exposure to sarin occurs through vapor contact, which is readily absorbable through not only the lungs and eyes but also the skin and intestinal tract.
Protective Equipment	Respiratory protection and chemical protective clothing required. Level A, B, and C may be used depending on air monitoring. Protective clothing will off-gas GB for approximately 30 minutes after contact with the vapor.

Material	**Soman**
Chemical Name	pinacolyl methylphosphonofluoridate
Structure	
History and Use	Discovered in Germany in 1944, laboratory testing of Soman was in progress in Germany at the end of World War II. Soman has never been used in combat, but was produced and stockpiled by the Soviet Union. It can and may be thickened to increase persistency. Because of the type of bonding between GD and the acetylcholinesterase (covalent as opposed to ionic), the poisoning is generally assumed to be irreversible after two minutes.
Military Designation	**GD**
CAS	96-64-0
Formula	$(CH_3)(C_6H_{13}O)FPO$
Appearance and Odor	Soman is a colorless, tasteless liquid when pure; the industrial product is yellow-brown. The pure compound has a fruity odor, and the industrial product contains impurities with a camphor-like odor.

Chemical and Physical Properties	Molecular Weight: 182
	Boiling point: 198°C (388°F)
	Freezing/melting point: -42°C (-44°F)
	Vapor pressure:
	    At 25°C (77°F): 0.4 mm Hg (0.008 psi)
	Vapor density: 6.3
	Volatility:
	    531 mg/m³ @ 0°C (32°F)
	    3,900 mg/m³ @ 25°C (77°F)
	    5,570 mg/m³ @ 30°C (86°F)
	Solubility in water: 34 g/l
	pH: unknown
	Odor threshold: unknown
	Specific gravity:
	    1.02
	    8.5 lb/gal
	Polymerization: will not occur.

Incompatibilities	Strong oxidizers and bases: steam.
Persistency	Heavily splashed liquid persists 1 to 2 days under average weather conditions. Thickened agent may last for over one week
Flammability	121°C (250°F) (Open cup) Will burn to produce HF and phosphorous

	oxides.
Physiological Properties	GD is a lethal anticholinesterase agent. Although it is primarily a vapor hazard, its toxic hazard is high for inhalation, ingestion, and eye and skin exposure. Signs and symptoms are the same regardless of route the poison enters the body (by inhalation, absorption, or ingestion): runny nose; tightness of chest; dimness of vision and myosis (pinpointing of the eye pupils); difficulty in breathing; drooling and excessive sweating; nausea; vomiting; cramps and involuntary defecation and urination; twitching, jerking, and staggering; and headache, confusion, drowsiness, coma, and convulsion. These signs and symptoms are followed by cessation of breathing and death. Symptoms appear more slowly from a percutaneous route of entry, with a lethal dose causing death within two hours. Respiratory doses can cause death within one to ten minutes. GD binds irreversibly with acetylcholinesterase in a few minutes; rapid treatment is required. Depending on the point of contact, pinpointing of the pupils may not be seen when absorbtion is through the skin.

Toxicity	ICt_{50} inhalation: 35 mg-min/m^3
	    4 ppm for a one-minute exposure
	LC_{50} inhalation: 70 mg-min/m^3
	    9 ppm for a one-minute exposure
	LD_{50} skin (5 mg/kg bare skin): 1.4 g/man (clothed skin)
	ICt_{50} skin vapor: 10,000 mg-min/m^3

Exposure Data	TLV: 0.00003 mg/m^3
Emergency Response Action Levels	None established.
Rate of Detoxification	Its rate of detoxification in the body is low.
First Aid	Inhalation: hold breath and don respiratory protection mask; if severe signs of agent exposure appear, administer immediately, in rapid succession, all three nerve agent antidote kits, Mark I injectors; use mouth-to-mouth resuscitation when approved mask-bag or oxygen delivery systems are not available, but do not use mouth-to-mouth resuscitation when facial contamination exists; administer oxygen if breathing is difficult; seek medical attention immediately. Eye Contact: flush eyes immediately with water for 10-15 minutes, then don a respiratory protective mask. Although myosis may be an early sign of agent exposure, do not administer an injection when myosis is the only sign present; seek medical attention immediately. Skin Contact: don respiratory mask and remove victim's contaminated clothing; wash contaminated skin with copious amounts of soap and water immediately using 10 percent sodium carbonate solution or 5 percent liquid

	household bleach; rinse well with water to remove decontamination; administer an intramuscular injection with the Mark I kit if local sweating and muscular symptoms occur; seek medical attention immediately. Ingestion: do not induce vomiting; first symptoms are likely to be gastrointestinal; administer immediately 2 milligrams intramuscular injection of the Mark I kit autoinjectors; seek medical attention immediately.
Decontamination	Soman and other G agents are rapidly hydrolyzed in basic solutions, e.g., Na_2CO_3, NaOH, or KOH; soman has a half-life of approximately 1 minute at pH 11 at 25°C. Catalysts for soman hydrolysis include copper (II) complexes and iodosobenzoic acid derivatives. Based on its chemical similarity to sarin, soman hydrolysis should be catalyzed by hypochlorite anion (OCl-). Current decontamination systems based on this chemistry include: solids, powders and solutions containing various types of bleach (NaOCl- or Ca[OCl-]2) DS2 (2 percent NaOH, 70 percent diethylenetriamine, 28 percent ethylene glycol monomethyl ether), towelettes moistened with NaOH dissolved in water, phenol, ethanol, and ammonia. Use of 10 percent NaOH is recommended; if NaOH is not available, then the following decontaminants may be used instead and are listed in the order of preference: decontaminating agent (DS2), sodium carbonate, supertropical bleach slurry (STB), and sodium hypochlorite solution.
Hydrolysis Rate	Hours to two days depending on acidity; 5 minutes in 5 percent solution of NaOH. Hydrolysis products: HF and organophosphorus acids.
Environmental Fate	Unknown.
Protective Equipment	Respiratory protection and chemical protective clothing required. Level A, B, and C may be used depending on air monitoring.

232

Material	**VX**
Chemical Name	O-ethyl S-(2-diisopropylamino) ethyl methylphosphonothiolate
Structure	VX — V-gas
History and Use	The phosphorylthiocholine class of compounds was discovered independently by Ranaji Ghosh of ICI, Gerhard Schrader of Bayer, and Lars-Erik Tammelin of the Swedish Institute of Defense Research, in 1952-1953. Shortly thereafter, the United States Army began a systematic investigation of this class of compounds at Edgewood Arsenal; as a result, VX was developed and stockpiled by the United States. A closely related compound referred to as V-gas was manufactured and stockpiled by the Soviet Union. VX was the US standard persistent nerve agent.
Military Designation	**VX**
CAS	50782-69-9
Formula	$C_{11}H_{26}NO_2PS$
Appearance and Odor	VX is a colorless to straw-colored oily liquid that is also odorless and tasteless, similar in appearance to motor oil.

Chemical and Physical Properties	Molecular weight: 267
	Boiling point: 298°C (568°F)
	Freezing/melting point: -39°C (-38°F)
	Vapor pressure:
	    At 25°C (77°F): 0 .0007 mm Hg (0.000013 psi)
	Vapor density: 9.2
	Volatility: 10.5 mg/m³ @ 25°C
	Solubility in water: moderate
	    50 g/l @ 20°C (68°F)
	    30 g/l @ 25°C (77°F)
	pH: basic
	Odor threshold: unknown
	Specific gravity:
	    1.01
	    8.4 lb/gal
	Polymerization: will not occur.

Incompatibilities	Unknown.

Persistency	Heavily splashed liquid persists for long periods of time under average weather conditions.
Flammability	159°C (318°F)
Physiological Properties	Nerve agent VX is a persistent, nonvolatile agent that is primarily a liquid exposure hazard to the skin or eyes, although small amounts of VX vapor may be generated under extremely high temperatures. Nerve agent VX affects the body by blocking the action of the enzyme acetylcholinesterase. When this enzyme is blocked, large amounts of the chemical acetylcholine build up at critical places within the nervous system, causing hyperactivity of the body organs stimulated by these nerves. The signs and symptoms of exposure to nerve agent VX depend upon the route of exposure and the amount of exposure. Whether inhaled, absorbed through the skin, or ingested, the symptoms of VX poisoning are basically the same: myosis (constriction of pupils) and visual effects, headache and pressure sensation, runny nose and nasal congestion, salivation, tightness in the chest, nausea, vomiting, giddiness, anxiety, difficulty in thinking, difficulty sleeping, nightmares, muscle twitches, tremors, weakness, abdominal cramps, diarrhea, and involuntary urination and defecation. Signs of severe exposure can progress to convulsions and respiratory failure. Symptoms appear more slowly from a percutaneous route of entry, with a lethal dose causing death within two hours. Respiratory doses can cause death within one to ten minutes. When absorbed through the skin, depending on the point of contact, pinpointing of the pupils may not be seen.
Toxicity	ICt_{50} inhalation: 3 ppm for a one-minute exposure (30 mg-min/m^3) ICt_{50} skin liquid: 10 mg/person ICt_{50} skin vapor: 6-360 mg-min/m^3 ICt_{50} respiratory: 2 ppm for a one-minute exposure (25 mg-min/m^3) ICt_{50} skin liquid: 0.005 gm/person LD_{50} skin: 0.142 mg/kg 1 percent lethality: 4.3 mg-min/m^3 No-deaths level: 2.5 mg-min/m^3 NOAEL: 1.6 mg-min/m^3 (estimated)
Exposure Data	TLV: 0.00001 mg/m^3
Emergency Response Action Levels	None established.
Rate of Detoxification	Very slow; essentially cumulative.
First Aid	Inhalation: hold breath and don respiratory protection mask; administer immediately, in rapid succession, all three nerve agent antidote kits, Mark I injectors, if severe signs of agent exposure appear; use mouth-to-mouth resuscitation when approved mask-bag or oxygen delivery systems are not available, but do not use mouth-to-mouth resuscitation when facial contamination exists; if breathing is difficult, administer oxygen; seek

	medical attention immediately.
	Eye Contact: flush eyes immediately with water for 10-15 minutes, then don a respiratory protective mask. Although myosis may be an early sign of agent exposure, do not administer an injection when myosis is the only sign present; seek medical attention immediately. Skin Contact: don respiratory mask and remove victim's contaminated clothing; wash contaminated skin with copious amounts of soap and water immediately using 10 percent sodium carbonate solution or 5 percent liquid household bleach; rinse well with water to remove decontamination; if local sweating and muscular symptoms occur, administer an intramuscular injection with the Mark I kit; seek medical attention immediately. Ingestion: do not induce vomiting; first symptoms are likely to be gastrointestinal; administer immediately 2 milligrams intramuscular injection of the Mark I kit autoinjectors; seek medical attention immediately.
Decontamination	A large-scale decontamination procedure, which uses both HTH and NaOH, destroys VX by oxidation and hydrolysis. Typically, the large-scale product contains 0.2-0.4 weight percent EA2192 at 24 hours. At pH 12, the EA2192 in the large-scale product has a half-life of about 14 days. Thus, a 90-day holding period at pH 12 results in about a 64-fold reduction of EA2192 (six half-lives). This holding period has been shown to be sufficient to reduce the toxicity of the product below that of a Class B poison. Other less toxic products are ethyl methylphosphonic acid, methylphosphonic acid, diisopropylaminoethyl mercaptan, diethyl methylphosphonate, and ethanol. A small-scale decontamination procedure uses sufficient HTH to oxidize all VX; thus no EA2192 is formed. Large amounts of hypochlorite need to be used to ensure oxidation of VX.
Hydrolysis Rate	Alkaline solutions: minutes Acidic solutions: hours to days During basic hydrolysis of VX, up to about 10 percent of the agent is converted to EA2191 (diisopropylaminoethyl methylphosphonothioic acid). Based on the concentration of EA2192 expected to be formed during hydrolysis and its toxicity (1.4 mg/kg dermal in rabbit at 24 hours in a 10/90 wt percent ethanol/water solution), a Class B poison would result.
Environmental Fate	O-Ethyl S-(2-diisopropylaminoethyl) methylphosphonothioate (VX) may be released to the environment during its production, storage, transport, disposal, and past use as a chemical warfare nerve agent. When used in chemical warfare, releases may be by aerial spraying or from bursting munitions that would shower droplets (typically 2 mm diameter) of VX over

	the terrain. When released on soil, the concentration of VX will decline to low levels in a few days, after which the degradation is much slower. This behavior is observed on different types of soil and soils with different moisture contents. Little VX is lost through evaporation. The half-life on vegetative surfaces is 1-2 days. If released into water, VX may adsorb to sediment and particulate matter in the water column and will decompose by hydrolysis, a process that is quite slow, especially at low pH. Recent experiments at 21°C gave a hydrolytic half-life of 57 days that was independent of pH. Earlier results had indicated that the hydrolysis was base-catalyzed. In seawater, the half-life of VX is approximately 230 days at 5°C. In the atmosphere, droplets of VX would be subject to gravitational settling. Vapor-phase VX will react with photochemically produced hydroxyl radicals with an estimated half-life of 0.24 days.
Protective Equipment	Respiratory protection and chemical protective clothing required. Level A, B, and C may be used depending on air monitoring.

Crowd-Control Agent Chemical Data Sheets

Crowd-control agents like CS have been used in both military and nonmilitary environments. Crowd-control agents are normally nonlethal in application although fatalities may occur among sensitive individuals or those experiencing significant exposure. Crowd-control agents may cause severe tearing, coughing, and disorientation to those exposed.

Material	**2-Chlorobenzalmalononitrile**
Chemical Name	[(2-chlorophenyl)methylene]propanedinitrile
Structure	
History and Use	CS was developed in the late 1950s as a crowd-control substance. It is a more potent irritant than chloroacetophenone but less incapacitating. In the late 1960s, stocks of CS replaced CN. Presently, the US Army uses CS for combat training and crowd-control purposes. When burned to create a colorless gas with an acrid, pepper-like smell, CS is used primarily as an incapacitating agent, both by military and law enforcement personnel. It can be disseminated in burning grenades and weapon-fired projectiles, as an aerosol from the finely divided solid chemical, or from a solution of the chemical dissolved in methylene chloride or acetone.
Military Designation	**CS**
CAS	2698-41-1
Formula	$C_{10}H_5ClN_2$
Appearance and Odor	CS is a white crystalline solid.
Chemical and Physical Properties	Molecular weight: 188 Boiling point: 310°C (590°F) to 315°C (599°F) Freezing/melting point: 93°C (199°F) to 95°C (203°F) Vapor pressure: At 20°C (68°F): 0.000034 mm Hg (0.00000066 psi) Vapor density: 6.7 Volatility: 0.71 mg/m^3 @ 25°C (77°F) Solubility in water: 1-5 g/l at 16C (61°F) pH: unknown Odor threshold: unknown Specific gravity: 1.04 g/cc (8.7 lb/gal) Polymerization: unknown
Incompatibilities	Incompatible with strong oxidizers.
Persistency	Varies, depending upon amount of contamination.
Flammability	Flash point: 197°C (386°F) When heated to decomposition, CS emits very toxic fumes.

Physiological Properties	CS is disseminated by burning, explosion, and aerosol formation. It is immediately irritating to the eyes and upper respiratory tract. Warm vapors mix with human sweat to cause a burning sensation to the eyes, nose, and mouth. Conjunctivitis and pain in the eyes, lacrimation, erythema of the eyelids, runny nose, burning throat, coughing, and constricted feeling in the chest are the effects that will occur immediately and will persist 5 to 20 minutes after removal from the contaminated area. It is immediately dangerous to life and health at a concentration of 2 mg/m^3. It is not an accumulative agent in the human body, although it accumulates in the landscape. CS is the most persistent of the tear agents, absorbing into the most porous surfaces including soil and plaster.
Toxicity	ICt_{50}: 10 to 20 mg-min/m^3 LCt_{50}: 61,000 mg-min/m^3
Exposure Data	Ceiling value: 0.05 ppm (0.4 mg/m^3)
Emergency Response Action Levels	IDLH 2 mg/m^3
Rate of Detoxification	Unknown.
First Aid	Inhalation: remove the victim to fresh air immediately; perform artificial respiration if breathing has stopped; keep the victim warm and at rest; seek medical attention immediately. Eye Contact: wash eyes immediately with copious amounts of water for at least 15 minutes; apply an ophthalmic corticosteroid ointment after decontamination; treat delayed erythema with a bland shake lotion (such as calamine lotion) or a topical corticosteroid depending on severity; do not wear contact lenses when working with this chemical; seek medical attention immediately. Skin Contact: wash the contaminated skin thoroughly using soap and water; remove the contaminated clothing immediately; if irritation persists after washing, seek medical attention immediately. Ingestion: give victim copious amounts of water immediately; induce vomiting by having victim touch the back of throat with finger; do not make an unconscious person vomit; seek medical attention immediately.
Decontamination	Do not use standard decontaminants or detergents that contain chlorine bleach because the materials can react to form compounds more toxic than CS. Contaminated surfaces should be decontaminated using a solution of equal parts (by volume) methanol and water with 18 percent (by weight) sodium hydroxide or commercial lye added to the solution. Also, an aqueous solution containing 10 percent monoethanolamine anionic detergent can be used as a decontaminant.
Hydrolysis Rate	Unknown.

Environmental Fate	2-Chlorobenzalmalononitrile is released directly to the environment through its use as a tear gas and crowd-control agent. If released to the atmosphere as a dust or powder, it will settle to the ground via dry deposition. If released to water or soil, the major degradation process is expected to be hydrolysis. Aqueous hydrolysis experiments in seawater have determined hydrolysis half-lives of 281.7 minutes at 0°C and 14.5 minutes at 25°C. However, actual environmental degradation rates may be much slower because the rate at which 2-chlorobenzalmalononitrile dissolves in water can be very slow. 2-Chlorobenzalmalononitrile released to water could float and travel for considerable distances before it dissolves. Insufficient data are available to predict the importance of biodegradation.
Protective Equipment	Respiratory protection and chemical protective clothing required. Level A, B, and C may be used depending on air monitoring.

Material	**2-Chloroacetophenone**
Chemical Name	2-chloro-1-phenylethanone, α-chloroacetophenone, phenacyl chloride
Structure	
History and Use	The United States considers agent CN (popularly known as mace or tear gas) and its mixtures with various chemicals to be obsolete for military deployment. It is highly toxic by inhalation and ingestion.
Military Designation	**CN**
CAS	532-27-4
Formula	C_8H_7ClO
Appearance and Odor	CN is a colorless-to gray crystalline solid with a sharp, irritating floral odor. In very low concentration in air, it has an odor resembling apple blossoms

Chemical and Physical Properties	Molecular Weight: 154.6
	Boiling point: 247°C (477°F)
	Freezing/melting point: 54°C (129°F)
	Vapor pressure:
	    At 0°C: 0.0026 mm Hg (0.00005 psi)
	    At 20°C: 0.0041 mm Hg (0.0007 psi)
	    At 51.7°C: 0.152 mm Hg (0.003 psi)
	Vapor density: 5.3
	Volatility:
	    2.36 mg/m^3 @ 0°C (32°F)
	    34.3 mg/m^3 @ 20°C (68°F)
	    1060 mg/m^3 @ 51.7°C (125°F)
	Solubility in water: 1g/l at 19°C
	pH: unknown
	Odor threshold: 0.1mg/m^3 (0.015 ppm)
	Specific gravity:
	    Solid: 1.318 @ 20°C (68°F)
	    Liquid: 1.187 @ 58°C (136°F)
	Polymerization: will not polymerize.

Incompatibilities	Water and steam.
Persistency	Short, because the compounds are disseminated as an aerosol.
Flammability	Flash point: 118°C (244°F)
Physiological Properties	Alpha-chloroacetophenone vapors may cause a tingling or runny nose, burning or pain of the eyes, blurred vision, and tears. Burning in the chest, difficult breathing, and nausea may also occur as well as skin irritation, rash,

	or burns. It can also cause difficulty if swallowed.
Toxicity	ICt_{50}: 80 mg-min/m^3 LCt_{50}: 7,000 mg-min/m^3 from solvent LCt_{50}: 14,000 mg-min/m^3 from grenade RfC inhalation: 0.00003 mg/m^3 Irritation thresholds range from 0.15-0.4 mg/m^3 Lacrimation thresholds from 0.3-0.4 mg/m^3 Irritant to eyes in concentration of 0.3 ppm LD_{50} rat ip: 36 mg/kg LD_{50} rabbit oral: 118 mg/kg
Exposure Data	TWA: 0.3 mg/m^3 (0.05 ppm)
Emergency Response Action Levels	None established.
Rate of Detoxification	Unknown.
First Aid	Inhalation: remove the victim to fresh air immediately; perform artificial respiration if breathing has stopped; keep victim warm and at rest; seek medical attention immediately. Eye Contact: wash eyes immediately with copious amounts of water, lifting the lower and upper lids occasionally; do not wear contact lenses when working with this chemical; seek medical attention immediately. Skin Contact: wash the contaminated skin using soap or mild detergent and water immediately; remove the contaminated clothing immediately and wash the skin using soap or mild detergent and water; seek medical attention immediately when there are chemical burns or evidence of skin irritation. Ingestion: induce vomiting by having victim touch the back of the throat with finger or by giving victim syrup of ipecac as directed; do not induce vomiting if victim is unconscious; seek medical attention immediately.
Decontamination	Wash with soap and water.
Hydrolysis Rate	Toxic and corrosive vapors are produced when combined with water or steam.
Environmental Fate	2-Chloroacetophenone may be released to the environment through its use as a crowd-control agent (tear gas) and in chemical mace. Waste streams generated at sites of its manufacture and use as a pharmaceutical intermediate are potential sources of release. If released to the atmosphere, 2-chloroacetophenone will degrade in the vapor phase by reaction with photochemically produced hydroxyl radicals (estimated half-life of 9.2 days). If released to soil, 2-chloroacetophenone will probably leach based on estimated K_{oc} values of 76–325. If released to water, 2-chloroacetophenone will volatilize slowly; the estimated volatilization

	half-lives from a model river (1 m deep) and model environmental pond (2 m deep) are 13.3 and 159 days, respectively. Direct photolysis may contribute to the environmental degradation of 2-chloroacetophenone, but potential rates are unknown. Insufficient data are available to predict the importance of biodegradation in soil or water. Occupational exposure to 2-chloroacetophenone can occur through inhalation of dusts and vapors and through skin contact. The use of chemical mace to disable attackers causes direct exposure to 2-chloroacetophenone through skin contact and inhalation.
Protective Equipment	Respiratory protection and chemical protective clothing required. Level A, B, and C may be used depending on air monitoring.

Material	**Chloropicrin**
Chemical Name	trichloronitromethane
Structure	
History and Use	PS was used in large quantities during World War I; it was stockpiled during World War II and is no longer authorized for military use. PS is more toxic than chlorine but less toxic than phosgene. Used as a fumigant for nondeciduous fruits, tomatoes, and tobacco, and for disinfecting cereals and grains; in synthesis, especially in manufacture of methyl violet; soil insecticide; war gas; tear gas; soil/space fumigant for nematodes, bacteria, fungi, insects and weeds; warning agent for use with odorless fumigants.
Military Designation	**PS**
CAS	76-06-2
Formula	CCl_3NO_2
Appearance and Odor	PS is a colorless, oily liquid with a stinging pungent odor.

Chemical and Physical Properties	Molecular weight: 164.5
	Boiling point: 112°C (234°F)
	Freezing/melting point: 69°C (156°F)
	Vapor pressure:
	    At 20°C (68°F): 20 mm Hg
	Vapor density: 5.6
	Volatility:
	    55,700 mg/m^3 @ 0°C (32°F)
	    99,000 mg/m^3 @ 10°C (50°F)
	    164,500 mg/m^3 @ 20°C (68°F)
	    210,700 mg/m^3 @ 25°C (77°F)
	    267,500 mg/m^3 @ 30°C (86°F)
	Solubility in water: 2.272 g/l at 0°C; 1.621g/l at 25°C
	pH: unknown
	Odor threshold: 1.1 ppm
	Specific gravity: 1.66 g/cc (13.8 lb/gal)
	Polymerization: material will not polymerize.

Incompatibilities	Contact with strong oxidizers may cause fires or explosions. Incompatible with strong base.
Persistency	Short.
Flammability	Not combustible, but with strong initiation, heated material under confinement will detonate. Toxic gases and vapors (such as oxides of

	nitrogen, phosgene, nitrosyl chloride, chlorine, and carbon monoxide) may be released when chloropicrin decomposes.
Physiological Properties	Chloropicrin is a powerful irritant whose vapors cause lung, skin, eye, nose, and throat irritation, coughing, and vomiting. As an eye irritant, it produces immediate burning, pain, and tearing. In high concentration, PS damages the lungs, causing pulmonary edema. Exposure to liquid PS can cause severe burns on the skin that generally result in blisters and lesions.
Toxicity	LCt_{50}: 2,000 mg-min/m^3 LD_{50}: 250 mg/kg (rat) 2000 mg/m^3 (297.6 ppm) for 10 min is lethal 100 mg/m^3 (15.0 ppm) for 1 min is intolerable Irritant at 9 mg-min/m^3 (1.3 ppm)
Exposure Data	TWA: 0.7 mg/m^3 OSHA PEL-TWA: 0.1 ppm
Emergency Response Action Levels	IDLH Value: 2 ppm
Rate of Detoxification	Unknown.
First Aid	Inhalation: remove the victim to fresh air immediately; perform artificial respiration if breathing has stopped; keep the victim warm and at rest; seek medical attention immediately. Eye Contact: wash eyes immediately with copious amounts of water, lifting the lower and upper lids occasionally; do not wear contact lenses when working with this chemical; seek medical attention immediately. Skin Contact: wash the contaminated skin using soap or mild detergent and water; remove the contaminated clothing immediately and wash the skin using soap or mild detergent and water; if irritation persists after washing, seek medical attention immediately. Ingestion: give victim copious amounts of water immediately; induce vomiting by having victim touch the back of his throat with his finger; do not make an unconscious person vomit; seek medical attention immediately.
Decontamination	Wash with soap and water. Soda ash may be used to neutralize material.
Hydrolysis Rate	Unknown.
Environmental Fate	Chloropicrin may be released to the environment as emissions and in wastewater; as a result of its manufacture, transport, and disposal; and from its use as a chemical intermediate, soil sterilant, fumigant for cereals and grain, fungicide, rat extermination agent, and war gas. Chloropicrin is formed in the chlorination of drinking water and wastewater and may be released during these processes. If applied to soil as would be the case in its use as a soil sterilant, chloropicrin will both rapidly volatilize and leach. It should photolyze on the soils surface. It may degrade in soil by chemical or

	biological processes. However, degradation rates are unknown. Chloropicrin has a high Henry's law constant and if released in water would readily volatilize (half-life in a model river and model lake are 4.3 hours and 5.2 days, respectively). It will photodegrade in the surface layers of water (half-life about 3 days). Its rate of biodegradation in natural water is unknown, as is its rate of other abiotic dechlorination reactions. Chloropicrin would not be expected to adsorb to sediment or bioconcentrate in fish. If released to the atmosphere, chloropicrin will photolyze (half-life 20 days), producing phosgene and nitrosyl chloride. Being relatively soluble in water, it may be washed out by rain. Exposure to chloropicrin would be primarily occupational via inhalation and dermal contact, especially to applicators of the fumigant. The general public may be exposed to chloropicrin in drinking water, especially chlorinated drinking water.
Protective Equipment	Respiratory protection and chemical protective clothing required. Level A, B, and C may be used depending on air monitoring.

Material	**Bromoacetone**
Chemical Name	1-bromo-2-propanone
Structure	
History and Use	Unknown.
Military Designation	**BA**
CAS	598-31-2
Formula	C_3H_5BrO
Appearance and Odor	Yellowish-brown liquid with a penetrating odor. Violet liquid when pure and unexposed to air.
Chemical and Physical Properties	Molecular weight: 137 Boiling point: 137°C (279°F) (partial decomposition) Freezing/melting point: -36.5°C (-33.7°F) Vapor pressure: At 20°C (68°F): 9 mm Hg (0.17 psi) Vapor density: 4.7 Volatility: unknown Solubility in water: 13 percent pH: unknown Odor threshold: 0.5 mg/m³ (0.09 ppm) Specific gravity: 1.63 (13.6 lb/gal) Polymerization: Unknown
Incompatibilities	Strong corrosives.
Persistency	Unknown.
Flammability	Flash point: 51°C (124°F)
Physiological Properties	Poisonous and intensely irritating to skin and mucous membranes. Harmful if swallowed or absorbed through the skin. Vapor is extremely irritating to the eyes, nose, throat, and upper respiratory system. Violent lacrimator. Liquid is corrosive to eyes, skin, and upper respiratory tract. Permanent dense opacification of cornea has resulted from splashing liquid bromoacetone in the eye. Relatively minor injury has occurred in a case in which only a few fine droplets came in contact with eye. Spots of gray opacity and necrosis appeared in corneal epithelium, but eye recovered completely in a few days.
Toxicity	LC_{Lo}: 572 ppm
Exposure Data	None established.

Emergency Response Action Levels	None established.
Rate of Detoxification	Unknown.
First Aid	Inhalation: move victim to fresh air. If breathing has stopped, give artificial respiration. If breathing is difficult, give oxygen.

Eye Contact: hold eyelids open and flush with water for at least 15 minutes.

Skin Contact: remove contaminated clothing and shoes, flush affected areas with plenty of water for at least 15 minutes.

Ingestion: do nothing except keep victim warm. DO NOT INDUCE VOMITING. |
Decontamination	Wash with lots of soap and water. Addition of soda ash will help neutralize the material.
Hydrolysis Rate	Unknown.
Environmental Fate	Bromoacetone occurs naturally in the essential oil of a seaweed species that grows in the ocean around the Hawaiian Islands. If released to the atmosphere, it will degrade via reaction with photochemically produced hydroxyl radicals (estimated half-life of 53 days in an average atmosphere), although degradation via photolysis may be more rapid. Physical removal from air by rainfall is possible. If released to water, photolysis may be an important degradation process. Volatilization from water is not rapid, but may be important in the absence of significant degradation processes. If bromoacetone is spilled into a body of water, it will sink to the bottom of the water column, dissolve slowly, and turn violet rapidly. If released to soil, significant leaching may be possible. Evaporation from dry surfaces is likely to occur. The potential significance of biodegradation in soil or water is not known. Exposure of bromoacetone can occur through consumption of specific seaweeds found in the region of the Hawaiian Islands. With the exception of this specific exposure, there is no evidence that the general population is exposed to bromoacetone.
Protective Equipment	Respiratory protection and chemical protective clothing required. Level A, B, and C may be used depending on air monitoring.

Material	**Bromobenzeneacetonitrile**
Chemical Name	bromobenzylcyanide
Structure	
History and Use	CA was the first tear agent that came into existence at the end of the World War I. It was outmoded in 1920 with the introduction of the CN series and is now obsolete in NATO inventories. The tear compounds cause a flow of tears and irritation of the skin. Because tear compounds produce only transient casualties, they are widely used for training, crowd control, and situations where long-term incapacitation is unacceptable. When used against poorly equipped guerrilla or revolutionary armies, these compounds have proved extremely effective. When released indoors, they can cause serious illness or death.
Military Designation	**CA**
CAS	5798-79-8
Formula	C_8H_6BrN
Appearance and Odor	Pure bromobenzylcyanide is a colorless crystalline solid with a sour or rotten fruit odor.

Chemical and Physical Properties	Molecular weight: 196
	Boiling point: 242°C (468°F)
	Freezing/melting point: 25.5°C (78°F)
	Vapor pressure:
	    At 20°C (68°F): 0.11 mm Hg (0.002 psi)
	Vapor density: 6.8
	Volatility:
	    17 mg/m^3 @ 0°C (32°F)
	    115 mg/m^3 @ 20°C (68°F)
	    217 mg/m^3 @ 30°C (86°F)
	Solubility in water: very slight
	pH: unknown
	Odor threshold: 0.09 mg/m^3 (0.01 ppm)
	Specific gravity:
	    Solid: 1.52 g/cc
	    Liquid: 1.47 g/cc (12.3 lb/gal)
	Polymerization: will not occur.

Incompatibilities	Stable in glass, lead-lined, or enamel-lined containers; reaction with iron may be explosive.
Persistency	Heavily splashed liquid persists one to two days under average weather conditions.

250

Flammability	Material is combustible and would produce HBr and HCN in a fire.
Physiological Properties	CA is usually used in solution with ether or acetone as an aerosol. It produces a severe burning sensation to the mucous membranes and equally severe lacrimation to the eyes accompanied by headache and nausea. The nausea may lead to vomiting, although the vomiting is more of a psychological reaction than physiological. CA will go into solution with human sweat and produce a burning sensation in the face, especially in the areas around the mouth, nose, and eyes. It will penetrate clothing, making the areas around the neck, armpits, the tender skin areas behind the elbows, knees, and around the buttocks and crotch susceptible to rashes and blisters. The vapors can be lethal in enclosed or confined spaces within a few minutes without prior respiratory protection. Nausea can lead to unconsciousness, which may mean suffocation.
Toxicity	ICt_{50}: 30 mg-min/m^3 (approximately) LCt_{50}: 8,000 to 11,000 mg-min/m^3 (estimated) 109 ppm lethal in 30 min Irritation at 0.00015 mg/m^3
Exposure Data	None established.
Emergency Response Action Levels	None established.
Rate of Detoxification	Unknown.
First Aid	Inhalation: remove victim from the source immediately; seek medical attention immediately. Eye Contact: don a respiratory protective mask; flush victim's eyes immediately with copious amounts of water; seek medical attention immediately. Skin Contact: remove victim from the source immediately; decontaminate the skin immediately with copious amounts of water; decontaminate clothing with steam or by boiling; 20 percent alcohol caustic soda is effective on material, but may damage material; seek medical attention immediately. Ingestion: give victim milk to drink; seek medical attention immediately.
Decontamination	Use soap and water. Alcohol/caustic mixtures may be used to neutralize material.
Hydrolysis Rate	Very slow.
Environmental Fate	Unknown.
Protective Equipment	Respiratory protection and chemical protective clothing required. Level A, B, and C may be used depending on air monitoring.

Material	**Adamsite**
Chemical Name	10-chloro-5,10-dihydrophenarsazine
Structure	
History and Use	DM was first produced during World War I. Adamsite was not toxic enough for the battlefield, but it proved to be too drastic for use against civilian mobs; it was banned for use against civilian populations in the 1930s in the western nations. DM was produced worldwide until superseded by the CN series of tear agents.
Military Designation	**DM**
CAS	578-94-9
Formula	$C_{12}H_9AsClN$
Appearance and Odor	Light green to yellow crystals at room temperature; no odor, but irritates nasal passages in a manner similar to the effects of pepper.

Chemical and Physical Properties	Molecular weight: 277.5
	Boiling point: 410°C (770°F)
	Freezing/melting point: 195°C (383°F)
	Vapor pressure: Forms no appreciable vapor.
	Vapor density: 9.6
	Volatility:
	    19,300 mg/m³ @ 0°C (32°F)
	    26,000 to 120,000 mg/m³ @ 20°C (68°F)
	    72,500 to 143,000 mg/m³ @ 25°C (86°F)
	Solubility in water: insoluble in water
	pH: unknown
	Odor threshold: unknown
	Specific gravity: 1.65 g/cc (solid)
	Polymerization: unknown

Incompatibilities	Unknown.
Persistency	Short, because compounds are disseminated as an aerosol. Soil: persistent Surface (wood, metal, masonry, rubber, paint): persistent Water: persistent; when material is covered with water, an insoluble film forms which prevents further hydrolysis.
Flammability	Does not flash.
Physiological Properties	DM is a vomiting compound. It is normally a solid, but upon heating, DM first vaporizes and then condenses to form aerosols. It is toxic through

	inhalation, ingestion, and skin contact. Adamsite is dispersed as an aerosol, irritating to the eyes and respiratory tract but not necessarily to the skin. Under field conditions, vomiting agents can cause great discomfort to the victims; when released indoors, they can cause serious illness or death. Symptoms include irritation of eyes and mucous membranes, coughing, sneezing, severe headache, acute pain and tightness in the chest, nausea, and vomiting. DM has been noted to cause necrosis of corneal epithelium in humans.
Toxicity	ICt_{50}: 22 to 150 mg-min/m^3 LCt_{50}: variable, average 11,000 mg-min/m^3 NOAEL (inhalation): 4 mg-min/m^3
Exposure Data	None determined.
Emergency Response Action Levels	None established.
Rate of Detoxification	The human body will detoxify the effects of mild exposures within 30 minutes of evacuation. Severe exposures may take several hours to detoxify and minor sensory disturbances may persist for up to one day.
First Aid	Inhalation: remove victim to fresh air; apply a mask/respirator in spite of coughing, sneezing, salivation, and nausea; lift the mask from the face briefly, if necessary, to permit vomiting or to drain saliva from the face piece; seek medical attention immediately. Eye Contact: don a respiratory protective mask; seek medical attention immediately. Skin Contact: rinse the nose and throat with saline water or bicarbonate of soda solution; wash exposed skin and scalp with soap and water and allow to dry on the skin; dust the skin with borated talcum. Ingestion: seek medical attention immediately; carry on duties as vigorously as possible; this will help to lessen and shorten the symptoms; combat duties usually can be performed in spite of the effects of sternutators.
Decontamination	Soap and water.
Hydrolysis Rate	Acidic (pH): 0.5 percent; prevents hydrolysis at room temperature; 9.8 percent HCl; prevents hydrolysis @ 70°C. Basic (pH): slowly hydrolyzes in water. Hydrolysis by products are still toxic: $NH(C_6H_4)_2As_5OH$ & HCl
Environmental Fate	Unknown.
Protective Equipment	Respiratory protection and chemical protective clothing required. Level A, B, and C may be used depending on air monitoring.

Material	**3-Quinuclidinyl Benzilate**
Chemical Name	α-hydroxy-α-phenylbenzeneacetic acid, 1-azabicyclo[2,2,2]oct-3-yl ester
Structure	
History and Use	BZ is usually disseminated as an aerosol. The primary route of entry into the body is through the respiratory system; the secondary route is through the digestive tract. BZ blocks the action of acetylcholine in both the peripheral and central nervous systems. As such, it lessens the degree and extent of the transmission of impulses from one nerve fiber to another through their connecting synaptic junctions. It stimulates the action of noradrenaline (norepinephrine) in the brain, much as do amphetamines and cocaine. Thus, it may induce vivid hallucinations as it sedates the victim. Toxic delirium is very common. Production of BZ in the United States began in 1962 at Pine Bluff Arsenal and lasted through the late 1960s. BZ was weaponized in bomblets with a pyrotechnic mixture. The pyrotechnic mixture was ignited to produced a solid aerosol of the high-melting BZ. Between 1988 and 1990, the BZ munitions were destroyed, also at Pine Bluff. No BZ munitions remain in the US stockpile. BZ is widely used in research.
Military Designation	**BZ**
CAS	6581-06-2
Formula	$C_{21}H_{23}NO_3$
Appearance and Odor	An odorless white crystalline solid.
Chemical and Physical Properties	Molecular weight: 337.4 Boiling point: 320°C (608°F) Freezing/melting point: 164-165°C (327-329°F) Vapor pressure: negligible Vapor density: 11.6 Volatility: not volatile Solubility in water: slightly soluble pH: unknown Odor threshold: unknown Specific gravity: 1.33 g/cc (solid) Polymerization: will not occur
Incompatibilities	Unknown.

Persistency	Unknown.
Flammability	Flash point: 246°C (475°F) (not a flammable hazard).
Physiological Properties	BZ is a very potent psychoactive chemical affecting the central nervous system as well as the organs of circulation, digestion, salivation, sweating, and vision. Its pharmacological action is similar to that of other anticholinergic drugs (e.g., atropine, scopolamine), but is longer lasting. Acute exposure produces increased heart and respiratory rates; mydriasis; mouth, skin, and lip dryness; cycloplegia; high temperature; ataxia; flushing of face and neck; hallucinations; stupor; forgetfulness; and confusion. The initial symptoms after ½ to 4 hours of exposure include: dizziness, mouth dryness, and increased heart rate; secondary symptoms, after 3 to 5 hours of exposure, include: restlessness, involuntary muscular movements, rear vision impairment, and total incapacitation; final symptoms, after 6 to 10 hours of exposure are psychotropic in nature. After 3 to 4 days, full recovery from BZ intoxication is expected.
Toxicity	ICt_{50}: 101 mg-min/m^3 (15 l/min) LCt_{50}: 200,000 mg-min/m^3 (estimated)
Exposure Data	TWA 0.004 mg/m^3
Emergency Response Action Levels	None established.
Rate of Detoxification	Slow.
First Aid	Inhalation: remove individual from exposure immediately; start resuscitation and administer oxygen if breathing is irregular or has stopped; seek medical attention immediately. Eye Contact: flush eyes with water for at least 15 minutes; do not rub eyes; seek medical attention immediately. Skin Contact: wash from skin and clothing with water; remove any contaminated clothing; seek medical attention immediately. Ingestion: do not induce vomiting; seek medical attention immediately.
Decontamination	Wash with soap and water.
Hydrolysis Rate	Unknown.
Environmental Fate	Unknown.
Protective Equipment	Respiratory protection and chemical protective clothing required. Level A, B, and C may be used depending on air monitoring.

13

Environmental Monitoring

Environmental monitoring at a hazardous materials incident is required by law and is used for a number of purposes. Environmental monitoring is an essential component of a health and safety program at any incident.

Environmental monitoring is used:
- To set response zones (hot, warm, cold) for an incident command system.
- To select levels of personal protective equipment for responders (level B vs level A).
- To determine where contamination is and, conversely, to identify safe areas that are not contaminated.
- To determine areas that are immediately dangerous to life and health.
- To identify flammable atmospheres, oxygen deficient atmospheres, or the presence of toxic substances.

Airborne contaminants can present a significant threat to human health. Determing the presence and concentration of hazardous substances at a hazardous material spill incident is essential for assessing the health risks to response personnel and the public. Levels of personal protective equipment and areas where it is required can be determined when the nature and quantity of the hazardous substances are known.

Monitoring allows responders to determine the effectiveness of their preventive or remedial actions and to evaluate the progress of the general cleanup effort. Identifying and quantifying these contaminants by air monitoring are essential components of a health and safety program at an incident scene.

Direct-reading instruments were developed as early-warning devices for use in industrial settings where leaks or an accident could release a high concentration of a known chemical. Today, some direct-reading instruments can detect concentrations of contaminants below one part contaminant per million parts of air (ppm). Direct-reading instruments provide information at the time of sampling and do not require sending samples to a laboratory for subsequent analysis. This characteristic of direct-reading instruments enables rapid decision-making.

Sampling the environment (air, water and soil) for later analysis by gas chromatography, high-performance liquid chromatography, or mass spectrometry can provide highly accurate information on the identity and concentration of contaminants present. However, these are generally sophisticated analyses requiring that samples be taken to another location or to a portable field laboratory that may be brought to major incidents.

256

In most cases, these more sophisticated analyses require hours to perform and may not be useful in immediately defining safe areas or areas of significant contamination for the purposes of safe and effective emergency response.

Initial assessment surveys should be used to set the priorities for ongoing air monitoring. When conditions are found that are immediately dangerous to life and health, such as flammable atmosphere, oxygen-deficient atmosphere, or the presence of toxic substances, extreme caution should be used by personnel entering the area, and appropriate personal protective equipment should be worn.

Open areas generally receive the lowest priority for monitoring because natural dispersal forces tend to be able to dilute atmospheric contaminants very readily from these areas. Low-lying areas, confined spaces, and containers can allow hazardous concentrations of substances to persist for extended periods of time and thus merit a higher priority for monitoring.

Sampling should be planned and done with specific objectives in mind. To define a contaminant plume, sampling should begin downwind from the source. Work along the axis of the wind until you reach the source or safety becomes a factor. Next, sample across the axis of the wind to find the width of the plume.

The capability to detect, identify, and quantify unknown inorganic vapors and gases in the field is limited. Colorimetric indicator tubes may have some application in this area and photoionization detectors (PIDs) can monitor a few inorganic materials. Concentrations of unknown organic compounds can be estimated by colorimetric indicator tubes, PIDs or flame ionization detectors (FIDs) when used in the survey mode and identified to a limited degree when using the gas chromatograph mode. Combustible gas indicators will detect the presence of many combustible gases and vapors at relatively high concentrations.

Personnel working in areas where conditions might become hazardous due to unexpected changes or events can use a personal monitor as a warning device. In other cases, it may be desirable or necessary to monitor the exposure of a worker to various contaminants during a work period and obtain a time-weighted average of the exposure.

Personal monitoring instruments for detection of acute hazards such as flammable vapors, low oxygen concentrations, and toxic gases should be small and compact and easily carried by the worker. Audible and visual alarm signals are desirable with accessories such as ear plug attachments if work is to be conducted in high noise environments. The power supply (batteries) should last for the entire work period. Calibration adjustment controls should be positioned or designed so that they cannot be knocked out of position or easily readjusted by the workers. Many devices can serve as both an area monitor and a personal monitor.

Obtaining the time-weighted average exposure for some individual contaminants can be done by instruments equipped with microprocessor-based electronics. These personal monitors eliminate the need for sending samples to a laboratory for analysis.

More commonly, we measure the time-weighted average exposure by collecting the contaminant of interest in an absorbent medium, then doing a laboratory analysis to measure the concentration. The badge or tube containing the absorbent to be worn by the worker is placed near the breathing zone. With some devices, a pump draws a continuous flow of air through the sampler. Other devices, such as passive dosimeter badges, rely on the process of diffusion or, in some cases, permeation to bring the contaminant into contact with the absorbent. Some types of passive dosimeters may be read directly, similar to colorimetric tube samplers.

Positive Characteristics of Air-Monitoring Instruments

To be useful, air-monitoring instruments must be portable and rugged, easy to operate, inherently safe, and able to generate reliable and useful results. The following discussion addresses these important features.

Portability
A prime consideration for field instruments is portability. Transportation shock resulting from the movement from one place to another, with unintentional abuse, shortens the usable life of an instrument. To reduce the effects of this trauma, instruments should be selected that have reinforced shells or frames, shock-mounted electronic packages, or padded containers for shipment, or that can be easily carried. Exposure to the elements and to the test atmosphere itself is of concern for those instruments repeatedly used in adverse conditions or as long-term monitors. Anodized or coated finishes, weather-resistant packaging, and remote sensors are effective in reducing downtime and increasing portability. An internal power supply is important for portability. Some instruments use replaceable or rechargeable batteries and some do not require a power supply. An instrument should not be so heavy or bulky that it is difficult for a response worker to carry.

Ease of Operation
Because many of these instruments were designed for industrial use, allowances may not have been made for using the instrument while wearing protective equipment. One must consider how easy it is to use the instrument while wearing gloves or how difficult it is to read the meter while wearing a respirator. Also, consider how quickly a worker can learn to operate the instrument correctly. Preparation time for use of the instrument should be short. Rapid warm-up, easy attachment of accessories, and quick instrument checks shorten preparation time.

Use in a Hazardous Environment
The portable instrumentation used to characterize hazardous material spills or waste sites must be safe to use in hazardous atmospheres. Electrical devices, including instruments, must be constructed in such a fashion as to prevent the ignition of a combustible atmosphere. The sources of this ignition could be an arc generated by the power source itself or the associated electronics, or a flame or heat source necessary for function of the instrument. Several engineering, insurance, and safety organizations have standardized test methods, established inclusive definitions, and developed codes for testing electrical devices used in hazardous locations.

The National Fire Protection Association (NFPA) has created minimum standards in its National Electrical Code (NEC), published every three years. This code explains the types of areas in which hazardous atmospheres can be generated, types of materials that generate hazardous atmospheres, and design safeguards acceptable for use in hazardous atmospheres.

Hazardous Atmospheres
Depending upon the response worker's background, the term "hazardous atmosphere" conjures up situations ranging from toxic air contaminants to flammable atmospheres. For National Electrical Code (NEC) purposes, an atmosphere is hazardous if it meets the following criteria:
- It is a mixture of any flammable material in air whose concentration is within the material's flammable range (i.e., between the material's lower flammable limit and its upper flammable limit).
- There is the potential for an ignition source to be present.

258

The resulting exothermic reaction could propagate beyond where it started.

To describe hazardous atmospheres, the NEC categorizes them according to their class, group, and division.

Class and Group
Class is used to describe the type of flammable material that produces the hazardous atmosphere:
- **Class I** is flammable vapors and gases, such as gasoline and hydrogen. Class I is further divided into groups A, B, C, and D, based on similar flammability characteristics.
- **Class II** consists of combustible dusts like coal or grain and is divided into groups E, F, and G.
- **Class III** is ignitable fibers such as those produced by cotton milling.

Division
Division is the term describing the location of generation and release of the flammable material.
- **Division 1** is a location where the generation and release are continuous, intermittent, or periodic into an open, unconfined area under normal conditions.
- **Division 2** is a location where the generation and release are only from ruptures, leaks, or other failures from closed systems or containers.

Using this system, a hazardous atmosphere can be routinely and adequately defined. As an example, an abandoned waste site containing intact closed drums of methyl ethyl ketone, toluene, and xylene would be considered a Class 1, Division 2, Group D environment. However, when transfer of flammable liquids takes place at the site or if release of flammable gases/vapors is considered normal, those areas would be considered Class I, Division 1, Group D.

The following three methods of construction exist to prevent a potential source from igniting a flammable atmosphere:
- **Explosion-proof**: Explosion-proof instruments do not allow the flammable atmosphere to enter the instrument casing. Should the flammable atmosphere enter the instrument and an arc be generated, the resulting explosion is contained within the specially built enclosure. Within it, any flames or hot gases are cooled before exiting into the ambient flammable atmosphere so that the explosion does not spread into the environment.
- **Intrinsically Safe**: The potential for arcing among components is reduced by encasing them in a solid insulating material. Also, reducing the instrument's operational current and voltage below the energy level necessary for ignition of the flammable atmosphere provides protection. An intrinsically safe device, as defined by the National Electrical Code, is incapable "of releasing sufficient electrical or thermal energy under normal or abnormal conditions to cause ignition of a specific hazardous atmospheric mixture in its most easily ignited concentration. Abnormal conditions shall include accidental damage to any wiring, failure of electrical components, application of over voltage, adjustment and maintenance operations and other similar conditions."
- **Purged**: The arcing or flame-producing device is buffered from the flammable atmosphere with an inert gas. In pressured or purged systems, a steady stream of nitrogen or helium passes by the potential arcing device, keeping the flammable atmosphere from the ignition source. This type of control, however, does not satisfactorily control analytical devices that use flame or heat for analysis, such as a combustible gas indicator (CGI). It also requires a source of gas that would reduce instrument portability.

If a device is certified as explosion-proof, intrinsically safe, or purged for a given class, division, and group, and is used, maintained, and serviced according to the manufacturer's instructions, it will not contribute to ignition. The device is not, however, certified for use in atmospheres other than those suggested. All certified devices must be marked to show class, division, and group. Any manufacturer wishing to have an electrical device certified must submit a prototype to a laboratory for testing. If it passes, it is certified as submitted. However, the manufacturer agrees to allow the testing laboratory to randomly check the manufacturing plant any time, as well as any marketed units. Furthermore, any change in the unit requires the manufacturer to notify the test laboratory, which can continue the certification or withdraw it until the modified unit can be retested. Testing is done by such organizations as Underwriters' Laboratory, Inc. (UL) or Factory Mutual Research Corp. (FM). Currently, these are the only two testing labs recognized by OSHA.

The response time, sensitivity, selectivity, accuracy, and precision of an instrument are important in evaluating the reliability and usefulness of the data the instrument generates.

- **Response time**: the interval between when an instrument senses a contaminant and generates data, is important to producing reliable and useful results in the field. Response time depends on: test(s) to be performed, dead time between sample periods (the time for analysis, data generation, and data display), and the sensitivity of the instrument. Response times for direct-reading instruments may range from a few seconds to several minutes.
- **Sensitivity**: defined as the ability of an instrument to accurately measure changes in concentration. Sensitivity is important when slight concentration changes can be dangerous. The lower detection limit is the lowest concentration to which an instrument will respond. The operating range is the lower and upper use limits of the instrument. It is defined by the lower detection limit at one end and the saturation concentration at the other end. It is important to use an instrument with an operating range that will accurately measure the concentration in the range of concern.
- **Amplification**: a term often confused with sensitivity, amplification is the instrument's ability to increase very small electronic signals emanating from the detector to the readout. Changing the amplification of the detector does not change its sensitivity. However, it may be useful in calibration. Instruments with amplifier circuits can be affected by radio frequency from pulsed DC or AC power lines, transformers, generators, and radio wave transmitters.
- **Accuracy**: defined as the relationship between a true value and the instrument reading. Accuracy is the indication of the reproducibility. These factors can be indicated by the error factor. For example, some detector tubes may have an error factor of +/- 35 percent of the true value; meaning the actual concentration of the chemical being measured is within a range of 35 percent higher and lower than the tube reading.
- **Selectivity**: is the ability of an instrument to detect and measure a specific chemical or group of similar chemicals. Additionally, selectivity depends upon interfering compounds that may produce a similar response. Selectivity and sensitivity must be reviewed and interpreted together. Interferences can affect the accuracy of the instrument reading.

Another consideration is that the instrument must give results that are immediately useful. Instruments should be direct-reading, with little or no need to interpolate, integrate, or compile large amounts of data. When selecting an instrument, compare the desired sensitivity, range, accuracy, selectivity, and ability to vary amplification of detector signals with the available instrument characteristics.

For an instrument to function properly in the field, it should be calibrated before use. Calibration is the process of adjusting the instrument readout so that it corresponds to the actual concentration. Calibration involves checking the instrument results with a known concentration of a gas or vapor to see that the instrument gives the proper response. For example, if a combustible gas meter is calibrated with a gas that is 20 percent of the lower explosive limit (LEL), then the instrument should read 20 percent of the LEL. If it does not read accurately, it is out of calibration and should be adjusted until accurate readings are obtained.

260

Although an instrument is calibrated to give a one-to-one response for a specific chemical (the calibration gas), its response to other chemicals may be different. This variability is called relative response. A combustible gas indicator calibrated to pentane will give a higher instrument reading for methane than the actual concentration. The relative response of an instrument to different chemicals can be calculated by dividing the instrument reading by the actual concentration and is expressed as a ratio or as a percent. Note that for the calibration standard the relative response should be 1.00 or 100 percent.

Relative Response of Selected Chemicals for a
Combustible Gas Indicator Calibrated to Pentane at 100 ppm

Chemical Response	Meter Relative %LEL
Methane	170%
Acetylene	120%
Pentene	106%
1,4 Dioxane	74%
Xylene	54%

If the instrument is being used for a chemical that is different from the calibration standard, then it may be possible to find a conversion factor in the instrument's technical manual. Then the actual concentration can be calculated. For example, if the instrument's relative response for xylene is 0.27 (27 percent) and the reading is 100 ppm (parts per million), then the actual concentration is 370 ppm (100 ppm/0.27 = actual concentration). If there is no relative response data for the chemical in question, it may be possible to recalibrate the instrument. If the instrument has adjustable settings and a known concentration is available, the instrument may be adjusted to read directly for the chemical. As recalibration takes time, this is usually done only if the instrument is going to be used for many measurements of the specific chemical.

Oxygen Indicators

Oxygen indicators are used to evaluate an atmosphere for the following:

- Oxygen content for respiratory purposes. Normal air contains 20.9 percent oxygen. Generally, if the oxygen content drops below 19.5 percent, it is considered oxygen-deficient and special respiratory protection is needed.
- Increased risk of combustion. Generally, concentrations above 25 percent are considered oxygen-enriched and increase the risk of combustion.

Use of other instruments. Some instruments require sufficient oxygen for operation. For example, some combustible gas indicators do not give reliable results at oxygen concentrations below 10 percent. Also, the safety approvals for instruments are granted for normal atmospheres and not for oxygen-enriched ones.

Presence of contaminants. A decrease in oxygen content can be due to the consumption (by combustion or a reaction such as rusting) of oxygen or the displacement of air by a chemical. If it is due to consumption, then the concern is the lack of oxygen. If it is due to displacement, then there is something present that could be flammable or toxic.

Chapter 13/Environmental Monitoring

Street Smart™ Chemistry

Oxygen-deficient atmospheres may occur in unventilated areas or may be due to terrain variations in cases where vapors heavier than air may collect. Most indicators have meters that display the oxygen concentration from 0–25 percent. There are also oxygen indicators available that measure concentrations from 0–5 percent and 0–100 percent. The most useful range for response is the 0–25 percent oxygen content readout since decisions involving air-supplying respirators and the use of combustible gas indicators fall into this range.

Many instrument manufacturers make oxygen meters. They can be small hand-held units with or without pumps to draw the sample across the detector cell. Some pumps are single-aspirating (hand-squeeze) bulbs, others are battery-powered diaphragm pumps. Units that combine O_2 meters and combustible gas indicators into one instrument are also widely available. Also, flashing lights and audible alarms can be found on many instruments. These alarms go off at a predetermined oxygen concentration to alert the users even if they are not watching the meter.

Principle of Operation

Oxygen indicators have two principle components for operation. These are the oxygen sensor and the meter readout. In some units, air is drawn into the oxygen detector with an aspirator bulb or pump; in other units, the ambient air is allowed to diffuse to the sensor. The oxygen detector uses an electrochemical sensor to determine the oxygen concentration in air. A typical sensor consists of: two electrodes, a housing containing a basic electrolytic solution, and a semipermeable membrane made of Teflon®.

Oxygen molecules (O_2) diffuse through the membrane into the solution. Reactions between the oxygen, the solution, and the electrodes produce a minute electric current proportional to the oxygen content. The current passes through the electronic circuit. The resulting signal is shown as a needle deflection on a meter or digital reading.

Limitations and Considerations

The operation of oxygen meters depends on the absolute atmospheric pressure. The concentration of natural oxygen (to differentiate it from manufactured or generated oxygen) depends on the atmospheric pressure at a given altitude.

While the actual percentage of oxygen does not change with altitude, at sea level the weight of the atmosphere above is greater, and more O_2 molecules (and the other components of air) are compressed into a given volume than at higher elevations. As elevation increases, this compression decreases, resulting in fewer air molecules being squeezed into a given volume. Consequently, an O_2 indicator calibrated at sea level and operated at an altitude of several thousand feet will falsely show an oxygen-deficient atmosphere because less oxygen is being pushed into the sensor. Therefore, it is necessary to calibrate at the altitude at which the instrument is used.

High concentrations of carbon dioxide (CO_2) shorten the useful life of the oxygen sensor.

Temperature can affect the response of oxygen indicators. The normal operating range for them is between 32°F and 120°F. Between 0°F and 32°F, the response of the unit is slower. Below 0°F, the sensor may be damaged by freezing solution. The instrument should be calibrated at the temperature at which it will be used.

Strong oxidizing chemicals, like ozone and chlorine, can cause increased readings and show high or normal O_2 content when the actual content is normal or even low.

Combustible Atmosphere Indicators

Combustible gas indicators (CGIs) measure the concentration of a flammable vapor or gas in air, indicating the results as a percentage of the lower explosive limit (LEL) of the calibration gas.

The LEL (or LFL [lower flammable limit]) of a combustible gas or vapor is the minimum concentration of that material in air that will propagate flame on contact with an ignition source. The upper explosive limit (UEL) is the maximum concentration. Above the UEL, the mixture is too rich to support combustion, so ignition is not possible. Below the LEL, there is insufficient fuel to support combustion.

CGIs are available in many styles and configurations. Some units have some type of pump to draw the air sample into the detector, while in other units, the ambient air is allowed to diffuse to the sensor. The pumps are either hand-operated squeeze bulbs or automatic (battery-powered) diaphragm types. Many units are combination meters. This means they have an O_2 meter and CGI (and sometimes one or two specific gas indicators) combined in the same instrument. There are two types: filament and electronic. Flashing lights and audible alarms are options on many units. The alarms go off at predetermined concentrations to warn the instrument operator of potentially hazardous atmospheres. Other options such as larger sampling lines, moisture taps, and dust filters are also available.

Principle of Operation
Combustible gas indicators use a combustion chamber containing a filament that burns the flammable gas or an electronic sensor. To facilitate combustion, the filament is heated or is coated with a catalyst (like platinum or palladium) or both. In the hot wire type, a filament is part of a balanced resistor circuit called a Whetstone Bridge. The hot filament burns the gas on the immediate surface of the element, thus raising the temperature of the filament. As the temperature of the filament increases, so does its resistance.
This change in resistance causes an imbalance in the Whetstone Bridge. This is measured as the ratio of combustible vapor present compared to the total required to reach the LEL. For example, if the meter reads 0.5 (or 50 percent, depending upon the readout), this means that 50 percent of the concentration of combustible gas needed to reach a flammable or explosive situation is present. If the LEL for the gas is 5 percent and the meter indicates 50 percent LEL, then the true concentration of the vapor is 2.5 percent. Thus, the typical meter readout indicates concentrations up to 100 percent LEL or the true LEL of the gas.

If a concentration greater than the LEL and lower than the UEL is present, then the meter needle will stay beyond the 1.0 (100 percent) level on the meter. This indicates that the ambient atmosphere is readily combustible. When the atmosphere has a gas concentration above the UEL, the meter needle will usually rise above the 1.0 (100 percent) mark and then return to zero. This occurs because the gas mixture in the combustion cell becomes too rich to burn. This permits the filament to conduct a current just as if the atmosphere contained no combustibles at all.

Some instruments have a lock mechanism that prevents the needle from returning to zero when it has reached 100 percent and must be reset in an atmosphere below the LEL.

Limitations and Considerations
The response of some instruments is temperature-dependent. If the temperature at which the instrument is zeroed differs from the sample temperature, the accuracy of the reading is affected. Hotter temperatures raise the temperature of the filament and produce a higher-than-actual reading. Cooler temperatures will reduce the reading. It works best to calibrate and zero the instrument at the temperature at which it will be used.

The instruments are intended for use only in normal oxygen atmospheres. Oxygen-deficient atmospheres will produce lowered readings. Also, the guards that prevent the combustion source from igniting a flammable atmosphere are not designed to operate in oxygen-enriched atmospheres.

Organic lead vapors (e.g., leaded gasoline vapors), sulfur compounds, and silicone compounds will foul the filament. Acid gases (e.g., hydrogen chloride and hydrogen fluoride) can corrode the filament. Silicone vapors and samples containing them even in small quantities will poison the sensor. Most units have an optional filter that protects the sensor from lead vapors.

To the CGI, there is no differentiation between petroleum vapors and other combustible gases. If the combined flammability of the vapors and gases in an area is the desired measurement, this is not a problem. However, if the instrument is being used to detect the presence of a released flammable liquid like gasoline in a sewer system where methane may be present, the operator cannot tell if the reading is from the gasoline or the methane. A filter can be used to remove the petroleum vapors but will not remove the methane.

Thus, if two readings are made, one with and one without the filter, the operator can compare the readings and can conclude that differences in the values indicate that the petroleum vapor is present.

Colorimetric Indicator Tubes (Detector Tubes)

Principle of Operation
Colorimetric indicator tubes consist of a glass tube impregnated with an indicating chemical. The tube is connected to a piston or bellows-type pump.

A known volume of contaminated air is pulled at a predetermined rate through the tube by the pump. The contaminant reacts with the indicator chemical in the tube, producing a change in color whose length is proportional to the contaminant concentration.

Detector tubes are normally chemical-specific. There are different tubes for different gases; for example, chlorine detector tube for chlorine gas, acrylonitrile tube for acrylonitrile, etc. Some manufacturers do produce tubes for groups of gases, such as aromatic hydrocarbons or alcohols. Concentration ranges on the tubes may be in the ppm or percent range.

A preconditioning filter may precede the indicating chemical to:
- Remove contaminants (other than the one in question) that may interfere with the measurement.
- Remove humidity.
- React with a contaminant to change it into a compound that reacts with the indicating chemical.

HAZMAT kits are available from at least three manufacturers (Drager, Sensidyne, MSA). These kits identify or classify the contaminants as a member of a chemical group such as acid gas, halogenated hydrocarbon, etc. This is done by sampling with certain combinations of tubes at the same time by using a special multiple tube holder or by using tubes in a specific sampling sequence.

Limitations and Considerations
Sometimes detector tubes are the only means of monitoring. However, detector tubes have the disadvantage of poor accuracy and precision.

In the past, the National Institute for Occupational Safety and Health (NIOSH) tested and certified detector tubes that were submitted to them. For the tubes tested, NIOSH certified the accuracy to be +/- 35 percent at concentrations at half the OSHA Permissible Exposure Limit (PEL) and +/- 25 percent at 1 to 5 times the PEL. NIOSH has discontinued testing and certification. Special studies have reported error factors of 50 percent and higher for some tubes.

The chemical reactions involved in the use of the tubes are affected by temperature. Cold weather slows the reactions and thus the response time. To reduce this problem, it is recommended that the tubes be kept warm (for example, inside a coat pocket) until they are used, if the measurement is done in cold weather. Hot temperatures increase the reaction and can cause a problem by discoloring the indicator when a contaminant is not present. This can happen even in unopened tubes. Therefore, the tubes should be stored at a moderate temperature.

Some tubes do not have a prefilter to remove humidity and may be affected by high humidity. The manufacturer's instructions usually indicate whether humidity is a problem and list any correction factors to use if the tube is affected by humidity.

The chemical used in the tubes deteriorates over time. Thus, the tubes are assigned a shelf life. This varies from 1 to 3 years. Shelf life can be extended by refrigeration, but the tube should be brought up to ambient temperature before use. Vendors should sell the old stock first. The tube is only good until the expiration date.

An advantage that detector tubes have over some other instruments is that it is possible to select a tube that is specific to a chemical. However, some tubes will respond to interfering compounds. Fortunately, the manufacturers provide information with the tubes on interfering gases and vapors.

Interpretation of results can be a problem. Since the tube's length of color change indicates the contaminant concentration, the user must be able to see the end of the stain. Color changes may not be precise or clear at times. Some stains are diffused and are not clear-cut; others may have an uneven endpoint. Time changes length of stain and some tubes need longer reaction times. When in doubt, use the highest value that would be obtained from reading the different aspects of the tube.

The total volume to be drawn through the tube varies with the tube type and the manufacturer. The volume needed is given as the number of pump strokes needed, i.e., the number of times the piston or bellows is manipulated. Also, the air does not instantaneously go through the tube. It may take 1 to 2 minutes for each volume (stroke) to be completely drawn. Therefore, sampling times can vary from 1 to 30 minutes per tube. This can make the use of detector tubes time-consuming.

Due to these many considerations, it is very important to read the instructions that are provided with, and are specific to, a set of tubes. The information includes the number of pump strokes needed, time for each pump stroke, interfering gases and vapors, effect of humidity and temperature, shelf life, proper color change, and whether the tube is reusable.

A pyrolyzer is required for some tubes. Gases are "burned" before entering the tubes. This is not always safe in hazardous atmospheres.

While there are many limitations and considerations for using detector tubes, they are versatile in being able to measure a wide range of chemicals with a single pump. Also, there are some chemicals for which detector tubes are the only direct-reading indicators.

Specific Chemical Monitors

There are several gas monitors that use utilize electrochemical cells or metal oxide semiconductors (MOS) for detecting specific chemicals. MOS detectors change conductivity when exposed to certain gases or vapors. They can be designed to respond to a large group of chemicals or to a specific chemical. The most common monitors are used to detect carbon monoxide or hydrogen sulfide, but there are also monitors available for hydrogen cyanide, ammonia, and chlorine. They are more accurate than detector tubes, but there are only about a dozen different chemicals they can monitor.

Photoionization Detectors (PID)

These instruments detect concentrations of gases and vapors in air by using an ultraviolet light source to ionize the airborne contaminant. Once the gas or vapor is ionized in the instrument, it can be detected and measured. Photoionization detectors are also used in gas chromatographs made by Photovac, HNU, and Thermo Environmental Instruments.

Principle of Operation
All atoms and molecules are composed of particles: electrons, protons, and neutrons. Electrons (negatively charged particles) rotate in orbit around the nucleus, the dense inner core. The nucleus consists of an equal number of protons (positively charged particles) as electrons found in the orbital cloud. The interaction of the oppositely charged particles and the laws of quantum mechanics keep the electrons in orbits outside the nucleus.

The energy required to remove the outermost electron from the molecule is called the ionization potential (IP) and is specific for any compound or atomic species. Ionization potentials are measured in electron volts (eV). High-frequency radiation (ultraviolet [UV] and above) is capable of causing ionization and is hence called ionizing radiation.

When a photon of ultraviolet radiation strikes a chemical compound, it ionizes the molecule if the energy of the radiation is equal to or greater than the IP of the compound. Since ions are charged particles, they may be collected on a charged plate and produce a current. The measured current will be directly proportional to the number of ionized molecules.

The photoionization process can be illustrated as:

$$R + h \rightarrow R^+ + e$$

where R is an organic or inorganic molecule and h represents a photon of UV light with energy equal to or greater than the ionization potential of that particular chemical species. R^+ is the ionized molecule.

PIDs use a fan or a pump to draw air into the detector of the instrument where the contaminants are exposed to UV light and the resulting negatively charged particles (ions) are collected and measured.

Ionization Potentials of Selected Chemicals

Chemical	Ionization Potential (eV)
Hydrogen Cyanide	13.9
Carbon Dioxide	13.8
Methane	13.0
Water	12.6
Hydrogen Chloride	12.5
Oxygen	12.1
Chlorine	11.5
Propane	11.1
Hydrogen Sulfide	10.5
Hexane	10.2
Ammonia	10.1
Vinyl Chloride	10.0
Acetone	9.7
Benzene	9.2
Ethyl Amine	8.9
Phenol	8.5

Photoionization Considerations and Limitations

Since the ability to detect a chemical depends on the ability to ionize it, the IP of a chemical to be detected must be compared to the energy generated by the UV lamp of the instrument. As can be seen in the previous table there is a limit imposed by the components of air. That is to say, the lamp cannot be too energetic or oxygen and nitrogen will ionize and interfere with the readings for contaminants. The energy of lamps available are 8.3, 8.4, 9.5, 10.2, 10.6, 10.9, 11.4, 11.7 and 11.8 eV. Not all lamps are available from a single manufacturer.

One use of the different lamps is for selective determination of chemicals. For example, if a spill of propane and vinyl chloride were to be monitored with a PID, the first check would be to see if they could be detected. The IP of propane is 11.1 eV and the IP of vinyl chloride is 10.0 eV. To detect both, a lamp with an energy greater than 11.1 eV is needed (like an 11.7 or 11.8 lamp). If vinyl chloride were the chemical of concern, then a lamp with an energy greater than 10.0 but less than 11.1 (such as 10.2 or 10.6) could be used. The propane would neither be ionized nor detected. Thus, propane would not interfere with the vinyl chloride readings.

The sample drawn into the instrument passes over the lamp to be ionized. Dust in the atmosphere can collect on the lamp and block the transmission of UV light. This will cause a reduction in instrument reading. This problem will be detected during calibration, and the lamp should be cleaned on a regular basis.

Humidity can cause two problems. When a cold instrument is taken into a warm moist atmosphere, the moisture can condense on the lamp. Like dust, this will reduce the available light. Moisture in the air also reduces the ionization of chemicals and causes a reduction in readings.

Since an electric field is generated in the sample chamber of the instrument, radio frequency interference from pulsed DC or AC power lines, transformers, generators, and radio wave transmission may produce an error in response.

As the lamp ages, the intensity of the light decreases. It will still have the same ionization energy, but the response will decline. This will be detected during calibration, and adjustments can be made. However, the lamp will eventually burn out.

Photoionization detectors are calibrated to a single chemical. The instrument's response to chemicals other than the calibration gas/vapor can vary. The table below shows the relative responses of several chemicals for a specific PID.

Relative Responses for Selected Chemicals Using the HNU Model Pi 101 with 10.2 Ev Probe Calibrated to Benzene

Chemical	Relative Response
m-xylene	1.12
Benzene	1.00
Phenol	0.78
Vinyl Chloride	0.63
Acetone	0.50
Hexane	0.22
Phosphine	0.20
Ammonia	0.03

In some cases, at high concentrations, the instrument response can decrease. While the response may be linear (i.e., 1 to 1 response) from 1 to 600 ppm for an instrument, a concentration of 900 ppm may only give a meter response of 700 ppm.

Portable Flame Ionization Detectors (FID)

These units use combustion as the means to ionize airborne contaminants. Once they are ionized, many contaminants can be detected and measured.

Principle of Operation
Flame ionization detectors use a hydrogen flame as the means to ionize organic (toxic) vapors. The FID responds to virtually all organic compounds: that is, compounds that contain carbon-hydrogen or carbon-carbon bonds.

Inside the detector chamber, the sample is exposed to a hydrogen flame that ionizes the organic vapors. When most organic vapors burn, positively charged carbon-containing ions are produced, which are collected by a negatively charged collecting electrode in the chamber. An electric field exists between the conductors surrounding the flame and a collecting electrode. As the positive ions are collected, a current proportional to the hydrocarbon concentration is generated on the input electrode.

This current is measured with a preamplifier that has an output signal proportional to the ionization current. A signal-conducting amplifier is used to amplify the signal from the preamp and to condition it for subsequent meter or external recorder display.

Flame ionization detectors have a more generalized response in detecting organic vapors. This generalized sensitivity is due to the breaking of chemical bonds, which requires a set amount of energy and is a known reproducible event. Flame ionization detectors are the most sensitive for saturated hydrocarbons, alkanes, and unsaturated hydrocarbon alkenes. Substances that contain substituted functional groups, such as hydroxide (OH) and chloride (Cl), tend to reduce the detector's sensitivity. Overall, however, the detectabilities remain good.

Flame Ionization Detector Considerations
Flame ionization detectors respond only to organic compounds. Thus, they do not detect inorganic compounds like chlorine, hydrogen cyanide, or ammonia.

Infrared Spectrophotometer (IR)

Principle of Operation
The infrared spectrophotometer is a compound-specific instrument. Each compound being analyzed will absorb radiation at discrete infrared wavelengths. The unit measures how much of the infrared energy (IR) is absorbed and gives readings of percent IR absorbed or ppm of chemical.

Molecules are composed of atoms that are held together by bonds of various types and lengths. These bonds have finite locations and discrete movements for each atom. These movements can be either vibrational, rotational, stretching, or bending of the chemical bonds. The frequencies of these movements are on the order of infrared radiation. A given bond movement can be initiated by stimulating the molecule with IR of varying frequency. As the bond moves, it absorbs the characteristic energy associated with that movement. The frequencies and intensity of IR absorbed are specific for a compound and its concentration, providing a fingerprint that can be used as an analytical tool.

Aerosol Monitors

Not all toxic materials dispersed in air are in the form of a gas or vapor. Solids and liquids can become suspended in air by combustion, splashing liquids, or by disturbing soil.

There are direct-reading instruments that measure aerosols (e.g., dust, mist, fume, smoke, fog, spray). Most of them use a light source and a light sensor that measures the amount of light scattered by the aerosol. Readouts are in milligrams per cubic meter (mg/m^3).

Other methods of detection are the piezoelectric crystal mass monitor and beta attenuation. The piezoelectric crystal mass monitor uses a crystal that resonates at a certain frequency as electric current is applied to it. As particles collect on the crystal, its resonant frequency changes and the change is measured.

Beta attenuation measures the attenuation of beta radiation by particles collected on a surface between the beta source and a beta detector.

It is important to remember that these instruments give the total amount of particulate and not the type of particulate. Individual content, e.g., lead or arsenic, must be analyzed separately. However, if the content of the sample is known, then the direct-reading instrument could be used if the content of the dust is assumed to remain constant.

For example, if the dust being detected is 5 percent lead and 1 percent arsenic and the concentration of dust is 2 mg/m^3, then the concentration of lead and arsenic are 0.1 mg/m^3 and 0.02 mg/m^3, respectively (0.05 x 2 mg/m^3= 0.1 mg/m^3 and 0.01 x 2 mg/m^3 = 0.02 mg/m^3).

Accessories/Options

As mentioned earlier, some instruments combine more than one detector. For example, trimeters and quadmeters combine an oxygen indicator, a combustible gas indicator, and one or two toxic monitors. There are also units with alarms that indicate readings that are above or below a concentration of concern, strip chart (printed) outputs, and electronic outputs for data storage.

Some instruments have an integrator that averages concentrations while the instrument is operating or over a specified time (e.g., 15 minutes). This permits use of the instrument as a long-term monitor as well as a direct-reading instrument.

One of the more recent additions is the microprocessor. This can be used with a gas chromatograph so the microprocessor reads the output and compares it to calibration information in its memory. That way, the instrument instead of the operator qualifies and quantifies the chemicals. In some cases, the operator asks the microprocessor to check for a chemical and the unit uses its memory to match retention time and peak height.

Monitoring Pesticides and Highly Toxic Components

Overview
Monitoring air, water, and soils for pesticides and other highly regulated or toxic materials presents significant and difficult problems to overcome. Unlike with "bulk chemicals" like acids or bases and the more common organic intermediates, there are few field analyses that can be done to confirm the presence of these types of materials at levels that could be hazardous or that could cause significant harm to the environment:
- There are no simple Draeger tube type analyses to measure air concentrations of most pesticides. Unless the pesticide contains organic inerts (such as organic solvents) that might be monitored, they are unlikely to show up on air monitoring equipment readily available to most responders.
- The amount of some pesticides in water that can cause serious environmental damage is small enough that simple tests like pH normally will not pick up the contamination.

There are some tests which can detect or measure pesticides at very low levels in air, soil, or water. These include infrared (IR) analyzers, gas chromatography (GC), high-perfomance liquid chromatography (HPLC), mass spectrometry coupled with GC or HPLC (GCMS or LCMS), and immunoassay (IA) tests. These instruments are becoming more available in "field versions," but still remain primarily laboratory tools requiring specialized training and sophisticated sample preparation. In most cases, the use of these tools requires that samples be taken in the field and transported to a laboratory for sample preparation and analysis.

One nonspecific tool that can be used in the field for air monitoring for pesticides is a photo-ionization detector (PID) several of which are sensitive down to the parts per billion (ppb) level. However, the response on these instruments is nonspecific, so the value measured is for the total ionizable components and not for any specific component in the air. The result for this measurement is thus a maximum value rather than a specific analysis for one contaminant in the air.

Infrared Analysis

Infrared analysis relies on the fact that organic compounds absorb infrared radiation at frequencies that are characteristic and different for different molecules. The patterns of infrared absorbance are distinct enough that a well-trained chemist can often interpret the patterns and identify the characteristics of the molecule, sometimes even down to identifying the specific molecule and identifying one isomer out of several possible structures. An additional and significant factor is that the amount of infrared energy absorbed by a sample can be related directly to the amount of a specific component in that sample. Even better, instruments (such as the Miran® analyzers) are available today for field use and can monitor specific compounds in air down to the sub-parts-per-million level for compounds in their on-board computerized library. Infrared technology is used extensively to control chemical processes and to analyze gas streams to ensure compliance with pollution control requirements.

Some of these instruments are field-programmable in that one can change the compound being monitored easily—presuming that the compound is already in the instrument's database. In most cases, setting up the instrument to measure a compound that is not already in the database is difficult (if not impossible) in the field and will often require laboratory preparation of standard gas mixtures to allow the choice of monitoring frequencies and calibration factors.

Gas sampling is typically done by pumping ambient air through a transparent chamber between the infrared light source and a detector. The infrared scan below is a plot of the amount of infrared radiation absorbed by the sample as a function of the wavelength of the IR radiation. The IR pattern is sometimes called a "fingerprint" because it is characteristic of a molecule, although very similar molecules will display similar–but not identical–IR fingerprints.

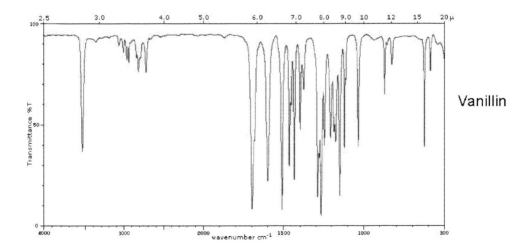

Vanillin

Gas Chromatography

Gas chromatography is a tool used extensively to measure contamination levels in air, water, and soil. Gas chromatography or (GC) is a technique used to separate and measure components in a mixture. This technique can be exceptionally sensitive and very specific depending on the component to be measured.

Principles of Gas Chromatography

In theory, the gas chromatograph is a fairly simple piece of equipment. You have:

- A supply of nonreactive carrier gas, which carries the sample to be analyzed through the equipment.
- A sampler or other means of introducing the sample into the carrier gas stream. This may be as simple as a valve to allow air to enter the gas stream or may involve introducing the sample with a syringe through a membrane called a septum. The injection port is usually heated to volatilize nonvolatile components.
- A chromatographic column, which may be metal or glass. The column allows the individual components in the sample to separate from each other as the gas mixture moves through the column. The theory of how this occurs is beyond the scope of this book.
- A column oven to maintain the column at constant temperature.
- A detector that responds to the presence of each individual component in the mixture as it comes out of the chromatographic column. Common detectors include:
    - A flame ionization detector which is similar in operation to a combustible gas detector
    - A thermal conductivity detector
    - A mass spectrometer
    - An electron capture detector, which uses a radioactive source to ionize the components in the gas mixture.
    - Specialized detectors that are sensitive to phosphorus or nitrogen compounds.

    Each type of detector has characteristics that make it most suitable for specific applications. Each type of detector also has certain limitations. For example, a thermal conductivity detector is relatively insensitive and may not detect toxic components present; a flame ionization detector will not detect compounds like chloroform or carbon tetrachloride that do not burn well.
- A recorder, computer, or other output device that takes the input from the detector and translates it into useable data. This may be as simple as a digital readout of the concentration of specific components or as sophisticated as a complete chromatogram with quantitation and calibration data.

A typical chromatogram is shown below for a wastewater standard intentionally contaminated with low parts per million contaminants. This chromatogram was run on a long glass capillary column with a flame ionization detector and a computer link to record and quantitate the chromatogram.

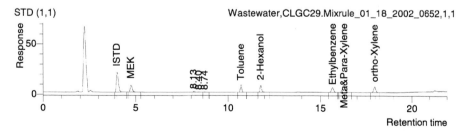

The chart above is a GC scan that shows the detector response as a function of time. The individual peaks are quantitated by measuring the peak area and comparing that to the peak areas of known standard concentrations of that component.

272

Potential Problems with Gas Chromatographic Data

A significant issue in gas chromatographic data is the possible misidentification of the impurity peak due to interferences in the chromatogram. For almost all GC work, the identification of a specific component in the mixture is done by comparing the retention time (the time it takes the component to come off the column into the detector) of the component with the retention time of that component in a standard. For example, a component that comes out of the column 4.2 minutes after injection will be assumed to be the same compound that comes at 4.2 minutes in a standard containing that component. This may NOT be correct. Depending on the chromatographic conditions, many different compounds might have the same retention time. It is thus possible to report the presence and concentration of Compound X in air, water, or soil when Compound X may not be present or may be present at a much lower level, and when you are actually measuring another compound. This phenomenon is called interference.

Sensitivity Issues and the Choice of Detectors

The results you get from a GC measurement of a component in air, water, or soil often depend on the type of detector chosen. Different detectors have different sensitivities to low-level components:

Flame Ionization Detectors are very sensitive to compounds like hydrocarbons that burn hot and clean. On the other hand, compounds like the components in Freon® or compounds like carbon tetrachloride that do not burn under the conditions in the detector may not be detected at all. Thus, analysis of a hydrocarbon mixture could be done at very low levels, but the same detector would not observe dangerously high levels of halocarbons present in the same sample.

Thermal Conductivity Detectors are inherently less sensitive to minor components in a mixture than other detectors. Typically this detector is good for measuring components present at high levels in a gas or liquid stream (say 1–25 percent) but may not detect components present at less than 0.1 percent in the mixture. This type detector probably would not detect low ppm levels of any component.

Mass Spectrometers are generally the most sensitive detectors for GC and may measure components in the low parts per million or even parts per billion (ppb) range. Mass spectrometers also have the decided advantage of being able to break down individual compounds into fragments and compare those fragments with the fragmentation pattern of a known sample of the component being measured. This means that the compound being measured is identified specifically rather than by retention time. Some mass spectrometers also have the ability to measure a compound even in the presence of another compound that elutes at or near the same retention time. The disadvantage of GCMs is that the equipment is not truly "field portable" and requires that it be set up at or near the scene in a stable environment, that samples be taken to the equipment, and that the operator be a highly trained technician.

Electron Capture Detectors (ECD) use a low-level radiation source, usually Ni^{63}, to provide a stream of electrons to ionize the compounds present. ECDs are extremely sensitive to compounds with halogens or other atoms that have a high affinity towards capturing electrons. Thus compounds like carbon tetrachloride can be measured at extremely low levels. On the other hand, compounds such as hydrocarbons that do not tend to capture electrons as easily tend to be nearly undetectable by ECDs.

Specialized detectors such as **Nitrogen-Phosphorus Detectors** (NPD) are used extensively on GCs for specific analyses. For example, an organophosphate pesticide or a nitrogen-containing herbicide may be analyzed at extremely low concentrations using an NPD detector. On the other hand, such specialized detectors may not be suitable for analyzing all samples because optimizing the detector to be most sensitive to low levels of nitrogen and phosphorus compounds makes them very insensitive to compounds not containing nitrogen or phosphorus.

Thermal Stability of the Analytes is a significant issue for some compounds. Some compounds decompose at the high temperature of the injection port, while others polymerize and make tar. In either case, those compounds that polymerize or decompose cannot be measured by GC.

Volatility and mobility of the analytes can also be an issue. Many potential contaminants that may be vaporized or entrained in air as a dust or mist and many contaminants in water and soil have relatively high melting and boiling points, and these contaminants may build up in the injection port. Obviously, compounds that collect in the injection port or at the inlet to the column do not reach the detector and cannot be measured.

High-Performance Liquid Chromatography (HPLC)

HPLC is a tool similar to gas chromatography in concept. A sample is injected into a solvent stream (called the eluent), which passes through a column packed with material that interacts with the components in the stream, causing them to separate from each other. The stream exits the column into a detector that measures the amount of each component. The detector outputs data to a computer. Similar to GC, the identification of peaks is normally done by comparing retention times of the component with the retention time of known standards.

HPLC instruments are rarely seen in the field. They typically are laboratory equipment that require excellent maintenance and technical support. Normal procedure would be to take samples in the field and bring them to the equipment for analysis.

Eluents

Most HPLC work today is done using a mixture of water and some organic solvent such as methanol, isopropanol, or acetonitrile. The eluent is frequently pH-adjusted to be slightly acidic or basic and may be buffered. HPLC eluents are often flammable liquids.

Columns and Separation of Components

In general, components in a mixture are separated by differences in how they interact with the column packing in the HPLC column. Compounds that interact strongly with the column packing tend to be retained on the column longer than those that are less strongly attracted to the column packing. Since there are a number of different kinds of columns available, the theory of why specific columns and specific compounds interact cannot be covered here.

Detectors

There are only a few basic types of HPLC detectors, although some of these detectors are quite sophisticated in design and operation:

- **Refractive Index Detectors** measure changes in the refractive index of the solution as it passes through the detectors. This type of detector has the advantage that it is effectively universal, in that almost anything that causes a change in refractive index will be detectable at a high enough concentration. A disadvantage of this type of detector is that it is relatively insensitive. It is doubtful whether it would detect pesticides at the low levels that would still cause environmental or toxicity problems.
- **Electrical Conductivity Detectors** measures the change in the electrical conductance of the eluent as it goes through the detector. This type of detector is normally used only to measure compounds that have electrical charges in solution (anions or cations), since this type of detector is not sensitive to compounds that are not ionic and that do not make a large change in the conductivity as they go through the detector.

- **Spectrophotometric Detectors** are the most common type of detectors. As the components elute through the detector, they absorb ultraviolet or visible light. The change in the amount of light passing through the analyzer is used to measure the amount of the desired component present. The advantages of spectrophotometric detectors are that they are relatively inexpensive and may be very sensitive to organic compounds. Older and cheaper instruments usually monitor one wavelength of light at a time, although it may be possible to select which wavelength to monitor. Newer instruments may measure many different wavelengths simultaneously to provide the most sensitive detection of low-level contaminant.
- **HPLC-Mass Spectrometry** is typically used only to verify the identity of a specific impurity or to measure the concentration of components at extremely low levels. With the proper sample preparation, HPLC-MS can often measure components at the parts per billion or parts per trillion level. Due to the extremely high cost of the equipment and the need for very high levels of technical skill to operate the equipment, most laboratories do not have HPLC-MS capability.

Immunoassay Techniques

Immunoassay methods are based on the response of specific antibodies to toxic materials. Living organisms, when exposed to toxic materials, will generate antibodies (proteins and enzymes) to respond to the attack as part of the organism's immune system. During subsequent exposures, these proteins and enzymes react to the presence of the toxic material rapidly and at very low concentrations. A limited number of tests have been developed that use this phenomenon to detect and identify very low levels of contaminants in soil and water. With the use of an air sparger to trap the contaminant in water solution, these tests can also be used for air analysis to identify the presence of a specific component.

Disadvantages and limitations of IA tests are:

- There are only a limited number of IA tests available for the larger sales–volume pesticides, many of which do not respond to reaction by-products or partially combusted pesticides.
- Those tests that have been developed may detect normal background levels of the pesticide. These compounds have been developed to be used in a broad range of applications, and it is not unusual to detect measurable levels of these compounds in the soil or water from farm runoff.

Methods for Monitoring Weapons of Mass Destruction

Chemical Warfare Agents

Just as there is no single system that will detect all HAZMATs, there is no single system that will detect all chemical warfare agents. A number of items are required, each of which will serve a specific role during the response. These range from the very simple items like papers (which work in seconds) to the very sophisticated laboratory instruments that can take from minutes to hours to give results). In general, we can say that the simpler a system is to use, the less specific the result. On the other hand, the more complex the system, the more information may be obtained. Some devices only respond to liquids, while others respond to vapors. The key point is that the response team will need to use the information provided by several different systems.

The ability to detect a chemical agent is a direct function of the volatility and freezing point of the agent as well as the ambient temperature. Agent volatility is based on its vapor pressure. An agent with low vapor pressure and low volatility, such as VX, will be harder to detect than an agent with a high vapor pressure and high volatility, such as sarin. Mustard, which freezes at 57°F but has a higher vapor pressure than VX, will be easier to detect at warmer temperatures than VX, but more difficult to detect than sarin.

An important use for chemical agent detection equipment is determining if casualties are free from detectable residual agent contamination. Because the most efficient equipment for performing this evaluation is the low-level detection equipment, which will not be readily available to pre-hospital providers, the best way of determining whether a patient is clean is by observing thorough decontamination of the casualty.

Most current detection methods rely on colorimetric reactions on detector paper, or the detection of specific atoms through gas chromatography. Many common pesticides, such as malathion and parathion, have similar molecular structures and can cause false positive alarms when tested using tests for chemical warfare agents.

There are two major categories of detection equipment available:
- **Gross-Level:** qualitative systems able to detect agent at fairly high concentrations (IDLH level), with a response time of 3 to 15 minutes.
- **Low-Level:** qualitative and quantitative systems able to detect and quantify agent at fairly low concentrations (AEL level), with a response time of 3 minutes to an hour.

There are several types of monitoring equipment available. These will be discussed using the US military designations in effect at the end of 2002.

Indicating Detection Papers

M8 and M9 Chemical Agent Detection Paper
M8 and M9 chemical agent detection papers are treated papers that react to give a color change in the presence of liquid nerve agents or blistering agents. M8 paper is dipped into the suspect liquid and the color change is compared to a color chart to identify specific chemical warfare agents. M9 paper will detect nerve and blister agents as droplets in the air. Both types of paper are easy to use but will only show that there is a probable toxic agent present and will not quantitate the level of material present. Both papers will also react with other chemicals, leading to false positive results. They are both extremely useful in that the response to a chemical warfare agent is immediate.

The Chemical Agent Monitor (CAM) or Improved Chemical Agent Detector (ICAD)
The chemical agent monitor (CAM) or improved chemical agent detector (ICAD) are gross-level detectors of nerve, blood, blister, and choking agents. They provide a visible and audible warning of agent doses, but only when the concentration is above the initial effects dose. These are hand-held, battery-operated, post-attack devices for monitoring chemical agent contamination on personnel or equipment. They contain a Ni^{63} radioactive source, which ionizes vapors from the agent and a detector to detect the ionized species generated when the vapor passes over the radiation source. Both detectors may give false positive readings if certain organic solvents are present.

The French AP2C
The French AP2C is a device similar to the CAM and ICAD. Like the CAM, it detects and differentiates between nerve and blister agents. It can detect both simultaneously and is slightly more sensitive for nerve agents. It also recovers more quickly than the CAM/ICAM; however, it costs nearly twice as much. The AP2C uses hydrogen flame spectrophotometry as a detection mechanism. It also comes in a model (the AP2Ce) for use in an explosive atmosphere.

Surface Acoustic Wave Minicad

The surface acoustic wave minicad (SAW MINICAD) is a pocket-sized instrument that detects trace levels of chemical agents. It is easy to operate, readily available, operates with off-the-shelf lithium batteries, and can detect both nerve and blister agents simultaneously. It has a shelf life of 5 years.

The MINICAD uses a pair of SAW microsensors that are extremely sensitive to small changes in the mass of the surface coatings that act as sponges for chemical warfare agents. A small pump collects the vapor samples, concentrates them, and passes them over the microsensors. An onboard microcomputer analyzes the responses to determine if a hazard exists. Analysis time is 1 minute. This equipment has yet to prove itself in a terrorism response environment and is extremely expensive.

M21 Remote Sensing Chemical Agent Alarm (RSCAAL)

The M21 can remotely detect the presence of nerve (G-series) and blister agent (HD and L) vapor clouds at a distance of up to 3 miles. It needs to see fairly dense clouds of agent. It might be best employed facing into the wind covering an area where large crowds in the open are expected.

The RSCAAL uses a passive infrared spectrometer with an on-board microcomputer that makes agent/no-agent decisions. The detector scans a 60-degree horizontal arc in less than 60 seconds.

Minicams

The final types of instruments for chemical detection and identification are the gas chromatographs. These are laboratory-type instruments that require skilled lab technicians to operate and interpret results. A few have been hardened for use in vans and in the field.

An example of this type instrument is the MINICAMS. It is a hardened GC (gas chromatograph) used by the Department of Defense in depot operations where toxic chemical agents might be present. These instruments can provide automatic quantitative identification of chemicals. They can be set to read only one agent at a time and must be calibrated daily. This kind of instrument would be best used by a local or state laboratory to precisely identify an agent and its concentration. It is capable of determining that agent concentrations are below TWA/AEL, which is important in terms of downgrading protection and verifying that decontamination is complete.

Gas Chromatograph/Mass Spectrometer (GC/MS)

Another field-deployable instrument is the gas chromatograph/mass spectrometer (GC/MS). It is packaged in a suitcase-sized box and can be used by trained personnel in a field location to quantitatively identify chemical agents in soil, vapor, or liquid samples. It can detect chemical agents below TWA/AEL levels.

Biological Agents

Having concluded the discussion of chemical detection and identification, we turn now to the biological agents. Because a biological agent attack may not be discovered until days after the actual event, there may be no first response per se, and all activity may be focused on the hospital providers.

Rapid detection of biological agents at the scene of a terrorist attack will probably not be possible given the limitations of current technology in this field. Realistically, the initial detectors of a biological attack will be symptomatic patients, possibly appearing in large numbers.

A detector kit formerly used by specialty military units could detect anthrax, ricin, SEB, and botulism toxins. The kits, however, require storage at room temperature and have storage life and reliability problems. They are being replaced by more complex systems that currently cost thousands of dollars and require extensive training to operate. These systems would probably not be readily available at the scene without significant pre-planning and investment.

Radiation

Detection and measurement of nuclear contamination will help responders avoid hazardous exposure at the scene of a nuclear incident. The proper detection equipment can also be used to certify casualties as actually being free from radiological contamination.

How Radiation Is Detected
Unfortunately, our body senses cannot detect radiation. We cannot see, smell, taste, feel, or hear radiation, but we have very good instrumentation to detect it. Radiation monitoring instruments usually detect the presence of radiation by collecting charged particles (ions). The radiation measured is usually expressed as exposure per unit time, using various units of measure, including the Curie (Ci), the Becquerel (Bq), and counts per minute (CPM). A variety of instruments are available for detecting and measuring radiation.

Radiation detection and measurement instruments are used routinely to monitor personnel working around or with radiation sources and to check for any leakage of radiation from containers used in the storage or transport of radioactive materials.

Radiation Surveys
Radiation surveys are conducted using a variety of instruments in order to determine:

- Radiation levels in a given area
- Lost or hidden sources
- Surveying facilities for radiation hazards
- The possible exposure in an area and the necessity of wearing personnel monitoring devices
- Contamination levels on equipment and personnel
- The need for posting warning signs

Personal Dosimeters
Personal dosimeters are small objects, such as film badges or objects resembling pens, wristwatches, or other easily carried items. Simple devices record the accumulated ionizing radiation to which the wearer has been exposed. More complex versions can sound an alarm when a preset exposure limit is reached.

Survey Instruments

Geiger-Mueller Counter
This device can be used for area monitoring and detection of beta and gamma radiation. Some versions detect both types of radiation simultaneously, while others have a filter that screens out beta particles and allows the exclusive measurement of gamma radiation. Operating procedures for this equipment can be learned in a few hours. This instrument is used to measure background radiation levels and to quickly evaluate potentially contaminated victims. If a greater level of radiation emission is anticipated, a higher-range instrument (such as an ionization chamber) should be used. At higher levels, the GM meter will often display incorrectly low or off-scale readings.

Scintillation Detectors

- **Alpha Detectors:** These detection devices are designed to detect the presence of much smaller and less penetrating alpha particles. Since alpha particles travel short distances, they might not be detected in wounds because blood and tissue fluids may shield the particles from reaching the monitor's surface. They cost approximately the same as Geiger-Mueller counters, but require additional training to operate correctly.
- **Ionization Chamber Detectors:** These devices measure gamma ray dose/rate when high-level radiation hazards are suspected. Low-level gamma contamination is not detected.
- **Dose Rate Meters:** These measure mrad/hour or rad/hour units of radiation. To find the dose an individual is receiving, multiply the dose rate by the time.

$$Dose = Dose\ Rate\ x\ Time$$

Other devices used include: TLD (thermoluminescent dosimeter, which is composed of lithium fluoride), QFD (quartz fiber dosimeter), and ERD (electromagnetic radiation detector).

14

Fire

As demonstrated previously, serious students of hazardous materials need a rudimentary background in chemistry to be able to understand the materials with which they will be dealing. Since almost all organic materials will burn, a closer look at the chemical reaction called combustion will ensure understanding of just what is happening while a material is burning. Understanding the combustion process and the clearly definable parts into which it is divisible imparts knowledge of how to interrupt that process. The interruption of the combustion process is called extinguishment.

Theories of Fire

The chemical reaction of fire, or combustion, is really an oxidation reaction. Oxidation is the chemical combination of oxygen with any substance. This definition is incomplete but will suffice for current purposes. In other words, whenever oxygen and other materials combine chemically with a substance, that substance is said to have been oxidized. Rust is an example of oxidized iron. Here, the chemical reaction is relatively very slow. The very rapid oxidation of a substance is called combustion or fire. The important thing to remember is that a chemical reaction is occurring, and it may be your job to stop it. Knowing the various theories of fire will give insight into the various ways of interrupting the reaction.

Currently, three theories of fire are generally accepted by the fire services. They are the fire triangle, the tetrahedron of fire, and the life cycle of fire. Of the three, the first is the oldest and best known. The second is accepted as more fully explaining the chemistry of fire. The third and least known is a more detailed version of the fire triangle, going more into the physical aspects of fire.

The Fire Triangle
The fire triangle is by far the oldest of the three theories; as far as it goes, it is still valid. It is quite simplistic in nature and gives a basic understanding of the three entities that are necessary for a fire. Simply put, the fire triangle theory states that three things are necessary to have a fire: fuel, oxygen, and heat. It likens these three things to the three sides of a triangle. It states that as long as the triangle is not complete (that is, the legs are not touching each other to form the closed or completed triangle), then one or more of the three essential ingredients is missing and having a fire is impossible. The theory, as stated, is still correct.

Fuel

Without fuel to burn, there can be no fire. If there is no oxygen present, there can be no fire. Technically, this is not correct, but the fire triangle theory can be made technically correct by changing the oxygen leg to an oxidizer leg. For example, chlorine is an oxidizer. Finally, without heat, there can be no fire. This last statement must also be brought up to date. The fact is that heat is just one form of energy; it is really energy that is necessary to start a fire. This difference is mentioned because in some instances light or another form of energy may be what is needed to start the combustion reaction. It is best to change the heat leg of the fire triangle to the energy leg. Therefore, the updated fire triangle now has three sides representing fuel, oxidizer, and energy. Look a little more closely at each of the three components.

Fuel

A fuel may be defined as anything that will burn. Grasping this definition is important, because some people consider only flammable gases and liquids as fuels. Many others include wood and coal as fuels, because they will burn. Sometimes forgotten are the metals and other inorganic material, which under many circumstances are more hazardous than almost any other type of fuel. By defining fuels as anything that will burn, we are sure to include everything.

Fuels may be categorized into the following classes:

- Elements that include the metals and some nonmetal such as carbon, sulfur, and phosphorus
- Hydrocarbons
- Carbohydrates (including mixtures made up partially of cellulose, like wood and paper)
- Many covalently bonded gases (including carbon monoxide, ammonia, and hydrogen cyanide)
- All other organic compounds

This list of materials that burn is quite long. Remember that the list includes not only the pure substances, such as the elements and compounds that make up the list, but mixtures of those elements and compounds. Examples of mixtures would include natural gas (which is a mixture of methane (principally), ethane, and a few other compounds) and gasoline, which is a mixture of the first six liquid alkanes (pentane, hexane, heptane, octane, nonane, and decane) and a few other compounds. Wood (another mixture) and wood-related products, like paper, are excellent fuels, as are many polymers such as rubber, plastics, wool, silk, and the above-mentioned cellulose, which makes wood and paper the excellent fuels that they are.

The second leg of the fire triangle is oxygen or, in our updated version, the oxidizer. We changed this because oxygen, although it is the most common oxidizing agent, is not the only oxidizer. While oxygen is the usual oxidizing agent during combustion, there are chemicals that can burn without oxygen present. For example, calcium and aluminum will burn in nitrogen. Similarly, oil and hydrocarbons will burn with a bright flame in an atmosphere containing chlorine even when no oxygen is present. Another problem with calling this second leg the oxygen leg is that most fire fighters consider only oxygen from the atmosphere when they think of oxygen and do not consider other sources. Since the greatest source of oxygen is the atmosphere, however, this has to be considered the source that must be eliminated as one way to control a fire. Whatever the source, keep in mind that oxygen does not burn.

The third leg of the fire triangle is what was once called the heat leg, but now it is referred to as the energy leg. All forms of energy capable of providing the source needed to start the combustion process will be considered. This energy can be provided in one or more of four ways:
- Chemical
- Mechanical action
- Electrical
- Nuclear

Energy can be generated chemically by the combustion of another fuel, or it can be generated by another exothermic chemical reaction. Exothermic means the emission or liberation of heat or energy. This is the opposite of endothermic, which means the taking in or absorption of heat or energy.

Energy may also be generated by mechanical action, that is, the application of physical force by one body upon another. Examples of this are the energy created by the friction of one matter upon another or the compression of a gas. As we compress a gas, we increase the incidence of collision of gas molecules against each other as more of them are packed ever more tightly in the same confined space. The force of friction in one case may produce energy that manifests itself as heat, while friction in another case may result in a discharge of static electricity. Static electricity is created whenever molecules move over and past other molecules. This happens whether the moving molecules are in the form of a gas, a liquid, or a solid. This is why leaking natural gas under high pressure will ignite. This is also the reason why two containers must be bonded when we pour or transfer flammable liquids from one container to another. In any case, the energy present or released could be more than enough to start the combustion reaction.

A third method of generation of energy is electrical, much like the discharge of static electricity. This method may manifest itself as heat, such as produced in an electrical heater; as arcing in an electrical motor or in a short circuit; or as the tremendous amount of energy released as lightning.

The fourth method of generation of energy is nuclear. Nuclear energy may be generated by the fission (splitting) of the atoms of certain elements or by the fusion (or joining together) of the nuclei of certain elements.

Once the energy, typically heat, is generated, it must be transmitted to the fuel (the touching of the fuel and energy legs). This process is accomplished in three ways: conduction (the transfer of heat through a medium, such as a pan on a stove's heating element), convection (the transfer of heat with a medium, such as the heated air in a hot-air furnace), and radiation (the transfer of heat that is not dependent on any medium).

These three entities–fuel, an oxidizer, and an energy source–make-up the three legs of the fire triangle. It is a law of nature that when fuel, oxidizers, and energy are brought together in the proper amounts, a fire will occur. If the three are brought together slowly, over a long time, the oxidation will occur slowly, as in the rusting of iron. If the three are of a particular combination, the resulting oxidation reaction might even be an explosion. Whatever form the final release of energy takes, the thing that cannot be changed is that the chemical reaction will occur.

The Fire Tetrahedron

The second popular theory of fire is the fire tetrahedron theory. This theory encompasses the three concepts in the fire triangle theory but adds a fourth side to the triangle, making it a pyramid, or tetrahedron; this fourth side is called the chain reaction of burning. This theory states that when energy is applied to a fuel like a hydrocarbon, some of the carbon-to-carbon bonds break. This leaves an unpaired electron attached to one of the molecular fragments caused by the cleavage of the bond, thus creating a free radical. This molecular fragment with the unpaired electron, or dangling bond, is highly reactive. The same energy source that provided the necessary energy to break the carbon-to-carbon bond may have also broken some carbon-to-hydrogen bonds, creating more free radicals, and some oxygen-to-oxygen bonds, creating oxide radicals. This mass breaking of bonds creates the free radicals in a particular space and in a number large enough to be near each other, which in turn helps the recombining of these free radicals with whatever other radicals or functional groups may be nearby. The breaking of bonds releases the energy stored in them, so that the subsequent release of energy becomes the energy source for still more bond breakage, which in turn releases more energy. Thus, the fire feeds upon itself by continuously creating and releasing more energy (the chain reaction), until one of several things happens: either the fuel is consumed, the oxygen is depleted, the energy is absorbed by something other than the fuel, or this chain reaction is broken. A fire usually begins as a very small amount of bond breakage by a relatively small energy (ignition) source. It builds itself up higher and higher, until it becomes a raging inferno. It is limited only by the fuel present (a fuel-regulated fire) or the influx of oxygen (an oxygen-regulated fire). The earlier in the process that the reaction can be interrupted, the easier the extinguishment of the fire will be.

For example, an internal combustion engine receives fuel and air into the cylinder. The cylinder is compressed and the spark plug fires (activation energy). The resulting explosion drives the piston down, powering a car. Removing either the fuel or air or stopping the spark will stop the reaction.

Run-Away Chain Reaction

Energy

Oxidizer

FIRE

Fuel

The fire tetrahedron theory is considerably more complex than the previous description suggests. It encompasses the actual mechanism of bond breakage and the step-wise formation of all sorts of free radicals. The theory claims that the propagation of all hydrocarbon fires (or fires involving hydrocarbon derivatives) depends upon the formation of the hydroxyl (-OH) radical, which is found in great quantities in all such fires. If this theory is correct, it would appear that the hydroxyl radical may be the key to the extinguishment of most fires.

The Life Cycle of Fire
The third theory of fire is the life cycle of fire theory. This particular theory breaks the combustion process down into six parts, rather than the three of the fire triangle or the four of the fire tetrahedron theory. Three of the steps in this theory are the same as the three in the fire triangle theory.

In the life cycle of fire theory, the first step is the input of heat, which means how much heat is required to produce the evolution of vapors from the solid or liquid. The input heat will also be the ignition source and must be high enough to reach the ignition temperature of the fuel; it must be continuing and self-generating and must heat enough of the fuel to produce the vapors necessary to form an ignitable mixture with the air near the source of the fuel.

The second part of the life cycle of fire theory is the fuel, essentially the same as the fuel in the fire tetrahedron and the fire triangle. It was assumed (without so stating) in the fire triangle theory, and is true in all three theories, that the fuel must be in the proper form to burn; that is, it must be vaporized, or, in the case of a metal, almost the entire piece must be raised to the proper temperature before it will begin to burn.

The third part is oxygen, because the theory centers around the diffusion flame, which is the flame produced by a spontaneous mixture (as opposed to a pre-mix) of fuel gases or vapors and air. This theory concerns itself with air-regulated fires, so airflow is crucial to the theory; this is why only atmospheric oxygen is discussed. Ignoring oxygen and the halogens generated from oxidizing agents is viewed by many as a flaw in this theory. The author of the theory, however, is very specific on the conditions that must exist for fire to be explained by his theory.

The fourth part of the theory is proportioning, or the occurrence of intermolecular collisions between oxygen and the hydrocarbon molecule (the touching together of the oxidizer leg and the fuel leg of the fire triangle). The speed of the molecules and the number of collisions depend on the heat of the mixture of oxygen and fuel, which is the hotter the mixture, the higher the speed. A rule of thumb used in chemistry states that the speed of any chemical reaction doubles for roughly every 10°C (18°F) rise in temperature.

The fifth step is mixing; that is, the ratio of fuel to oxygen must be right before ignition can occur (flammable range). Proper mixing after heat has been applied to the fuel will produce the vapors needed to burn. This is the reason for the backdraft explosion that occurs when a fresh supply of air is admitted to a room where a fire has been smoldering.

The sixth step is ignition continuity, which is provided by the heat being radiated from the flame back to the surface of the fuel; this heat must be high enough to act as the input heat for the continuing cycle of fire. In a fire, chemical energy is converted to heat. If this heat is converted at a rate faster than the rate of heat loss from the fire, the heat of the fire increases; therefore the reaction will continue faster, producing more heat faster than it can be carried away from the fire and increasing the rate of reaction even more. When the rate of conversion of chemical energy falls below the rate of dissipation, the fire goes out. That is to say, the sixth step, ignition continuity, is also the first step of the next cycle, the input heat. If the rate of generation of heat is such that enough energy is produced to raise or maintain the heat of the reaction, the cycle will be broken, and the fire will go out.

As stated above, the life cycle of fire theory expands the fire triangle. The fire triangle simply states that when three essential ingredients (fuel, oxidizer, and energy source) are brought together in the proper amounts, there will be a fire. The life cycle of fire theory adds the concepts of flashpoint and ignition points (heat input) and flammable range (mixing).

Theories of Fire Extinguishment

Remembering that the theories of fire were presented to illustrate the components or steps of the combustion process, it must follow logically that if the reaction can be interrupted at any particular step, the reactions should stop. In the fire triangle, if the three components can be prevented from coming together, a fire is prevented . It is equally logical that if, while a fire is in progress, we can remove one or more of the legs, the fire will go out. Either remove the fuel, prevent the energy from reaching the fuel oxidizer mixture, or remove the heat so the temperature drops below the ignition temperature.

In the fire tetrahedron theory, the only difference is the fourth side, the chain reaction of burning, which is caused by the formation and subsequent reaction of free radicals, particularly the hydroxyl radical. Again, it is logical to assume that if the formation and reaction of free radicals are occurring in a fire, the prevention of the formation or the reaction of these radicals should extinguish the fire. The tetrahedron of fire theory calls for the application of free radical quenchants to the fire. They will either prevent the formation of or react with the free radicals after they are formed. This will keep them from reacting with more fuel or oxygen radicals. Whatever can be done that will prevent either the formation of free radicals–or the interception of those already formed so that they will not react to cause the formation of more free radicals–will extinguish the fire. The dry chemical and Halon® fire extinguishing agents work in this way.

In the life cycle of fire theory, the interruption or the prevention of any of the six steps will result in the extinguishment of the fire. In this theory, an interesting option appears to be the interruption of the ignition continuity, such as using dynamite to blow out the flame of an oil well fire, so that the fire is extinguished. The use of one's your breath to blow out the flame from a burning match or candle is a more common way of interrupting ignition continuity. The breath will redirect the heat away from the fuel (and the fuel away from the heat), preventing the radiated heat from contacting the surface and causing the generation of flammable vapors by pyrolysis. The breath removes the energy faster than it was being generated.

No matter how sophisticated an approach a theory presents, all fires are extinguished in the same way: by interruption of some vital step in their sequence of events. A theory of fire can probably be developed individually; the chances are that the more steps into which the reaction is broken down, the more opportunities there are to extinguish the fire.

How Water Acts as a Fire Extinguisher
Recognize the fact that fire is an exothermic (heat-liberating) reaction; as explained in the preceding discussion of the various theories of fire, there must be a continuous feedback of energy (heat) to keep the reaction going. Heat is dissipated from the fire by one or more of the methods of transferring heat: conduction, convection, and radiation. Heat energy is also fed back to the fire by radiation from the flame, and this source of heat keeps the fire going. If a way could be devised to interrupt that feedback of heat to the fuel, the continuity of the fire would be broken, and the fire would go out. What is needed is a fire-extinguishing agent that would somehow siphon heat energy away from the fire. It would reduce the temperature of the material burning and cool the surroundings below the ignition temperature of the fuel. Therefore, no re-ignition of the flammable vapors after the fire was extinguished could occur. Not only would such an extinguishing agent be needed, a way to deliver it to the seat of the fire would also be needed.

Water is an extinguishing agent that performs this task. There are also many ways to deliver it, not only to the seat of the fire, but also above it and around it if the situation dictates. Water really has many drawbacks, however, and after reviewing them one may wonder why it is used.

Some of the drawbacks to the use of water as an extinguishing agent include its propensity to conduct electricity, which, of course, is deadly if the water is applied incorrectly. Water has a low viscosity, which allows it to run off a wall instead of sticking there. It also has a high surface tension that prevents it from penetrating tightly arranged materials. Water also allows heat to be radiated through it, freezes at a relatively high temperature, splashes about, and displaces many flammable liquids, causing them to spread rapidly. This list of problems also includes the fact that water itself will violently react with many of the hazardous materials it is supposed to control. With all these problems, why even think about using water to extinguish fires?

Besides the fact that water is relatively inexpensive and is usually available in large quantities, two specific properties of water make it invaluable. Those properties are its latent heat of vaporization and its specific heat. The latent heat of vaporization of a substance is defined as how much heat a material must absorb when it changes from a liquid to a vapor or gas. The specific heat of a substance is defined as the ratio between the heat necessary to raise the temperature of a substance and the heat necessary to raise the same weight of water by the same number of degrees.

The specific heat of water is important because it is so high in relation to the specific heat of other materials; this fact means that it takes more energy to raise the temperature of water than just about any other material. Therefore the temperature of the materials to which water has been applied will drop faster than the temperature of water will rise. The specific heat may be reported as the number of calories needed to raise the temperature of one gram of the material 1°C, or the number of British thermal units (BTUs) needed to raise one pound of the material 1°F. This latter measurement for water is more familiar to fire fighters; the value is 1.0 BTU per pound; it is also 1.0 calorie per gram.

Therefore, when water is applied to a fire, it begins absorbing heat from the fire, thereby cooling the fire down while the water heats up. For every BTU absorbed, the temperature of the water will rise 1°F per pound of water involved. The important thing to remember here is that the rise in temperature of the water is caused by heat energy absorbed from the fire. The water is "siphoning" the heat away from the burning material. The temperature of the water will continue to rise, since the fire is producing heat, until it reaches its boiling point of 212°F. At this time the latent heat of vaporization of water comes into play. At 212°F the water is still a liquid and will remain a liquid unless more energy is received from the fire. At this time, a phase change from liquid to vapor occurs, with no increase in temperature; that is, water as a liquid at 212°F converts to water vapor at 212°F. It is at this phase change that the latent heat of vaporization of water does its work. Water will absorb 1 BTU per pound for every increase of 1°F, up to 212°F. At 212°F, when the phase change occurs, 970 BTUs are absorbed per pound. That sudden, rapid, and massive withdrawal of heat energy from the fire at this time is what gives water its tremendous fire extinguishing capabilities, which are so valuable as to overcome the previously mentioned disadvantages. Heat is withdrawn from the burning material so rapidly and in such large quantities that the temperature of the burning fuel drops dramatically, usually well below its ignition temperature. When this happens, of course, the fire goes out. The latent heat of vaporization also explains why steam (which is invisible) at 212°F is hotter than boiling water at 212°F. The live steam has 970 BTUs of energy more per pound than the boiling water.

This latent heat of vaporization also explains why materials wet with water are difficult, and sometimes impossible, to ignite. If a combustible substance has absorbed enough water to be considered wet, or just damp, this water will act as a homer to ignition by its evaporation as it is heated. As heat is applied to the wet substance, the water begins to evaporate (go through the phase change from a liquid to a vapor). To make this phase change, the water must absorb 1 BTU for every pound of water present for every 1°F it rises until it reaches 212°F, when it must absorb 970 BTUs for every pound of water present. Before any combustible material that has been wet with water can burn, the water (which has preferentially been absorbing the applied heat and thus keeping the combustible material itself from heating to its ignition temperature) must be driven off. If, while driving off the water, enough heat energy from the potential ignition source has been used up, there may not be enough energy left to raise the combustible to its ignition temperature, and there will be no fire.

Pyrolysis

The word pyrolysis comes from two Greek words meaning "fire" and "breakdown." Pyrolysis, therefore, is defined as breakdown by heat. The "breaking down" is actually the cleavage of covalent bonds in hydrocarbon compounds and in hydrocarbon derivative compounds. This breaking of the bonds between carbon atoms is also called cracking. Indeed, it is the same reaction that takes place in a catalytic cracking tower (cat cracker) at an oil refinery. This process is used to pyrolytically crack long-chain hydrocarbons from petroleum into short-chain hydrocarbons (pentane, hexane, heptane, octane, and so on) to use as fuels (gasoline, kerosene, fuel oils, and the like). Pyrolysis is different from combustion in that pyrolysis takes place in the absence of air, or at least where there is not enough oxygen or other oxidizer to support combustion. Pyrolysis does occur in air, simply because near the surface of the material that is undergoing pyrolysis, the fuel is too rich to ignite. Once the fuel enters the flammable range, and the heat energy is sufficient to reach the ignition temperature of the gases, combustion will occur.

Recall that wood is not a compound but instead a mixture of compounds, the principal compound being cellulose, a naturally occurring polymer that contains bonded carbon, hydrogen, and oxygen. The repeating unit in the naturally occurring polymer (cellulose) is the glucose molecule, a six-carbon molecule. This six-carbon molecule that is connected to another six-carbon molecule, which is connected to another, and so on, until we have a new compound (cellulose). This giant molecule is called the cellulose polymer. Visualize these thousands and thousands of carbon atoms strung together in a long chain. When energy is applied to the molecule in the form of heat, the molecule, which had been vibrating slowly, begins to vibrate rapidly, until this vigorous motion causes one of the carbon to carbon bonds to break (cleave). As more heat is applied, the molecule moves faster and faster, causing more bonds to break on both the remaining long-chain molecules and the shorter-chain molecules that resulted from earlier bond cleavage. As all the compounds near the heat source absorb more heat, more bonds break, and the resulting compounds are shorter and shorter chains. The result of breaking bonds between carbon atoms in hydrocarbons and hydrocarbon derivative compounds is the formation of molecules of the simplest hydrocarbon, methane–similar to the process that takes place in many organisms (for example, the bacteria that reside in ruminants or the microorganisms that breakdown municiple or biodegradable waste). Methane, as we know, is a highly flammable gas; it is the methane and other short chain hydrocarbons (ethane, propane, and so on) that actually burns when mixed with the right amount of oxygen and in contact with the proper ignition source.

The key to pyrolysis, of course, is heat. The original source of heat is the ignition source; before it can raise the fuel to ignition temperature, it must first produce the fuel by breaking down the solid cellulose. Once the methane and other short-chain hydrocarbons have been created and have begun to rise from the solid material, the continuing energy from the ignition source produces combustion. As the gases are consumed, the energy needed to continue the processes of pyrolysis and combustion comes from the heat of the flame radiated back to the surface of the fuel. If the ignition source is constant and oxygen is excluded from the process, pyrolysis alone will occur; there will be a large buildup of flammable gases, many or most of them heated to energy levels above their ignition temperatures, just waiting for that third leg of the fire triangle to snap shut and complete the triangle. When the air comes rushing into the super-heated gases, the dreaded backdraft explosion will occur.

Within the same room, as flammable vapors are formed pyrolytically, they are heated to temperatures below their ignition temperatures. These vapors rise toward the ceiling (some gases are lighter than air, while others rise because they are hot) and gather there. They are further heated by heat radiating from the ignition source or a fire burning on or near the floor. The gases will also radiate heat back to unburned portions of the room. When the gases, or at least one of them, are heated to the ignition temperature, all the gases (assuming they are in the flammable range) will ignite, producing a flashover.

Pyrolysis explains all flaming combustion by producing the fuels that burn in the flame. Solids, like liquids, do not burn; it is only the flammable gases produced by the breakdown of solids that burn. Flames consist of a diffusion of simple gases, not always hydrocarbon gases, because carbon monoxide and hydrogen cyanide may have been formed by the combustion reaction. Liquids do not burn; the fuels that burn are the gases volatilized and sometimes pyrolyzed from the liquid. Gases that are liberated and cracked from solid organic fuels mix in the flame over the solid and burn. Some solids like wood, coal, and other solid organic fuels will burn on their surfaces. This is called glowing, or surface burning, as opposed to flaming, or space burning, which is the process that occurs because of a pyrolytic breakdown of solid organic fuel. This glowing, or surface burning, is obvious to anyone who has enjoyed a fire in the fireplace; after all the gases are driven off in the flaming, or space burning, what remains is a solid char, or charcoal, if preferred, that produces the pleasant glowing fire long after the flames are gone. Of course, glowing, or surface burning, is how charcoal burns. It is also how soft or hard coal will burn, once the volatile gases are driven off.

Another example of surface burning is the manner in which metals burn. No space burning occurs because there are no gases generated (pyrolyzed) by the heated metal. The glowing combustion, or surface burning of metals, is the same phenomenon as the glowing combustion of charcoal. It is direct combination of the metal with oxygen at the surface of the metal.

288

The flame itself is explained by pyrolysis. All flames appear above the fuel, as the hot gases, rise with the thermal column. Many gases are not fully cracked (broken down completely to methane); as they rise (including the methane and ethane), they will be too concentrated (too rich) right near the surface of the fuel and will not begin to burn until the proper amount of oxygen is mixed with them. Once the proper mixture is achieved, the gases begin to burn, radiating more heat to the surface, producing more flammable gases. The space between the fuel surface and the bottom of the flame is the area where the gases are too rich to burn; once they do burn, they produce even more heat. This contributes to the turbidity of the thermal column causing the flame to quiver and dance.

The final products of pyrolysis, the simplest hydrocarbons such as methane, are still not the materials that burn. Further input of energy is necessary to break a carbon-to-hydrogen bond on the molecules of these hydrocarbons and produce a free radical. It is the reaction of these free radicals with the oxygen radicals formed from the bond cleavage of O_2 that is actually the combustion process. The breaking of the carbon hydrogen bonds (from the simple hydrocarbons formed) and the oxygen-to-oxygen bonds (from atmospheric oxygen) produce carbon monoxide (CO), carbon dioxide (CO_2), and the hydroxyl radical ($^{\cdot}OH$). The hydroxyl radical then reacts with more hydrogen radicals ($H^{\cdot}$) to form water (H-O-H or H_2O). All this is usually accompanied by the diffusion flame in which these reactions take place and by the evolution of heat energy.

Pyrolysis explains the crown fires in a burning forest. As the heat from the approaching fire radiates out in all directions, pyrolyzing the trees, it produces flammable gases that are further heated by radiation. They reach their ignition temperatures, and, when properly mixed with oxygen, produce a rolling flame across the top of the forest. As trees are heated by the radiated energy of an approaching fire, not only will the water trapped in the trunk cause a cracking and splitting of the tree, but the ignition of pyrolyzed gases will cause the tree to appear to explode. All fires produced by radiated heat undergo pyrolysis first, followed by the explosive breaking into flame of the gases produced.

This process explains how fires are spread from one building to the interior of another, by radiated heat through the windows, producing pyrolysis of the combustibles present, which generates tremendous quantities of flammable gases. Further radiated heat raises these gases to their ignition temperatures and a fire can jump from one building to another through a closed window! This is also how fires, which have broken out of a window below, start a fire on the floor above. The fire radiates heat through the intact window and then proceeds to leapfrog to the top of the building.

Pyrolysis of liquids is possible, but only in liquids of very high molecular weight, such as asphalt, tar, and heavy oils, simply because the heating of a lighter liquid may produce evaporation first. Once these vapors are in the air, combustion will occur almost instantaneously. Pyrolysis of plastics is another matter. Theoretically, since plastics are polymers just as cellulose is, one would expect them to be subject to pyrolysis just as cellulose is. Plastics, however, are different in their properties; while it is possible for plastics to pyrolyze, they usually melt and flow away before pyrolysis occurs. When the molten material stops flowing and is contained then the pyrolysis occurs.

Pyrolysis is also the explanation of why pesticide fires produce such toxic by-products. It is this process that produces the toxic gases like hydrogen cyanide, phosgene, methyl isocyanate, and other toxic materials. This is why getting the heat and fire temperature up on a pesticide fire to destroy these materials completely is important. Remember that combustion of these materials will still produce acid gases like HCl, HF, and SO_2.

15
Pesticides

Introduction

The benefits of pesticides may be measured in terms of enhancing the ability to grow bountiful crops or create beautiful landscapes. However, the misuse of pesticides can have an extremely negative effect on the environment. Improper application of insecticides or fungicides can ruin growing areas. Long-term effects may be observed if the residue from a pesticide spill is allowed to contaminate waterways or ground water sources.

Nearly all hazardous materials responders will be confronted at one time or another with an incident involving pesticides.

These materials are stored and used in nearly every community in grocery and hardware stores, garden shops, discount stores, etc. The ability to react properly by assessing the situation and identifying the hazards will play a major role in reducing property and environmental damages while avoiding serious permanent injuries.

The Federal Insecticide, Fungicide and Rodenticide Act as Amended (FIFRA) is the basis for the regulations governing the distribution, sale, and use of pesticides in the United States. On December 2, 1970, the Environmental Protection Agency (EPA) was established and given responsibility for administering the regulations governing pesticides. From 1947 until the formation of EPA, the US Department of Agriculture (USDA) had this responsibility.

FIFRA grants the states significant latitude in regulating the distribution, sale, and use of pesticides. It is important to appreciate that many of the federal laws have comparable state laws that require compliance also.

Pesticides and Registration

A pesticide, as defined by FIFRA, includes "any substance or mixture of substances intended for preventing, destroying, repelling or mitigating any pest, and any substance or mixture of substances intended for use as a plant regulator, defoliant, or desiccant." This definition is broad and comprehensive.

EPA defines registration as the "formal listing with EPA of a new pesticide before it can be sold or distributed in intrastate or interstate commerce." An EPA registration is often referred to as a FIFRA Section 3 registration. This pre-marketing licensing by EPA is based on data "demonstrating that the pesticide will not cause unreasonable adverse effects on human health or the environment when it is used according to approved label directions." It also considers economic and social costs and benefits. Under FIFRA, it is the responsibility of the applicant to demonstrate that the pesticide product meets all requirements for registration.

It is imperative that a pesticide be registered with the appropriate agency in each state before it can be marketed or used. Pesticides are also deregistrated or removed from sale. However, a responder may still encounter these no-longer-sold pesticides.

Common Types of Pesticides

As defined by FIFRA, a pesticide is a chemical or mixture of chemicals used to destroy or control any living thing regarded as a pest. Pesticides include any of the groups of chemicals designated as:

- Fungicides
- Herbicides
- Insecticides
- Fumigants
- Rodenticides
- Acaricides
- Bactericides

These materials control or destroy insects, plant diseases, and other pests. There are approximately 860 pesticide active ingredients formulated into 21,000 pesticide products sold and used in the United States today. For most practical purposes, the terms formulation and product can be used interchangeably.

There are many more types of pesticides than these seven. You should associate the ending of pesticide, "-cide," with materials that have the characteristics of pesticides. You should also associate the cide with its Latin meaning: to kill.

Types of Pesticides

Fungicides
These chemicals, employed to eradicate fungi and protect material from rot and decay, include many inorganic and organic compounds. Some are highly toxic to humans, while others are of little danger under ordinary circumstances.

Fungicides are used on farm crops, preferably as prophylactic rather than curative treatments applied to the surface of the plant in water suspensions or dusts before the attack of a fungus. Deciduous fruit trees and numerous vegetable crops and ornamentals, as well as germinating seeds, are usually subject to attack unless protected. Fungicides include inorganic forms of copper and sulfur, mercury, and metallic complexes of cadmium, chromium, and zinc, along with a wide variety of organic compounds and materials used in control of specific plant diseases. Use of some metallic compounds, especially mercurials, is now forbidden in many countries because of the hazard of poisonous residues. Some organic fungicides are systematic in action, absorbed, and distributed within the plant.

A classification of fungicides is as follows:
- **Inorganic:** sulfur, copper salts, and mercury salts
- **Organic:** dithiocarbamates, thiazoles, triazines, substituted aromatics, dicarboximides, oxathiins, benzimidazoles, dinitrophenols, organotins, aliphatic nitrogens, and organomercury compounds

Any or all of these types of compounds may be found in warehouses, farms, golf courses, farm and feed stores, garden supply shops, and department stores.

Herbicides

These chemicals are used primarily to eradicate weeds and include many inorganic and organic compounds. Some are highly toxic to humans, while others are of little danger under ordinary circumstances.

Herbicides are used in five general ways:

- **Preplanting:** Applied after the soil has been prepared but before seeding.
- **Preemergence** (Contact): Nonresidual dosages are used after seeding but before emergence of the crop seedlings.
- **Preemergence** (Residuals): Applied at time of seeding or just prior to crop emergence; kills weed seeds and germinating seedlings.
- **Postemergence:** Application after emergence of a crop.
- **Sterilant** (Nonselective): Used to kill all treated plant life.

Classification of herbicides is as follows: inorganic, petroleum oils, organic arsenicals, phenoxy-aliphatic acids, substituted amines, nitroanilines, substituted ureas, sulfonylureas, carbamates, thiocarbamates, heterocyclic nitrogens, triazines, uracils, aliphatic acids, arylaliphatic acids, phenol derivatives, substituted nitriles, bipyridyliums, and organophosphates.

Insecticides

The Association of American Pesticide Control Officials, AAPCO, has adopted this definition of insecticides:

- A substance or mixture of substances intended to prevent, destroy, repel, or mitigate any insects that may be present in any environment whatsoever.
- A material used primarily for the control of insects. The various insecticides fall into six general categories according to the way in which they affect insects:
  - **Stomach:** Toxic quantities are ingested by the insect.
  - **Contact:** Kills upon contact with an external portion of the body.
  - **Residual contact:** Remains toxic to insects for long periods after application.
  - **Fumigant:** Possesses sufficient natural or induced vapor pressure to produce lethal concentrations.
  - **Repellent:** Does not kill but is distasteful enough to insects to keep them away from treated areas.
  - **Systemic:** Capable of being absorbed into the plant system where they make plant parts insecticidal.

Classification of insecticides is as follows: organochlorines, organophosphates, organosulfurs, carbamates, formamidines, thiocyanates, dinitrophenols, organotins, botanicals, synthetic pyrethroids, inorganics, fumigants, and microbials.

Fumigants and Repellents

Fumigant

The AAPCO has adopted this fumigant definition: "A substance or mixture of substances which produce gas, vapor, fume or smoke intended to destroy insects, bacteria or rodents."

292

Fumigants may be volatile liquids or solids as well as substances already gaseous. They may be used to disinfest the interiors of buildings, objects, and materials that can be enclosed so as to retain the fumigant, and the soil where crops are valuable enough to warrant the treatment.

The most toxic are the cyanides and halogenated hydrocarbons. Most important, mainly because of their use in the home as moth balls or flakes, are naphthalene and para-dichlorobenzene.

Repellent (Insect)
A material used primarily for the control of insects, birds and other vertebrates.

Oil of citronella, prior to World War II, was the standard insect repellent. Now, many much more effective compounds are in use. These products include a wide variety of chemical compounds, many of which are highly toxic to humans and animals when ingested or inhaled. Those least dangerous are those repellents designed to be applied directly to the skin. These include benzyl benzoate for chiggers; dimethyl phthalate for mosquitos and mites; and ethyl hexandiol, indalone, and dimethyl carbonate for mosquitoes, chiggers, and fleas. Various combinations of these are used as all-purpose repellents.

Rodenticides
These materials are used to kill rodents of different types. The rat and mouse are thought of as the main targets for rodenticides, but rodenticides work equally well on any member of the rodent family.

Commonly used rodenticides are inorganic salts and synthetic and naturally occurring organic compounds. Inorganic compounds such as arsenic, thallium salts, phosphorus compounds, barium salts, and zinc salts are also used. They are used selectively but are found in many places.

Acaricides
These chemicals are effective on spiders, mites, and ticks.

Bactericides
These materials kill bacteria, especially those causing disease. Bactericides vary greatly in their potency and specificity. They may be other organisms (bactericides), chemical compounds, or short-wave radiation.

Pesticide Toxicity and the Corresponding Label Signal Word

Pesticides can be grouped into three categories in terms of toxicity: high, moderate, low.

The degree of toxicity is indicated by the signal word used on the pesticide label. The signal words–DANGER, WARNING, CAUTION–are the most important information that can be obtained from the label. Signal words are found at the center of the front panel of the label. Highly toxic pesticides display the signal word DANGER. Moderately toxic pesticides may be identified by the signal word WARNING, while the low toxicity materials are characterized by the signal word CAUTION.

The use of these signal words on pesticide labels is required by law. Other warnings that may be found on the label are the toxicity categories. Toxicity Category I (signal word DANGER), Toxicity Category II (signal word WARNING), and Toxicity Categories III and IV (signal word CAUTION) may appear on the label or in the accompanying information such as the MSDS. The following table provides an idea of how hazards compare to toxicity class and signal word.

Toxicity Category by Hazard Indicator

Hazard Indicators	Oral LD$_{50}$ (mg/kg)	Inhalation LC$_{50}$ (mg/l)	Dermal LD$_{50}$ (mg/kg)	Eye Effects	Skin Effects
Danger I	Up to 50	Up to 0.2	up to 200	Corrosive corneal opacity not reversible within 7 days	Corrosive
Warning II	50 to 500	0.2 to 2	200 to 2,000	Corneal opacity reversible within 7 days; irritation persisting for 7 days	Severe irritation at 72 hours
Caution III	500 to 5,000	2 to 20	2,000 to 20,000	No corneal opacity; irritation reversible within 7 days	Moderate irritation at 72 hours
Caution IV	Greater than 5,000	Greater than 20	Greater than 20,000	No irritation	Mild or slight irritation at 72 hours

Routes of Pesticide Entry into the Human Body

Pesticides may poison or cause harm to a person by entering the body through one or more of the following routes:

- Through the eyes
- Through the skin
- Inhalation
- Ingestion (swallowing)

The quickest route of entry for pesticide poisoning is through the eyes. The eyes contain relatively large amounts of moisture and blood vessels, which enhance the ability of the pesticide to absorb into the membranes. Most pesticides attack the central nervous system and the eyes represent the closest point of entry. Proper personal protective equipment is essential to avoid injury from pesticide exposure.

Any unusual appearance or feeling of discomfort or illness can be a symptom of pesticide poisoning. Signs/symptoms may be delayed up to 72 hours. It is important to develop the ability to assess the involvement of pesticides in a hazardous material incident and protect responders accordingly.

Identify the Signs and Symptoms of Pesticide Poisoning

The signs and symptoms of pesticide poisoning may differ due to the type of formulation used in the manufacturing process. Examples of symptoms associated with different types of pesticides are listed below.

Organophosphates and Carbamates (Insecticides)

Organophosphates
Symptoms of acute organophosphate poisoning develop during exposure or within 12 hours (nearly always within four hours) of contact. The most commonly reported early symptoms are headache, nausea, and dizziness. Anxiety and restlessness are prominent. Worsening of the poisoned state is indicated by muscle twitching, weakness, incoordination, tremor, vomiting, abdominal cramps, and diarrhea. Hypersecretion is often prominent: sweating, salivation, tearing, rhinorrhea, and bronchorrhea. Blurred or dark vision may be reported, and miosis is often a helpful diagnostic sign. Tightness in the chest, wheezing, and productive cough may progress to pulmonary edema. Bradycardia may progress to sinus arrest, or may be superseded by tachycardia and hypertension from nicotinic (sympathetic ganglia) stimulation. Toxic psychosis, manifest as confusion or bizarre behavior, has been misdiagnosed as acute alcoholism. Toxic myocardiopathy has been a prominent feature of some severe organophosphate poisonings. Unconsciousness, incontinence, convulsions, and depression of respiratory drive signify life-threatening severity of poisoning.

Carbamates
Malaise, muscle weakness, dizziness, and sweating are commonly reported early symptoms of carbamate poisoning. Headache, diarrhea, nausea, vomiting, abdominal pain, and salivation are often prominent. Miosis, incoordination, and slurred speech are reported. Dyspnea, bronchospasm, and chest tightness may progress to pulmonary edema. Blurred vision, muscle twitching, and spasms characterize some cases. Severe neurologic manifestations, including convulsions, are less common than in organophosphate poisonings. Bradycardia occurs infrequently. Poisonings by N-methyl carbamates tend to be of shorter duration than poisonings by organophosphates, but they are not easily differentiated from organophosphate poisoning in the acute phase in the absence of an accurate exposure history.

Pinpoint pupils can be the first sign for both organophosphates and carbonates. To distinguish between smoke inhalation and pesticide poisoning, remember that victims of smoke inhalation have dilated pupils, while pesticide exposures are characterized by pinpoint pupils.

Organochlorines (Insecticides)
Early manifestations of poisoning by some organochlorine pesticides, particularly DDT, are often sensory disturbances: hyperesthesia and paresthesia of the face and extremities. Headache, dizziness, nausea, vomiting, incoordination, tremor, and mental confusion are also reported. More severe poisoning causes myoclonic jerking movements, then generalized tonic-clonic convulsions. The seizures may be followed by coma and respiratory depression.

Poisoning by the cyclodienes and toxaphene is more likely to begin with the sudden onset of convulsions, often not preceded by the premonitory manifestations mentioned above. Seizures caused by cyclodienes may appear as long as 48 hours after exposure and may then recur periodically over several days following the initial episode. Because lindane and toxaphene are more rapidly biotransformed in the body and excreted, they are less likely than dieldrin, aldrin, and chlordane to cause delayed or recurrent seizures.

Poisoning by chlordecone has occurred as a result of extraordinary occupational exposure over many days. Principal manifestations were weight loss, tremor, muscle weakness, involuntary eye movements, pain in the chest and joints, skin rash, slurred speech, mental changes, and abnormalities of liver function. Seizures did not occur. Recovery was slow.

Nitro and Chlorophenols (Herbicides, Wood Preservatives, and Fungicides)

Chlorophenols
Chlorophenoxy compounds are moderately irritating to skin and mucous membranes. Inhalations of sprays may cause burning sensations in the nasopharynx and chest, and coughing may result. Prolonged inhalation sometimes causes dizziness. Adjuvant chemicals added to enhance foliage penetration may account for the irritant effects of some formulations.

Manifestations of systemic toxicity of chlorophenoxy compounds are known mainly from clinical experience with cases of deliberate suicidal ingestion of large quantities. The agents most often involved in these incidents have been 2,4-D and mecoprop. The toxic effects of other chlorophenoxy compounds are probably similar but not identical. Few cases of deliberate ingestion of chlorophenoxy compounds have terminated fatally.

Irritation of the stomach usually leads to vomiting soon after ingestion. Pain in the chest and abdomen and diarrhea may ensue. Headache, mental confusion, and bizarre behavior are early manifestations of severe poisoning, which may progress to unconsciousness. Myotonia (muscular stiffness on passive movement of the limbs) has occurred in persons poisoned by 2,4-D. Areflexia is sometimes observed. Muscle twitching may or may not be evident. Convulsions occur very rarely. Respiratory drive is not depressed; hyperventilation is sometimes evident. Body temperature may be moderately elevated, but this is rarely a life-threatening feature of the poisoning. With effective urinary excretion of the toxicant, consciousness returns in 48–96 hours.

Nitrophenols
Yellow staining of skin and hair often signify contact with a nitroaromatic chemical. Staining of the sclerae and urine indicate absorption of potentially toxic amounts. Profuse sweating, headache, thirst, fever, confusion, malaise, and lassitude are common early symptoms of poisoning. Warm, flushed skin, tachycardia, and tachypnea indicate a serious degree of poisoning. Restlessness, apprehension, anxiety, manic behavior, or unconsciousness reflect cerebral injury. Convulsions signify an immediate life-threatening intoxication. Labored breathing and cyanosis are consequences of the stimulated metabolism and tissue anoxia. Weight loss occurs in persons continually exposed to relatively low doses of nitrophenols or nitrocresols.

Identify the Information Found on a Pesticide Label

Labels are required on all pesticide products regardless of the type or application. The label will include information concerning physical or chemical hazards and will detail any special flammability, corrosivity, or other notable hazards that the product may pose to response personnel. The product name will be clearly visible on the front panel of the label. An EPA registration number will also appear on the label and will provide a positive means of identification for responders. The label will also provide a list of active and inert ingredients. Regulations require that the active ingredients in a pesticide be listed by chemical names and many times will also include a common name if applicable. However, the inert ingredients, such as solvents or clays, are not required to be specified by name. The label may only list the total percentage of inert ingredients, making identification of these nearly impossible.

Other portions of the pesticide label may contain information on storage and disposal procedures, or detail specific environmental or wildlife hazards that might occur from misuse or accidental spillage of the material. This information could prove helpful in cleanup operations or decontamination procedures. If the pesticides are involved in a fire, the inhalation of the smoke and fumes may pose additional hazards to responders, bystanders, and the environment. A pesticide label may also contain precautionary information and instructions for treating exposure. Clearly, the labels on pesticide products are an invaluable source for assessment of hazards, and development of a safe entry plan for response personnel.

Labeling, as provided by the manufacturer, gives additional information concerning the pesticide product. Labeling includes booklets, brochures, flyers and other information distributed by the pesticide dealer or manufacturer. Labeling also may include information provided by the Environmental Protection Agency (EPA) on maps indicating the habitats of endangered species.

Label Requirements

- **Brand, trade, or product name:** A single pesticide active ingredient may be marketed at the same time under several brand names. Each label may designate a different use of the product. A specific brand name, usually registered as a trademark, will identify a product from a particular manufacturer.
- **Ingredient statement:** Every pesticide product label must include the active and inert ingredients. The amounts (percentage by weight) of the ingredients are also printed on the label. Often, the chemical name of the active ingredient is stated. If an approved common name of the active ingredient exists, it may be listed and followed by a chemical name. Brand or trade names are indicated on the front panel of the label and are used in advertisements and by company representatives and pesticide dealers. The names of inert ingredients sometimes are not stated, but the label must indicate their percentage of the total contents.
- **Net weight or measures of content:** The net contents are displayed prominently on the front of the label. Net weight often is expressed as fluid ounces, pints, quarts, or gallons for liquid formulations. If the formulation is dry, semi-solid, viscous or pressurized, or a mixture of solid and liquid, the contents are expressed in ounces and/or pounds. Sometimes, the liquid formulations also list the pounds of active ingredient per volume of the product. Net contents may be expressed in metric units.
- **Manufacturer:** The name and address of the manufacturer, registrant, or formulator who makes the product must be printed on the label. If the registrant's name appears on the label and the registrant is not the manufacturer, then qualifying wording such as "packed for," "distributed by," or "sold by" is required.
- **Registration number:** An EPA registration number is proof the label was approved by the US Environmental Protection Agency before sale in the marketplace. In the case of a special local need registration, a pesticide product may be approved in a specific state for additional usage. This type of registration number is designated as EPA SLN No. __ __ __ __.
- **Establishment number:** An establishment number identifies the specific facility that produced the product. A given pesticide product with the establishment number can be traced to the manufacturing plant of origin. This information is beneficial if problems occur with the product or if it has been found to be adulterated.
- **Classification statement:** All uses of pesticides are classified on the basis of hazards, the intended use, and the effect upon the environment. Pesticide use is classified either for general use or restricted use. General use pesticides are less likely to harm users or the environment when used according to the label. Restricted use pesticides have a greater potential to harm the environment or the applicator when not used as directed. Training and certification is required for an applicator to purchase, apply, or supervise the application of a restricted use pesticide.
- **Directions for use:** The instructions for applying the pesticide are most important. These directions provide the rate of application, the site (crop, animal, location, etc.) the product is intended to protect, the pests controlled, mixing directions, when and where the material is to be

applied, and the necessary application equipment. A preharvest interval (in days) may be listed, especially if the product is to be used on crops or vegetables. This time period must pass after a pesticide application before harvest or grazing by animals can occur. The waiting period after application may vary with the type of livestock.

- **Signal words and symbol:** Each label will display a prominent signal word that indicates the relative toxicity of the active ingredient to humans. The three signal words, in order of increasing toxicity, are CAUTION, WARNING, and DANGER. A signal word must appear on the front panel of the label. A product with the CAUTION signal word would require an ounce to more than a pint to kill an average person. Products with a CAUTION signal word are slightly toxic orally, dermally, or through inhalation. They may cause slight eye and skin irritation. A lethal dose for a product with the WARNING signal word generally would be one teaspoon to one tablespoon. Products in this category are moderately toxic. Highly toxic products with the DANGER signal word only require a taste to a teaspoonful of the product to be lethal to an adult. The word poison and the skull-and-crossbones symbol also are associated with products having the DANGER signal word. Products with the DANGER signal word are highly toxic orally, dermally, or through inhalation. They may cause severe eye and skin irritation.

- **Precautionary statements:** These statements guide the applicator in taking proper precautions to protect humans or animals that could be exposed. Sometimes these statements are listed under the heading "Hazards to Humans and Domestic Animals." Other statements may be under several headings.

  - Route of entry statement: Pesticides may enter the body in three ways: 1) through the skin (dermal); 2) through the lungs (inhalation); 3) by mouth (oral). A route of entry statement suggests the route(s) more likely for a specific product and suggests specific actions to prevent exposure.
  - Protective clothing and equipment statements: Guidelines or requirements specifying the correct type(s) of protective equipment are found in this portion of the label. Although not required to be on every label, protective clothing and equipment guidelines commonly are provided for the safety of the applicator. The toxicity of the product influences the selection of the clothing and equipment.
  - Every pesticide label must include the statement "Keep out of reach of children" on the front panel. This warning must be heeded.

- **Statement of practical treatment:** First-aid treatment guidelines are recommended in this statement in case of over-exposure. These guidelines are very concise and this information should be read before the product is used and again in case of emergency. For example, a statement may read: "In case of contact with skin, wash immediately with plenty of soap and water." The label contains a "Note to Physicians" describing the appropriate medical procedure for poisoning cases, and may indicate an antidote.

- **Environmental hazard statement:** This statement includes commonsense reminders to avoid contamination of the environment. Special warning statements on the label cover hazards to the environment. Examples include "This product is highly toxic to bees," or "This product is highly toxic to fish," and "Do not allow drift to contact nontarget plants or trees."

- **Re-entry statement:** Some labels may contain a precaution to protect people after a pesticide application. This statement indicates how much time must pass before a person can reenter a treated area without appropriate protective clothing.

- **Storage and disposal statement:** The storage of the pesticide after purchase and the disposal of the empty container are important responsibilities. Use the best storage and disposal guidelines for the specific situation and location. Pesticide inventories should be stored securely, preferably under lock and key, and separate from food and feed supplies. State and local laws may include additional requirements, especially for proper pesticide disposal procedures.

**Harmony
HERBICIDE
DRY FLOWABLE**

ACTIVE INGREDIENT
   Methyl 3-[[[[(4-methoxy-6-methyl-1,3,5-triazin-2-yl).............................75%
   amino] carbonyl] amino] sulfonyl]-2-thlophenecarboxylate
INERT INGREDIENTS...25%

EPA Reg No. 352-446

**KEEP OUT OF REACH OF CHILDREN
PRECAUTIONARY STATEMENTS-HAZARDS TO HUMANS
WARNING! CAUSES EYE IRRITATION. DO NOT GET IN EYES.**

Avoid contact with skin, eyes and clothing. In case of contact with eyes, immediately flush with plenty of water. Get medical attention if irritation persists. Wash thoroughly after handling. Remove and wash contaminated clothing before reuse. For medical emergencies involving this product, call toll free 1-800-441-3637.

Environmental Hazards

Do not apply directly to any body of water. Do not contaminate water by cleaning of equipment or disposal of wastes.

Storage and Disposal

STORAGE: Store product in original container only, away from other pesticides, fertilizer, food or feed.

DISPOSAL: Do not contaminate water, food, or feed by storage or disposal. Wastes resulting from the use of this product may be disposed of on alto or at an approved waste disposal facility. Triple rinse (or equivalent) the container. Then offer for recycling or reconditioning, or puncture and dispose of in a sanitary landfill, or by incineration, or, if allowed by state and local authorities, by burning. If burned, stay out of smoke.

Formulations Ingredients and the Hazards of Inert Pesticide Ingredients

An Overview of the Formulation Process
The active ingredients in pesticide products come from many sources. Some, such as nicotine, pyrethrum, and rotenone, are extracted from plants. Others have a mineral origin, while a few are derived from microbes. However, the vast majority of active ingredients are synthetic.

Regardless of their source, pesticide active ingredients have different solubilities. Some dissolve readily in water, others only in oils. Some active ingredients may be relatively insoluble in either water or oils. These different solubility characteristics, coupled with the intended use of the pesticide, define the types of formulations in which the active ingredient may be delivered.

It is preferable from the manufacturer's perspective to use the active ingredient in original form when possible (e.g., a water-soluble active ingredient formulated as a water-soluble concentrate). Usually, an active ingredient will be combined with appropriate inert materials prior to packaging. This formulation gives the product its unique physical form and specific characteristics, enabling it to fill a market niche.

Solid Formulations
Solid formulations can be divided into two types: ready-to-use and concentrates that must be mixed with water to be applied as a spray. There are six solid formulations. Three of the solid formulations (dusts, granules, and pellets) are ready-to-use, and three (wettable powders, dry flowables, and soluble powders) are intended to be mixed with water.

DUSTS are manufactured by the sorption of an active ingredient onto a finely-ground, solid inert such as talc, clay, or chalk. They are relatively easy to use because no mixing is required and the application equipment (e.g., hand bellows and bulb dusters) is lightweight and simple. Dusts can provide excellent coverage, but the small particle size that allows for this advantage also creates an inhalation and drift hazard. In general, dust formulations are no longer used in large-scale outdoor situations due to their high drift potential. However, dusts are still applied as spot treatments for insect and disease control outside. Commercial pest control operators use dusts effectively in residential and institutional settings for control of various insect pests. Indoors, this type of formulation permits the delivery of an insecticide into cracks and crevices, behind baseboards and cabinets, etc. Thus, the insecticide is placed into the pest's habitat and away from contact by people and pets.

GRANULES are manufactured in a way that is similar to that of dusts except that the active ingredient is sorbed onto a larger particle. The inert solid may be clay, sand, or ground plant materials. A granule is defined by size: granule-sized products will pass through a 4-mesh (number of wires per inch) sieve and be retained on an 80-mesh sieve. Granules are applied dry and usually are intended for soil applications where they have the advantage of weight to carry them through foliage to the ground below. The larger particle size of granules, relative to dusts, minimizes the potential for drift. There is also a reduced inhalation hazard, but fines are associated with the formulation — especially when a bag is being emptied. In addition, granules have a low dermal hazard. The primary drawbacks of granules are their bulk, the problems they present in handling, and the difficulty inherent in achieving a uniform application with this type of product. Granules also may have to be incorporated into the soil to work, and they are sometimes attractive to nontarget organisms such as birds.

PELLETS are very similar to granules, but their manufacture is different. The active ingredient is combined with inert materials to form a slurry (a thick liquid mixture). This slurry is then extruded under pressure through a die and cut at desired lengths to produce a particle that is relatively uniform in size and shape. Pellets are typically used in spot applications. Pelleted formulations provide a high degree of safety to the applicator. They do have the potential to roll on steep or frozen slopes and thereby harm nontarget vegetation or contaminate surface water.

WETTABLE POWDERS are finely divided solids, typically mineral clays, to which an active ingredient is sorbed. This formulation is diluted with water and applied as a liquid spray. Upon dilution, a suspension is formed in the spray tank. Wettable powders will likely contain wetting and dispersing agents as part of the formulation. These are chemicals used to help wet the powder and disperse it throughout the tank. Wettable powders are a very common type of formulation. They provide an ideal way to apply an active ingredient in spray form that is not readily soluble in water. Wettable powders tend to pose a lower dermal hazard in comparison to liquid formulations, and they do not burn vegetation as readily as many oil-based formulations. This formulation does present an inhalation hazard to the applicator during mixing and loading because of the powdery nature of the particles. Furthermore, there are disadvantages associated with all formulations that form a suspension in the spray tank: they require agitation to prevent settling out; they can be abrasive to equipment; and they may plug strainers and screens.

DRY FLOWABLES or water-dispersible granules, as they are sometimes called, are manufactured in the same way as wettable powders except that the powder is aggregated into granular particles. They are diluted with water and applied in a spray exactly as if they were a wettable powder. Dry flowables, as would be expected, form a suspension in the spray tank; they have basically the same advantages and disadvantages as wettable powders, with several important exceptions. During the mixing and loading process, dry flowables pour more easily from the container and, because of their larger particle size, reduce inhalation hazard to the applicator.

SOLUBLE POWDERS are not particularly common, but they are worth mentioning for purposes of contrast with the wettable powders and dry flowables. Their lack of availability is due to the fact that not many solid active ingredients are soluble in water. Those that do exist and are formulated in this fashion are mixed with water prior to spraying, dissolve in the spray tank, and form a true solution. Soluble powders provide most of the same benefits as wettable powders without the need for agitation once dissolved in the tank. They are also nonabrasive to application equipment. Soluble powders, like any finely divided particle, can present an inhalation hazard to applicators during mixing and loading.

Liquid Formulations

There are four common liquid formulations that are mixed with a carrier. The carrier will generally be water, but in some instances labels may permit the use of crop oil, diesel fuel, kerosene, or some other light fuel oil as a carrier.

LIQUID FLOWABLES are manufactured like wettable powders, with the additional step of mixing the powder, dispersing agents, wetting agents, etc., with water before packaging. The result is a suspension that is further diluted with water before use. The product is applied as a spray with all the advantages of a wettable powder. The benefit of this formulation is that there is no inhalation hazard to the applicator during mixing and loading because the powder already is suspended in water, permitting it to be poured. Liquid flowables form a suspension in the spray tank and have the same problems inherent in any suspension.

However, they usually do not require agitation during application due to the extremely small size of the suspended particle but will settle if not tended to. One further problem noted with this formulation is the difficulty in removing all of the product from the container during mixing, loading, and container rinsing.

MICRO ENCAPSULATES consist of a solid or liquid inert (containing an active ingredient) surrounded by a plastic or starch coating. The resulting capsules can be aggregated to form dispersible granules (see dry flowables), or they can be suspended in water and the product sold as a liquid formulation. Encapsulation enhances applicator safety while providing timed release of the active ingredient. Liquid forms of micro encapsulates are further diluted with water and applied as sprays. They form suspensions in the spray tank and have many of the same properties as liquid flowables.

EMULSIFIABLE CONCENTRATES consist of an oil-soluble active ingredient dissolved in an appropriate oil-based solvent to which is added an emulsifying agent. Emulsifiable concentrates are mixed with water and applied as a spray. As their name implies, they form an emulsion in the spray tank. The emulsifying agents are long-chain chemicals that orient themselves around the droplets of oil and bind the oil-water surfaces together to prevent the oil and water from separating. Emulsifiable concentrates allow oil-soluble active ingredients to be sprayed in water as a carrier. Some agitation is typically required to maintain dispersion of the oil droplets. They are not abrasive to application equipment, nor do they plug screens and strainers. Emulsifiable concentrates have several disadvantages. There is a dermal hazard associated with this formulation. Emulsifiable concentrates readily penetrate oily barriers like human skin. They usually have an odor problem and can also burn foliage and cause the deterioration of rubber and plastic equipment parts.

SOLUTIONS (water-soluble concentrates) consist of water-soluble active ingredients dissolved in water for sale to the applicator for further dilution prior to field application. They will obviously form a true solution in the spray tank and require no agitation after they are thoroughly dissolved. Solutions are not abrasive to equipment and will not plug strainers and screens. Although solutions are not a particularly common formulation, several major herbicides with wide-scale use are formulated in this way. They include products containing paraquat, glyphosate, and 2,4-D. Aside from lack of availability, solutions have few disadvantages; however, some that are produced as dissolved salts can be caustic to human skin.

Miscellaneous Liquid Formulations

Most liquid formulations are designed to be mixed with a carrier before application. However, some products are sold ready-to-use (RTU). This type of formulation generally will have a low concentration of active ingredient. Low- and ultralow-volume concentrates used in specialty situations (e.g., space spraying and fogging) are frequently applied undiluted. Dermal hazards are a problem during mixing and loading of these products because of the high concentration of active ingredient. Low- and ultralow-volume concentrated formulations use special equipment to deliver the product in the form of very tiny droplets. Consequently, while they provide excellent coverage, drift potential and inhalation problems during application can be quite high.

Miscellaneous Liquid Formulations

Suffix	Meaning	Suffix	Meaning
Describe the formulation:		**Describe how a pesticide is used:**	
AF	Aqueous Flowable	GS	For Treatment of Grass Seed
AS	Aqueous Suspension	LSR	For Leaf Spot and Rust
D	Dust	PM	For Powdery Mildew
DF	Dry Flowable	RP	For Range and Pasture
E	Emulsifiable Concentrate	RTU	Ready-to-Use
EC	Emulsifiable Concentrate	SD	For Use as a Side Dressing
ES	Emulsifiable Solution	TC	Termiticide Concentrate
F	Flowable	TG	Turfgrass Fungicide
FL	Flowable	WL	To Be Used with Weed Killers
G	Granule		
OL	Oil-Soluble Liquid	**Describe characteristics of the formulation:**	
P	Pelleted		
PS	Pelleted	BE	The Butyl Ester of 2,4-D
S	Soluble Powder	D	An Ester of 2,4-D
SG	Sand Granules	K	A Potassium Salt of the Active Ingredient
SL	Slurry	LO	Low Odor
ULV	Ultralow-Volume Concentrate	LV	Low Volatility
W	Wettable Powder	MF	Modified Formulation
WDG	Water-Dispersible Granules	T A	Triazole
WP	Wettable Powder	2X	Double Strength
		Label for use in special locations:	
		PNW	For Use in the Pacific Northwest
		TVA	For Use in the Waterways of the Tennessee Valley Authority

Inerts

The label will have a listing of inert ingredients. It does not specify what that inert is unless it is harmful or regulated in some way. Most inerts in dry flowables are sugar, clay, and surfactants of some type. For liquids, the inerts are usually surfactants and some type of carrier. If it is flammable the label will say so, but it may not indicate what is flammable until the MSDS is consulted. There are many other inerts that can be in a pesticide product. Some of these inerts are very toxic in their own right and could cause death upon exposure to them. The following table lists some of the inerts that may be of concern.

Table of Inerts

Acetonitrile	Ethyl Acrylate
Aniline	Ethylbenzene
Asbestos Fiber	Ethylene Glycol Monomethyl Ether
Benzenediol	Ethylene Dichloride
Benzotriazole	Hexane
Benzyl 4-Chlorophenol	Hydrazine
Butoxy-2-Propanol	Isophorone
Butoxy-1-Ethanol	Isopropyl Phenols
Butoxyethoxy-2-Propanol	Lead Compounds
Butyl Benzyl Phthalate	m-Cresol
Butyl Methacrylate	Malachite Green
Butylene Oxide	Mercaptobenzothiazole
Cadmium Compounds	Mesityl Oxide
Carbon Tetrachloride	Methoxy-2-Propanol
Chlorobenzene	Methyl Bromide
Chlorodifluoroethane	Methyl Methacrylate
Chlorodifluoromethane	Methyl Ethyl Ketoxime
Chloroethane	Methyl Isobutyl Ketone
Chloroform	Methyl n-Butyl Ketone
Chlorotoluene	Methyl Chloride
Cresols	Methylene Chloride
Cyclohexanone	Nitroethane
Di-(2-Ethylhexyl) Phthalate (DEHP)	Nitromethane
Di-(2-Ethylhexyl) Adipate	Nitrophenol
Dibutyl Phthalate	Nonylphenol Oxide

Dichloroanilines	Perchloroethylene
Dichlorobenzene	Petroleum Hydrocarbons
Dichlorodifluoromethane	Phenol
Dichloromonofluoromethane	Phenylphenol
Dichlorophene	Propylene Glycol Monobutyl Ether
Dichlorotetrafluoroethane	Propylene Dichloride (1,2- Dichloropropane)
Diethanolamine	Pyrethrin
Diethyl Phthalate	Rhodamine B
Diethylene Glycol Monomethyl Ether	Sodium Dichromate
Diethylene Glycol Monobutyl Ether	Toluene Diisocyanate
Diethylene Glycol Monoethyl Ether	Toluene
Difluoroethane	Tolyl Triazole
Dimethyl Formamide	Tri-orthocresylphoshate (TOCP)
Dimethyl Phthalate	Tributyl Tin Oxide
Dioctyl Phthalate	Trichloroethane
Dioxane	Trichloroethylene
Diphenyl Ether	Trichlorofluoromethane
Dipropylene Glycol Monomethyl Ether	Trichlorotrifluoroethane
Epichlorohydrin	Triethanolamine
Ethanol, 2-Ethoxy (Cellusolve)	Tripropylene Glycol Monomethyl Ether
Ethanol Ethoxy Acetate	Xylene

Dangers Involved in Pesticide Fires and Spills

Fires

The seriousness of an agricultural chemical fire is largely determined by the temperature of the fire and whether the product is actually on fire or is being vaporized by the heat of burning materials. Vaporization and decomposition by the heat of the fire without combustion create a dangerous situation for fire fighters. The smoke residue from the fire may contain significant quantities of active pesticides and toxic decomposition products. These burning pesticide by-products may be more toxic than the original pesticide. They may be up to more than 1000 times more toxic than the original product.

Any slow, smoldering fire involving nitrogen-containing compounds may produce hydrogen cyanide in significant concentrations. Air monitoring for cyanide is recommended. The residue from smoldering fires

304

may contain significant amounts of pesticides and toxic by-products. Proper protective equipment must be worn to prevent exposure to these residues. In a fire involving many different types of pesticides, the following chemicals may be given off: hydrogen cyanide, sulfur oxides, methyl isocyanate, nitrogen oxides, hydrogen chloride, hydrogen fluoride, phosgene, phosphorus oxides, carbon monoxide, and carbon dioxide. In order to provide complete destruction of pesticides and residues, the fire temperature must be in excess of 1800°F for two seconds. This will destroy all pesticides and residues; however, materials like sulfur oxides, nitrogen oxides, acid gases, and carbon dioxide will still be present in the smoke cloud.

A hot fire involving agricultural products may produce significant amounts of nitrogen oxides and sulfur oxides in addition to the normal by-products of fire. Air monitoring should be performed downwind to determine whether additional precautions need to be taken to protect the surrounding population.

Spills

Generally confine the spilled material and prevent material from entering sewers, waterways, or low areas. For small liquid spills, absorb with vermiculite, sand, oil dry, etc., and shovel or sweep up. For dry materials, shovel or sweep up. Beware that material vapors of some products may reach toxic levels in a confined space.

Personal Protective Equipment Requirements when Working with Pesticides

For any pesticide incident, the protective equipment that needs to be worn will vary depending on the nature of the emergency. Some general guidelines are listed below. Contact the manufacturer or other technical resources for specific PPE recommendations.

Nontoxic to moderately toxic:
- Use: Long-sleeved shirt, long-legged pants, waterproof gloves, shoes and socks.
- Early entry: Coveralls, waterproof gloves, shoes and socks.
- Emergency response: Chemical-resistant coveralls, waterproof gloves, waterproof boots, and face/eye splash protection. If dusting occurs or the product has a high vapor pressure, a cartridge respirator or SCBA should be used.

Moderately toxic to extremely toxic:
- Use: Long-sleeved shirt, long-legged pants, chemical-resistant gloves, chemical-resistant boots, goggles, head covering, and pesticide respirator.
- Early entry: Coveralls, chemical-resistant gloves, chemical-resistant boots, goggles, head covering, and pesticide respirator.
- Emergency response: At a minimum Level B response equipment, should be worn. Level B consists of chemical-resistant one-piece encapsulated suit or three-piece acid suit with chemical-resistant gloves and boots. SCBA is also required.

Difficulties in Decontamination of Pesticides

Decontamination methods

Decontamination of pesticides can be very difficult. It may take very strong chemicals or combinations of chemicals to detoxify or neutralize the pesticide. For many pesticides, a strong surfactant (detergent) will increase solubility but will not detoxify. For some pesticides, bleach (sodium hypochlorite) will cause decomposition to inactive or relatively nontoxic by-products. For others, a boiling caustic solution is required. It is best to get help from the manufacturer on how to decontaminate/neutralize the pesticide.

16

DOT Class Chemistry

Each DOT hazard class exists due to specific properties for each material or group of materials that fall within the descriptive characteristics of each class. The nine DOT hazard classes are outlined below.

CLASS 1

49 CFR 173.50: Explosive; this describes any substance or article, including a device, that is designed to function by explosion. An explosion is an extremely rapid release of gas and heat or by chemical reaction within itself, can function in a similar manner, even if not designed to function by explosion, unless the substance or article is otherwise classified. Explosives, when exposed to heat, shock, or contamination, can result in thermal and mechanical hazards. Heat, light, and sound are generated when something goes wrong. Explosives in Class 1 are divided into six divisions.

- **DIVISION 1.1:** Explosives that have a mass explosion hazard. A mass explosion is one that affects almost the entire load instantaneously.

  Major hazard is mass detonation.

  Examples: black powder, TNT, dynamite, ammonium perchlorate

- **DIVISION 1.2:** Explosives that have a projection hazard, but not a mass explosion hazard.

  Major hazards are dangerous projections.

  Examples: aerial flares, ammunition, bombs

- **DIVISION 1.3:** Explosives that have a fire hazard and either a minor blast hazard or minor projection hazards or both, but not a mass explosion hazard.

  Major hazard is radiant heat, violent burning, or both, but there is no blast or projection hazard.

  Examples: small-arms ammunition, liquid-fueled rocket motors, common fireworks

308

- **DIVISION 1.4:** Explosives that present a minor explosion hazard. The explosive effects are largely confined to the package and no projection of fragments of appreciable size or range is to be expected. An external fire must not cause a virtually instantaneous explosion of contents of the package.

  Small hazard with no mass explosion and no projection of fragments of appreciable size or range.

  Examples: igniter cord, shaped charges without detonators, signal cartridges

- **DIVISION 1.5:** Explosives that are very insensitive. This division is composed of substances that have a mass explosion hazard but are so insensitive that there is very little probability of initiation of transition from burning to detonation under normal conditions of transport.

  Examples: ammonium nitrate, fuel oil mixtures

- **DIVISION 1.6:** Explosives that are extremely insensitive articles that do not have a mass explosive hazard. This division is composed of articles that contain only extremely insensitive detonating substances and which demonstrate a negligible probability of accidental initiation or propagation.

CLASS 2

Under pressure; containers may rupture violently (fire and nonfire); may be flammable, a corrosive, an asphyxiant, or an oxidizer; may cause frostbite.

- **DIVISION 2.1 (FLAMMABLE GAS)–49 CFR 173.115(a):** Flammable gas means any material that is a gas at 20°C (68°F) or less than 101.3 kPa (14.7 psi) of pressure; that is ignitable at 101.3 kPa (14.7 psi) when in a mixture of 13 percent or less by volume of air; or that has a flammable range at 101.3 kPa (14.7 psi) with air of at least 12 percent no matter the lower limit.

  Examples: propane, butadiene (inhibited), methyl chloride

- **DIVISION 2.2 (NONFLAMMABLE GAS)–49 CFR 173.115(b):** Nonflammable, nonpoisonous compressed gas, including compressed gas, liquefied gas, pressurized cryogenic gas, and compressed gas in solution. A nonflammable, nonpoisonous compressed gas means any material or mixture that exerts an absolute pressure of 280 kPa (41 psi) at 20°C (68°F) and does not meet the definition of Division 2.1 or 2.3.

  Examples: carbon dioxide, nitrogen, anhydrous ammonia, cryogenic argon

- **DIVISION 2.3 (POISONOUS GAS BY INHALATION)–49 CFR 173.115(c):** Poisonous gas by inhalation means a material that is a gas at 20°C (68°F) or less and a pressure of 101.3 kPa (14.7 psi). It is known to be so toxic to humans as to pose a hazard to health during transportation; or, in the absence of adequate data on human toxicity, it is presumed to be toxic to humans because when tested on laboratory animals it has an LC_{50} value not more than 5000 ppm.

  Examples: methyl bromide, chlorine, phosgene

CLASS 3

Flammable; containers may rupture violently; may be corrosive, toxic, or thermally unstable.

- **FLAMMABLE LIQUID**–49 CFR 173.120(a): Flammable liquid means any liquid having a flash point of not more than 60.5°C (141°F), or any material in a liquid phase with a flash point at or above 37.8°C (100°F) that is intentionally heated and offered for transportation or transported at or above its flash point in a bulk packaging.

  Examples: gasoline, ethyl chloride, methanol, acetone

- **COMBUSTIBLE LIQUID**–49 CFR 173.120(b): Combustible liquid means any liquid that does not meet the definition of any other hazard class except Class 9 and that has a flash point at or above 60.5°C (141°F) and below 93.3°C (200°F). Domestically, the flash point can be between 101°F and 200°F.

  Examples: # 6 fuel oil, creosote, mineral oil

CLASS 4

These materials are solid materials offered for transportation that may be flammable, water-reactive, toxic or corrosive, or are extremely difficult to extinguish when involved in fire.

- **DIVISION 4.1** (FLAMMABLE SOLIDS)–49 CFR 173.124(a): Flammable solid means any of the following:
  - Explosives that are wetted with sufficient water, alcohol, or plasticizer to suppress explosive properties that when dry are Explosive Class 1.
  - Self-reactive materials that are liable to undergo, at normal or elevated temperature, a strongly exothermic decomposition caused by excessively high transport tempertures or contamination.
  - Readily combustible solids that may cause a fire through friction or show a burning rate faster than 2 mm (0.087 inches) per second.

  Examples: phosphorus trioxide, magnesium pellets, nitrocellulose

- **DIVISION 4.2** (SPONTANEOUSLY COMBUSTIBLE MATERIAL)–49 CFR 173.124(b): Spontaneously combustible material means any of the following materials:
  - Pyrophoric materials that can be a solid or a liquid and that even in small quantities and without an external ignition source can ignite within 5 minutes after coming in contact with air.
  - Self-heating material that in contact with air and without energy supply is liable to self-heat and ignite or heat to above 200°C (392°F).

  Examples: white phosphorus, charcoal, titanium powder

- **DIVISION 4.3** (DANGEROUS WHEN WET) - 49 CFR 173.124(c): Dangerous when wet material means a material that by contact with water is liable to become spontaneously flammable or will give off flammable or toxic gas at a rate greater than 1 liter per kilogram of material per hour.

  Examples: metallic sodium, calcium carbide, magnesium powder

CLASS 5

These materials supply oxygen to support combustion. They may be sensitive to heat, shock, friction, or contamination.

- **DIVISION 5.1** (OXIDIZER)–49 CFR 173.127(a): Oxidizer means a material that may supply oxygen to cause or enhance combustion. These materials may also be sensitive to heat, shock, friction, or contamination. A substance, such as chlorate, permanganate, inorganic peroxide, or a nitrate that yields oxygen readily to stimulate the combustion of organic matter.

  Examples: perchloric acid, ammonium nitrate, calcium hypochlorite

- **DIVISION 5.2** (ORGANIC PEROXIDES)–49 CFR 173.128: Organic peroxide means any organic compound that contains the bivalent O-O structure and that may be considered a derivative of hydrogen peroxide where one or more of the hydrogen atoms have been replaced by organic radicals. Organic peroxides are assigned to one of seven types:
  - Type A: an organic peroxide that can detonate or deflagrate rapidly as packaged for transport. Transportation of Type A organic peroxides is forbidden.
  - Type B: an organic peroxide that neither detonates nor deflagrates rapidly, but that can undergo a thermal explosion.
  - Type C: an organic peroxide that neither detonates nor deflagrates rapidly and that cannot undergo a thermal explosion.
  - Type D: an organic peroxide that detonates only partially or deflagrates slowly, with medium to no effect when heated under confinement.
  - Type E: an organic peroxide that neither detonates nor deflagrates and shows low or no effect when heated under confinement.
  - Type F: an organic peroxide that will not detonate, does not deflagrate, shows only a low or no effect if heated when confined, and has low or no explosive power.
  - Type G: an organic peroxide that will not detonate, does not deflagrate, shows no effect if heated when confined, has no explosive power, is thermally stable, and is desensitized.

  Examples: benzoylperoxide, peroxyacetic acid

CLASS 6

These materials may be toxic by inhalation, ingestion, and skin and eye absorption; may be flammable or corrosive.

- **DIVISION 6.1** (POISONOUS MATERIALS)–49 CFR 173.132(a): Poisonous material means a material, other than a gas, that is known to be so toxic to humans as to afford a hazard to health during transportation; or that, in the absence of adequate data on human toxicity, is presumed to be toxic to man and fall into one of the following categories:

- Oral toxicity: a liquid with an LD_{50} for acute oral toxicity of not more than 500 mg/kg or a solid with an LD_{50} for acute oral toxicity of not more than 200 mg/kg.
- Dermal toxicity: material with an LD_{50} for acute dermal toxicity of not more than 1000 mg/kg.
- Inhalation toxicity: material with an LC_{50} for acute toxicity on inhalation of not more than 10 mg/l.

Examples: dibromomethane, epichlorohydrin, aniline, hydrocyanic acid

Hazard class 6.1, PGIII has a placard known as the Saint Andrews Cross. The symbol is a shaft of wheat with an X through it.

- **DIVISION 6.2** (INFECTIOUS SUBSTANCES)–49 CFR 173.134: Infectious substance is a material that is:
  - An infectious substance such as a viable microorganism, or its toxin, that causes or may cause disease in humans or animals.
  - Any human or animal material including, but not limited to, excreta, secreta, blood and its components, tissue, and tissue fluids being shipped for diagnosis.
  - Biological products.
  - Regulated medical waste.

Examples: anthrax, botulism

CLASS 7

49 CFR 173.401: Radioactive material; this means any material or combination of material that spontaneously emits ionizing radiation and has a specific activity greater than 0.002 microcuries per gram. Extremely variable, includes solids, liquids, and gases.

Examples: Plutonium, cobalt

CLASS 8

49 CFR 173.136: Corrosive material; this means any liquid or solid that causes visible destruction or irreversible alterations in human skin tissue at its site of contact, or a liquid that has a severe corrosion rate on steel or aluminum.

Examples: sulfuric acid, sodium hydroxide, ethanolamine, phosphorus trichloride

CLASS 9

49 CFR 173.140: Miscellaneous hazardous materials; this means a material that presents a hazard during transport, but that is not included in another hazard class, including:

- Any material that has an anesthetic, noxious, or other similar property that could cause extreme annoyance or discomfort to a flight crew member.
- Meets the definition of a hazardous substance or hazardous waste.
- Other Regulated Materials (ORM-D) are considered a consumer commodity that although regulated, present a limited hazard during transportation.

Examples: blue asbestos, molten sulfur, adipic acid

Other Resources

DuPont Safety Resources offers Emergency Response training in the following areas:

- First Responder: Hazardous Materials Operations/WMD
- Operations for EMS/WMD
- Operations for Law Enforcement/WMD
- Hazardous Materials Technician/WMD
- Weapons of Mass Destruction
- Street Smart™ Chemistry/WMD
- Incident Command
- Protective Clothing

For more information, call 1-800-532-SAFE or visit us at www.dupont.com.safety.

Periodic Table of the Elements

1   2   3   4   5   6   7   8   9

In the periodic table the elements are arranged in order of increasing atomic number. Vertical columns headed by Arabic numerals are called *Groups*. A horizontal sequence of elements is called a *Period*. The most active elements are at the bottom left of Group 1 and the top right of Group 17. The staggered line (Groups 13-17) roughly separates metallic from non-metallic elements.

Groups—Elements within a Group have similar properties and contain the same number of electrons in their outside energy shell.
—The first Group (1) contains

hydrogen and the *alkali metals*.
— The last (18) contains the *noble gases*.
— Group (17) contains the *halogens*.
— The elements intervening between Groups 2 and 13 are called *transition elements*.
— Short vertical columns without Arabic numerical headings are called *Subgroups*.

Periods—in a given Period the properties of the elements gradually pass from a metallic to a non-metallic nature, with the last number of a period being a noble gas.

d ORBITALS FILLING

Hydrogen 1.0079 **H** 1	

Lithium 6.941 **Li** 3	Beryllium 9.012 **Be** 4

Sodium 22.990 **Na** 11	Magnesium 24.305 **Mg** 12

Potassium 39.098 **K** 19	Calcium 40.08 **Ca** 20	Scandium 44.956 **Sc** 21	Titanium 47.88 **Ti** 22	Vanadium 50.942 **V** 23	Chromium 51.996 **Cr** 24	Manganese 54.938 **Mn** 25	Iron 55.847 **Fe** 26	Cobalt 58.933 **Co** 27
Rubidium 85.47 **Rb** 37	Strontium 87.62 **Sr** 38	Yttrium 88.906 **Y** 39	Zirconium 91.224 **Zr** 40	Niobium 92.906 **Nb** 41	Molybdenum 95.94 **Mo** 42	Technetium (98) **Tc** 43	Ruthenium 101.07 **Ru** 44	Rhodium 102.91 **Rh** 45
Cesium 132.90 **Cs** 55	Barium 137.33 **Ba** 56	Lanthanum 138.91 **La** 57	Hafnium 178.49 **Hf** 72	Tantalum 180.95 **Ta** 73	Tungsten 183.85 **W** 74	Rhenium 186.21 **Re** 75	Osmium 190.2 **Os** 76	Iridium 192.22 **Ir** 77
Francium (223) **Fr** 87	Radium (226) **Ra** 88	Actinium (227) **Ac** 89	Unnilquadium (261) **Unq** 104	Unnilpentium (262) **Unp** 105	Unnihexium (263) **Unh** 106	Unnilseptium (262) **Uns** 107	Unniloctium (265) **Uno** 108	Unnilennium (266) **Une** 109

Lanthanide Series

Cerium 140.12 **Ce** 58	Praseodymium 140.91 **Pr** 59	Neodymium 144.24 **Nd** 60	Promethium (145) **Pm** 61	Samarium 150.36 **Sm** 62	Europium 151.96 **Eu** 63	Gadolinium 157.25 **Gd** 64	Terbium 158.92 **Tb** 65

Actinide Series

Thorium 232.04 **Th** 90	Protactinium 231.04 **Pa** 91	Uranium 238.03 **U** 92	Neptunium (237.05) **Np** 93	Plutonium (244) **Pu** 94	Americium (243) **Am** 95	Curium (247) **Cm** 96	Berkelium (247) **Bk** 97

f ORBITALS FILLING